Mrs. H. Lasko

Y0-AAQ-724

Reading
Grade 5

This workbook belongs to:

Table of Contents

All About Me!

Glue a photo of yourself here or draw a self-portrait.

These are my hobbies: _____

_____

If I had a free hour every day during school, I might like to _____

_____

I would like to learn more about _____ because _____

_____

The library I usually visit is called _____

I go there   ☐ once a week   ☐ once a month

          ☐ once a school term   ☐ when I am doing a project

          ☐ only in the summer   ☐ or _____

This is how much I enjoy reading.

          ☐ I love it!   ☐ It's OK.

          ☐ I do it if I have to.   ☐ Not if I have a choice!

I've marked the kind of books I enjoy most with a ☺.
I've put a ☹ on the kind books I don't like much.

_____ fantasy	_____ adventure	_____ science
_____ folklore	_____ biography	_____ mystery
_____ history	_____ animal	_____ humour
_____ fine arts	_____ science fiction	_____ comic books

These are some of my favourite books: _____

_____

_____

I do most of my fun reading

☐ every day
☐ over the weekend
☐ over the summer

I do most of my reading

☐ on a chair at school
☐ on a comfortable couch
☐ on my bed
☐ in the car

I prefer to read a book

☐ that is fiction
☐ that teaches me about things
☐ that is funny
☐ that is scary

I just like to finish a good book and daydream about it.

Book reports for school are _____

_____

_____

These are the magazines that come to my home: _____

_____

_____

My parents often get a newspaper at home.   ☐ yes   ☐ no

I read some part of the newspaper

☐ every day
☐ once a week
☐ when my parents show me
   something interesting
☐ when our class is using a newspaper
☐ never

I'm a ☐ good reader   ☐ OK reader   ☐ weak reader

From Morning Till Night

Use these words to tell about a typical day for someone in your grade 5 class.

schedule	time	problem	boxes	announcements
instructions	profits	homework	name	bottles
sign	headline	peanut butter	chart	clipboard
book	menu	roster	weather	DEAR
science	buddies	aloud	list	score
chalkboard	planner	French	recipe	telephone directory
TV				

When the clock radio came on, I rolled over and checked the ___time___. It couldn't be 7 a.m. already. As usual, I went into the bathroom and I showered and washed my hair. I had to read three _____ because I didn't want to use the wrong stuff on my hair.

I got dressed and went down to breakfast. Last night I helped put out the bottles of peanut butter and jam and two boxes of cereal. I choose some chunky _____ _____ instead of the smooth kind for my toast and while I was eating this, I read the two cereal _____. One had a sports hero's picture on it so I decided to eat that kind.

When I got on the bus at the corner, I noticed that it wasn't my regular driver. I read the _____ and made sure she was going to my school and not to the senior school. I also read her _____ tag after she asked me to find my name on her _____. She didn't call it a list though, she called it a _____.

When my friends and I went to our homeroom, I noticed that the teacher had a newspaper on her desk. I had a quick look at the _____. It was something about a hurricane in the Caribbean. I figured we would be talking about it in _____ class later in the day because we are studying weather.

This morning the _____ were late coming over the PA. One of the kids in my class was supposed to read them but she was away, so I had to run downstairs to help her partner. I liked doing that. My turn reading the announcements was a while ago. It was nice to do it again. I think I read _____ in a clear voice. I like to read out loud. It is great when our reading _____ from grade 1 come to see our class every Thursday and I read stories to my buddy, Nunio.

After math class, we were asked to talk about the challenge question that had been on the _____ since last Friday. I was proud that I had been able to figure it out. It was an arithmetic _____ about money.

I was getting hungry and found myself watching the clock until the lunch bell rang. According to the _____ at my school, lunch is from 11:45 a.m. to 1 p.m. When the bell rang I rushed to see what was on the _____. Great, my favourites—chicken and pasta!

I was also excited about today because we had a meeting of the Environment Club. We are having a bake sale tomorrow to earn some money. I helped by making muffins. I read the _____ on the package of the muffin mix very carefully. Ms Shriver says that this kind is just as good as her _____ and it's quicker because you don't need to measure so many things. One of my other jobs was to make some signs and put them up all over the school. I did that last week. I'll be selling tomorrow and counting our _____ .

Just after lunch, it was _____ time in our class. That means Drop Everything And Read. I like this time every day because there are no interruptions. I'm reading a great _____. I read one by the same author last week.

When science class time arrived, we had to show that our _____ was done. All of us had to fill in the huge _____ on the side wall with the information we found out about yesterday's weather in our assigned Canadian city. My city was Winnipeg, Manitoba. Tonight we have to watch the _____ channel and find out more about the hurricane. Ms Shriver read the article about it in today's paper to us.

After the bell went, I played basketball at the community centre. Tonight was our first game as a team. We had just been practicing until now. I had to find my name and number on the team _____. The game went until five o'clock. We won: the _____ was 10 to 8.

After dinner, I was checking the _____ schedule. Mom didn't believe me at first that it was for my homework. I showed her where I had written it in my _____. "Watch TV—weather channel—take notes." She laughed and said, "OK, but don't switch channels!"

I had other reading to do for my _____ homework, too. It's getting a little easier this year because we're still reviewing last year's work. Learning another language is hard work! I had to call my best friend to ask her about our math homework. She was staying at her grandparents' house so I had to look their phone number up in the _____ _____ .

I'm sure glad I can read…it's something I do from morning till night!

Fan Mail

R.L. Stine, the author of the *Goosebumps* series said in a TV interview that sometimes he gets 2 000 letters a week. He has written many stories that have been made into television shows, plays and movies.

Stine has been telling adventure and horror stories since he was nine years old. He used to tell his brother a story and then stop at the scariest and most exciting part. His brother had to imagine the rest of the story.

Stine commented that he likes to write for kids in the middle grades but that he wants you to know that the stories will always turn out OK. He doesn't want you to have nightmares.

In the first draft of one story he planned to have the librarian eat kids. But in the revisions he changed it so that the librarian ate turtles and snails. He thought that this was better for his readers and he also liked the idea of the crunchy sounds.

Stine's books became popular in the mid-1990s. Ask your parents what books were popular when they were your age. Many of them will tell you about a mystery series that they loved. Perhaps they will find some copies to share with you.

I'm not afraid when I read scary stories.

Children's authors like to receive letters from kids just like you. Sometimes they use ideas that are sent to them by kids in creating their next book. Authors like to know what kinds of things hook their readers, so tell them what parts of their stories really caught your attention and made you excited.

You can mail your letters to the company where the author's books are published or you can look up their name on the Internet. They might have a Web site that would make for some interesting reading and would also give you an e-mail or a regular address.

Write a first draft of a letter to _____.
(Name of your favourite author)

Dear _____ ,

_____

_____

_____

_____

_____

_____

_____

_____

_____

_____

_____

_____

_____

_____

_____

Now revise it.

Check for correct spelling, proper paragraphs, complete sentences, interesting comments and ideas. Look it over once yourself, then have a friend or a parent take a look. Check out pages 94 and 95 for the format.

Some people can revise work they do on the computer onscreen. Others need to print out a hard copy to check over.

Now rewrite your letter and send it off. Be sure to put your return address on the envelope. If the letter can't be delivered, it will be returned to you. Also put your address on the inside in case your favourite author decides to send you back a picture or a note.

Parking Lot Search

Take a walk through a parking lot and write down a list of all the kinds of cars you find. Be careful! Make sure that you are visible at all times so you don't get clobbered by a careless driver. We'll be doing some sorting with this list on the next page.

Here's a list of 20 to start.

Write the cars you find here:

Taurus _____

Volkswagen _____

Sunbird _____

Pontiac _____

Subaru _____

Chevrolet _____

Jimmy _____

Geo _____

Cavalier _____

Caravan _____

Buick _____

Toyota _____

Hyundi _____

Honda _____

Blazer _____

Land Rover _____

Intrepid _____

Beetle _____

Mazda _____

Explorer _____

This could be an imaginary walk and you might add to this list just by talking with your family!

You can also find car names in the newspaper

Now we can decide how to sort these names on a separate piece of paper.

1. Make an alphabetical list.

2. Sort them by dealer and name like Chevrolet: Cavalier
Blazer
Geo

3. Find those car models that use the name of something else. For instance, some of the Volkswagen cars have names of insects, animals and sports.

You can do the three sorts noted above on another sheet of paper. On this page we'll sort cars by the sounds of the vowels in their names. One car name may be in more than one column.

short a	short e	short i	short o	short u
Toyota				

long a	long e	long i	long o	long u

silent vowels	y - long e	y - long i	r - controlled vowels	special vowel sounds

Which One Is It?

Cute kids like kites.

Do chrome kettles work quicker in the dark?

Say these sentences out loud. What sound do you hear repeated many times? ____

AT THE BEGINNING OF A WORD
There are several ways to make the sound of "k":
- before i or e it is usually spelled "k"
- before a, o, u, r and l it is usually spelled "c"
- and sometimes it is spelled "ch"

Add the correct "k" sound to complete each of these words:

1. __k_id   ___at   ___orus   ___it   ___lip

2. ___oir   ___rush   ___ot   ___ite   ___ill

3. ___ristmas   ___evin   ___up   ___abin   ___offee

AT THE END OF A WORD
The "k" sound is usually spelled:
- "ck" after a short vowel sound—clock
- "ke" after a long vowel sound—spoke
- and "k" after a consonant or vowel digraph (ee/ea)—dark and peek

Now, which one will finish these words?

4. tra_ck_   lea___   si___   ba___e   du___

5. spar___   jo___e   ma___   wee___   hul___

6. bris___   bri___   de___   bi___e   fa___e

7. mar___   ca___e   sul___   cho___e   tru___

8. brea___   ta___e   stea___   cra___   ne___

9. yo___e   bu___   pa___   qua___   bar___

10. li___e   pe___   ki___   ti___-to___   ra___e

The sound of "k" is also heard in words like quit (kw) and tax (ks).
This is a tricky part of spelling in English.

Use these words in the following sentences:

quick	quiz	quilt	quite	quake	quiet
box	fix	tax	wax	fox	mix

11. The librarian pointed to the sign that said, "Be ___*quiet*___."

12. The _____ of _____ crayons tipped onto the carpet.

13. There will be sales _____ and GST added to the price of the _____.

14. The _____ red _____ dashed away from the hikers.

15. Everyone stayed away for fear of another earth _____.

16. That was _____ a difficult surprise _____ the teacher gave us.

17. We'll _____ the broken bike after lunch.

18. Please _____ up your groups and then make three new groups.

Some more "k" sounds that might confuse you or mess up your spelling come at the end of a word. They are –cal and –cle.

Just remember that you will see: –cal at the end of an adjective and –cle at the end of a noun

> My uncle rides a vertical bicycle—it's a miracle.

Sort these words and use them in a short sentence:

uncle	bicycle	vertical	physical
article	musical	miracle	practical

Adjectives	Sentence	Nouns	Sentence
vertical			

I'm Not Triskaidekaphobic!

Triska—what? I don't know if I am or not.

Maybe some of the parts of this word will give you a clue about what this word means. What language does it look like? The word *phobia* means *afraid* so that's a start. Maybe that prefix tri- is important!

Find out about these words and use them in a sentence to show that you understand their meaning.

UNI– means one when you see it added to a base word.

unique

I am the only person in the world who is just like me. I am unique. When I look in the mirror, I see many things about myself that make me unique.

unison

_____

_____

universal

_____

_____

unicorn

 A picture might be the best way to show that you know this word.

BI– means two when you see it added to a base word.

biceps

_____

_____

bilingual

_____

_____

bicentennial

_____

_____

bicycle

_____

_____

TRI– means three when you see it added to a base word.

triplets

_____

_____

triangle

_____

_____

triplicate

_____

_____

Ahhh! I looked up that tri–word. It means being afraid of the number thirteen.

Yikes! And we're on page 13...hmmm... coincidence?

I Want the Biggest Half!

You know that in mathematics the title of this page is impossible, but this is language arts, so we can take poetic licence.

There is a prefix that means half. It is SEMI–.

I've heard kids say it when a chocolate bar or something really yummy is being split in two.

Choose words that fit in these sentences. In some of these sentences the prefix means *partly*.

semidetached   semiconscious   semicolon   semifinal   semicircle

1. If you are a sports fan you have watched many ___semifinal___ games on TV.

2. I will move into a _____ house next fall. My aunt will live beside me.

3. In some sentences, it is correct to use a _____.

4. The pattern for the angel had a large _____ for the wings.

5. After the accident he was _____ for an hour.

Some prefixes help the word mean the opposite of the base word.

ANTI– means against.

Use these words in the following sentences:

antifreeze   antisocial   antidote   antiperspirants   anti-aircraft

6. The ___anti-aircraft___ missiles were successful.

I'm anti-pollution, if that's a word.

7. The doctor gave him an _____ for the snake bite.

8. They were _____ sitting by themselves all evening.

9. Every fall you need to check the _____ in your car.

10. There are many kinds of deodorants and _____ in the drugstore.

Changing Again!

These prefixes make the words they join mean the **opposite** but always in a **negative** way.

in–   im–   il–   un–   non–   ir–   dis–

Match a prefix to the marked word in these sentence to change the meaning.

1. He told me it was _____ legal to park there.

2. That ring must have been very _____ expensive.

3. They were _____ responsible in the way they cared for their dogs.

4. She showed her _____ maturity by her behaviour at the theatre.

5. It was _____ necessary to have the police walk through Confederation Park each day.

The meanings of these prefixes help to make the next part of the word change.

PRE– means before (preview, precaution)
POST– means after (postdate, postscript)
PRO– means in forward or favour (projector, proceed)

SUB– means under, beneath (submarine, substitute)
INTER– means between, among (interrupt, intercom)
TRANS– means across, over, down or beyond (translate, transport)

> I'm pro-reading but anti-homework.

Use one word from each pair of words in a sentence.

1. _____

2. _____

3. _____

4. _____

5. _____

6. _____

Lost and Found

A suffix is a word ending. Each of the nouns lost in the word search has a suffix.

Underline the suffix and draw a shape around the entire word when you find it in the word search.

awareness	friendliness	freedom	wisdom
accomplishment	argument	electrician	librarian
labourer	researcher	spectator	director
fixture	signature	opinion	complexion
expression	television	detention	population
combination	occupation	definition	preposition

```
C D L L V R O T A T C E P S L U H M F
Z Q E C S L I B R A R I A N H M Y S J
O H V J O P R E P O S I T I O N Z L N
R H Y R G S S E N E R A W A X G O H Y
S J N O I T N E T E D L X Z K M K B G
A N O I X E L P M O C E A N O I R E W
N O I T A N I B M O C L T A F K E X N
C J W G S S E N I L D N E I R F S P O
N O I N I P O U T M O D S I W N E R I
O C C U P A T I O N O Y S P U A A E S
T Z E I O B C L A B O U R E R I R S I
R E U E R L S I G N A T U R E C C S V
U N O F O N O I T I N I F E D I H I E
A R G U M E N T V U U W S J W R E O L
D A C C O M P L I S H M E N T T R N E
J O E R U T X I F P I M D K U C N N T
K P Z K C R O T C E R I D L K E N N J
Y W T I V X Z L F R E E D O M L U N H
R D Y Q A N O I T A L U P O P E M N V
```

Why did you go to Mars and Venus before you came to Earth?

I didn't planet that way!

Find the right endings to these words to help these sentences make sense.
Some endings may be used more than once.

–ible	–able	–ery	–ary	–ory	–ous	–ious
–ent	–ence	–ant	–ance	–ise	–ize	

1. I apolog*ize*_____ for forgetting the date and missing the party.

2. In sports, it helps to have flex_____ joints.

3. What are you writing? Is it an imagin_____ story or a factual report?

4. You must stay at home if you have an infect_____ disease.

5. Everyone should try for excell_____ in their work.

6. The fall merchand_____ arrives in the stores in July.

7. The new green_____ is attractive at the entr_____ to the school.

8. The continu_____ noise from the traffic doesn't bother me.

9. A signific_____ amount of snow fell on Winnipeg.

10. Her excuse for being late is unbeliev_____.

11. The stories they told the police were contradict_____.

12. Are you a resid_____ of Calgary?

Mixed-up Words

If you are a fan of the word game Scrabble™ you will be interested to know that the wooden tiles are no longer being made. The newer versions of the game are made with plastic tiles. The letters are printed on top of the smooth tiles and not engraved as they used to be.

During tournaments, expert Scrabble™ players using the old tiles were able to identify the letters as they were pulling them from the bag just by the feel of the carved letters. If you have an older game, try it and see if you can feel the letter while it is in the bag! How many times were you right? Keep a tally by marking "I" for each time you are correct. Your tally might go like this:

I, II, III, IIII, IIII, IIII I, IIII II, IIII III, IIII IIII, IIII IIII, IIII IIII I, etc.

Suppose these were the seven letters that you pulled out. What words could you make?

Two-letter words	**BE**
Three-letter words	**BEE RIB**
Four-letter words	**BEER**
Five-letter words	(You won't be able to make words for every line.)
Six-letter words	(Look carefully, maybe you can see some words.)
Seven-letter words	**RECEIVE**

Try these yourself!

E E A R D L C

Two-letter words	_____	Five-letter words	_____
Three-letter words	_____	Six-letter words	_____
Four-letter words	_____	Seven-letter words	_____

R A U C T T S B

Two-letter words	_____	Five-letter words	_____
Three-letter words	_____	Six-letter words	_____
Four-letter words	_____	Seven-letter words	_____
Eight-letter word	_____		

Find as many smaller words as you can in these big words.

Graduation	Microwave	Alligators
drag		

Vacation	Opportunity	Certificate

Now try some of your own words. How many smaller words can you find in the words you chose?

The letters in my name can also spell ear, gear, dear, drag, dreg, rage and egad!

(Word for a product you use)	(Name of another country)	(A word in another language)

That's Good for a Laugh

I like the jokes in bubble gum!

Do you like jokes and riddles? _____

Which of your friends tells jokes the best?

_____

_____

_____

Why is he or she so good?

_____

_____

_____

Who is your favourite comedian on TV or in the movies?

_____

_____

_____

Why do you think he or she is a funny person?

_____

_____

_____

What is the difference between a joke and a riddle?

_____

_____

_____

Write three of your favourite jokes or riddles here.

1. _____

_____

2. _____

_____

3. _____

_____

PUNS are another way to have fun with words. Puns make jokes from the many meanings that one word can have. They're considered a cheap joke by most comedians.

Illustrate two of these puns.

1. Student: What is more intelligent than a talking parrot?
Teacher: A spelling bee!

2. Choir Director: I think you would be better singing tenor.
Choir Member: Tenor?
Choir Director: Yeah! Ten or twelve kilometres away!

3. Boy 1: What do you mean you brought your doghouse with you?
Boy 2: It's a pup tent, isn't it?

4. Mother: Can't you play tennis without making all that noise?
Son: No one can play tennis, Mum, without raising a racket!

Pun # _____	Pun # _____

Rapunzel's Walkman

"Rapunzel, Rapunzel, let down your hair," cried the prince.

"Wait a minute," Rapunzel shouted down to him. "I've got to unplug my Walkman." With a quick flip of her fingers, Rapunzel popped the earphones from her ears and then walked over to the balcony.

"What was that you were saying?" Rapunzel, unfortunately, had suffered some hearing loss from so many years of being locked up in the castle with no one but her Walkman for company. On the other hand, she did know every Céline Dion song by heart.

"I said, 'let down your hair,'" the prince cried again.

"Are you going to try to climb up it, like all the others?" Rapunzel asked.

"Of course," the prince replied.

Rapunzel knew it wouldn't work. The problem was in the tensile strength of the hair and the distance between her castle balcony and the ground. Somebody once said there was a formula to figure it out. All Rapunzel knew was that five other princes had tried climbing up the castle by yanking at her hair like a rope. This simply left her with a painful scalp and, even worse, with split ends.

"Couldn't you just get a ladder?" Rapunzel asked.

"Then this wouldn't be a fairy tale," shouted the prince. "I want to rescue you, take you away from this terrible castle, marry you and make you my beloved."

Rapunzel groaned. First, the castle really wasn't that terrible. She had her Walkman, a large TV, wall-to-wall carpeting and a refrigerator that was always full of great snacks. Second, she wasn't sure that this particular prince was good enough to be her beloved.

"Listen, I'm kind of picky about my princes," Rapunzel said.

"Picky?"

"Like, how do I know you're the prince of my dreams? At least the last prince, Harold of Burgundy, told me a few good jokes before he climbed up my hair."

"Good jokes?" asked the prince.

"Yes, I was laughing at one of them when he lost his grip on my hair. Naturally he blamed me, just like all you prince guys."

"I wouldn't do that," said the prince. "I am a good, true and noble prince!"

Rapunzel tried not to groan. "But are you smart?" she asked.

"Indeed, I am," the prince told her. "I can do complex division, and I've studied frog biology and I know the words to all of Céline Dion's songs."

Rapunzel's ears perked up at this last achievement. "In that case," she said, "don't bother trying to climb up my hair. It won't work. You'll have to come up with something else."

The prince thought and thought—he paced and pondered—until he came upon an idea. "How many headphones do you have?" he asked.

"Tons," Rapunzel replied.

"And if you just tied them all together...."

The rest, of course, is history. The prince and Rapunzel lived a prosperous life, raised a number of delightful children and spent many happy hours singing Céline Dion songs—from memory.

VOCABULARY

What do these phrases mean? You can use a dictionary to check on the meaning of some words. It's always a good idea to look back at the story and read the phrase in context.

1. tensile strength: _____

_____

2. split ends: _____

_____

3. lost his grip: _____

_____

4. kind of picky: _____

_____

5. paced and pondered: _____

_____

6. prosperous life: _____

_____

7. delightful children: _____

_____

Illustrate the technique the prince used to reach Rapunzel.
Do you think he climbed up to the balcony, or did Rapunzel climb down?

COMPREHENSION

Make a list of the things Rapunzel liked about her room in the castle.
Make a list of the disadvantages of Rapunzel's life at the beginning of the story.

Advantages	Disadvantages

8. Why didn't Rapunzel choose Harold of Burgundy for her prince?

_____

_____

_____

9. What characteristic did Rapunzel think was the most important for a prince to have?

_____

_____

_____

10. How did the Prince and Rapunzel get together? Explain.

_____

_____

_____

_____

_____

_____

_____

From My Point of View

Make up a telephone conversation for one of these famous fairy-tale characters. You probably know one side, but there is always another part of the story that is not often told.

Jack and the Beanstalk

Jack's mother is calling a gardener because the plant that grew from the magic beans is getting gigantic!

or

Jack's mother calls an ambulance when a huge giant falls into her garden!

Cinderella

The prince is calling everyone he knows in his kingdom to find out who the mysterious woman at the ball was.

or

One of Cinderella's stepsisters is telling her girlfriend about the party at the palace.

Snow White and the Seven Dwarfs

One of the seven dwarfs is phoning a real estate agent to rent a house for Snow White and the other dwarfs.

or

Snow White's stepmother is calling the department store to complain about her mirror.

Hello, this is _____ *calling.*

_____

_____

_____

_____

_____

_____

_____

_____

_____

_____

Now write the story from your point of view. Use some of your phone dialogue.

_____
(Title)

_____

_____

_____

_____

_____

_____

_____

_____

_____

(Draw a picture to illustrate your story.)

_____

_____

_____

_____

_____

_____

_____

_____

_____

_____

_____

_____

_____

MODERN FAIRY TALES

How would the story of the *Three Little Pigs* be different if the setting changed? Instead of building houses out of straw, sticks and bricks, what would happen if the first little pig bought a condominium in downtown Toronto, the second little pig bought a ski resort at Whistler and the third little pig bought a yacht and took off from Halifax to see the world!

Use your imagination and answer these questions.

How would the wolf, who has been chasing the Pig family for years, find out where the pigs had moved?

_____

_____

_____

How would the wolf travel to see them?

_____

_____

_____

Why would the wolf want to meet up with them? Do you think he is just hungry for pork?

_____

_____

_____

How would the three Pig brothers keep in touch with each other?

_____

_____

_____

My two brothers and I have moved to different places, too! I'm glad I chose Earth!

What would they think of each other's choice?

_____

_____

_____

Runaway Spaceship

The spaceship careened out of control as Alex tried to take the controls.

"Shut down the engines!" he screamed. "Shut them down!"

His words were wasted. Everyone else on the giant spaceship was passed out, lying helpless in the halls and cabins. In the otherwise silent spaceship, there was only one human voice to be heard over the roar of the engines.

The ship's computer had taken over, of course, when the captain passed out at the controls and no one else seemed to be in charge. It kept flying the ship forward, on a path that went straight to Romular—and to certain death for everyone on board.

Alex understood the situation as soon as he reached the bridge. He wondered, for a moment, why he wasn't affected by whatever had knocked out the crew. But there was no time to ask questions, only time to act.

"If I knock out the computer…" he said to himself. But Alex quickly dismissed that idea. The computer ran all the life-support systems on the ship. Without its giant brain clicking away, there'd be no light or heat or air to breathe. In a few seconds, everyone on board would be dead.

That left the engines themselves. Alex raced back through the huge ship, past the robot arm, down miles of tunnels. He looked at his watch and saw that he had, at most, twenty minutes before the ship would be caught by the Romular landing beams.

When he reached the engine room, he saw a bank of controls that stretched along an entire wall. It would take him more than twenty minutes just to read all the labels.

"I've got to stop and think," Alex said to himself, "think of something…."

He looked over the situation: a ship hurtling through space, the crew on the floor, a maze of lights and switches. This was hopeless, he said to himself. I'm just a kid. What do I know?

And then he had an idea. There was only one being on this ship who could help him, and that being wasn't a person—it was a computer.

"Computer!" Alex shouted.

"Yes, sir," came the synthesized voice of the machine.

"How do I shut the engines down?"

"We are under orders to fly to Romular, sir, and shutting the engines would make that impossible."

"I know your orders," Alex cried out. "I just…I just…" he kept thinking about the problem. "I need to know how…for a…crossword puzzle."

There was a brief pause while the computer searched its memory for "crossword puzzle." It was a term from the distant past. Crossword puzzles were some kind of game that humans played back in the twentieth century. Surely, the computer reasoned, there would be nothing wrong with helping a young boy play an historic game.

The computer thought that an honest answer would do no harm. "Switch B74 will shut down some, B76 the rest, or the red emergency handle will."

Alex lunged for the red handle and…

COMPREHENSION

1. Number these events from the story in the correct order.

_____ Alex saw a bank of controls with labels.

_____ Alex tricked the computer into revealing the secret.

_____ The spaceship careened out of control.

_____ Alex lunged for the red handle.

_____ The ship was being run by its master computer.

_____ Everyone but Alex was unconscious.

_____ Alex decided that the engines had to be disabled.

_____ Alex spoke to the voice-activated computer.

_____ The computer refused to shut down the engines.

2. What is the meaning of "the computer ran all the life-support systems."

_____

_____

3. Why do you think Alex was on board the spaceship headed to Romular?

_____

_____

4. How would you compare Alex's brain and the computer on the spaceship?

_____

_____

5. What words would describe Alex's emotions as he tried to save the spaceship and everyone on board?

_____

_____

6. What do you predict will happen after Alex touches the red handle?

_____

_____

VOCABULARY

Design your own crossword puzzle. If someone in the future finds it in a time capsule from the year _____, maybe this will be the first crossword puzzle they will ever see.

1. Place these words from the story on the large grid. The crossword puzzle has been started for you.

careened	engines	helpless	computer	situation	Romular
death	systems	controls	switches	maze	synthesized
impossible	distant	humans	historic	honest	emergency
orders	brief				

Try to find places where the same letter in two words will overlap. Put one of the words in the **across** section. Put the other word in the **down** section.

2. Put as many of these words as you can into the puzzle. You may add some others.
3. Darken the boxes that won't be used for any letters.
4. Print tiny numbers on the first box used by each word. Match these numbers to the **across** and **down** lists of clues.
5. Now write definitions or sentences with a missing word to help someone else figure out your puzzle.
6. Make a copy of the numbers and the shape of the puzzle, but leave out the words so that your friend can have fun figuring out the answers.

Across		Down	
#	Clue	#	Clue
1	opposite of possible	2	people are _____
2	from the past	3	a word that means far away

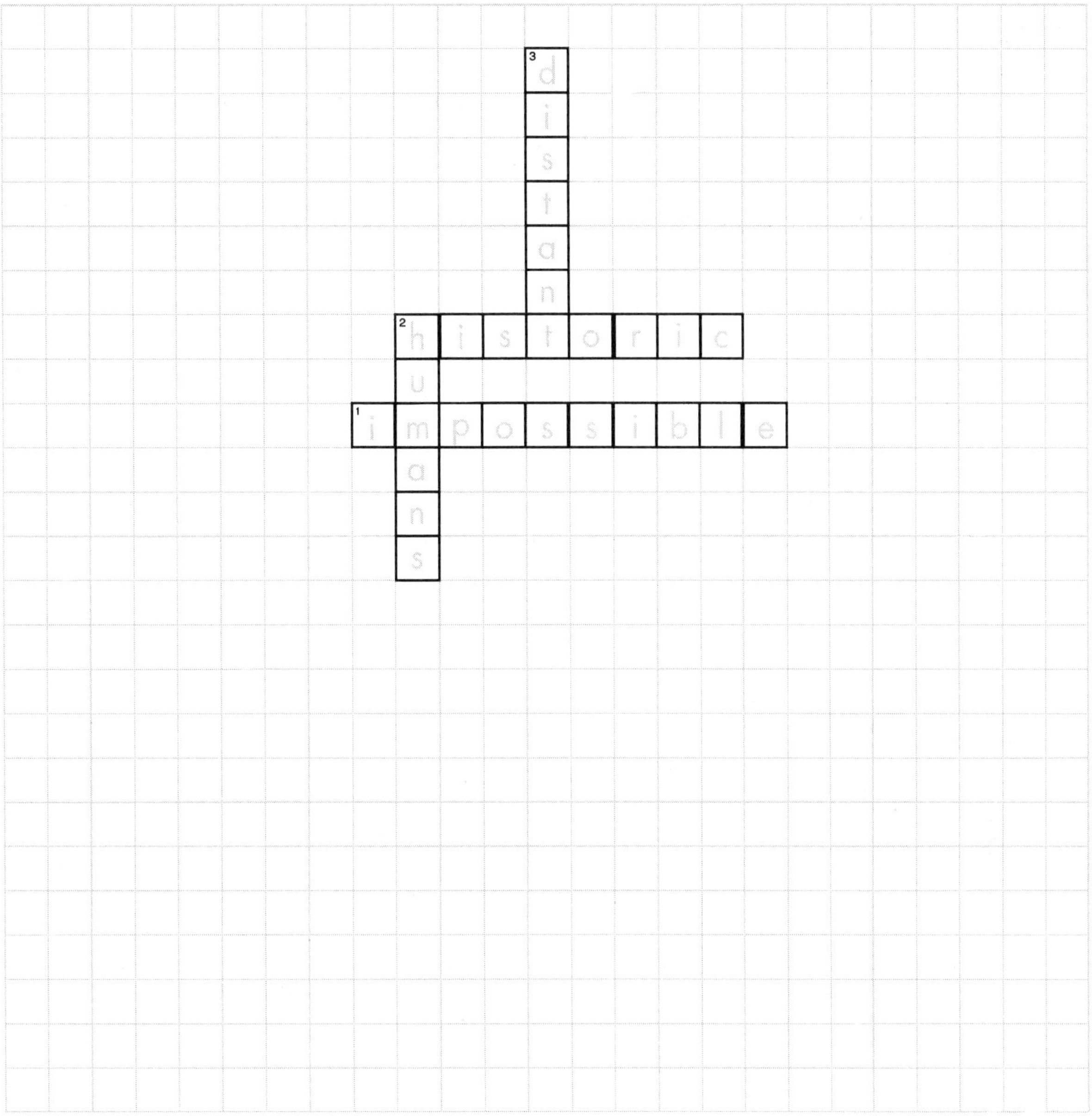
1 impossible
2 historic
2 humans
3 distant

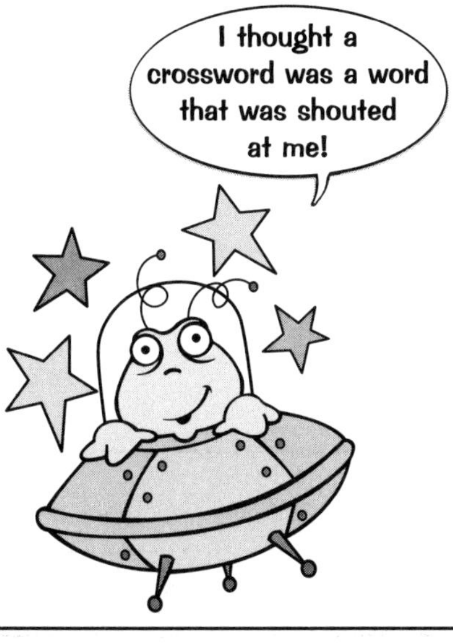
I thought a crossword was a word that was shouted at me!

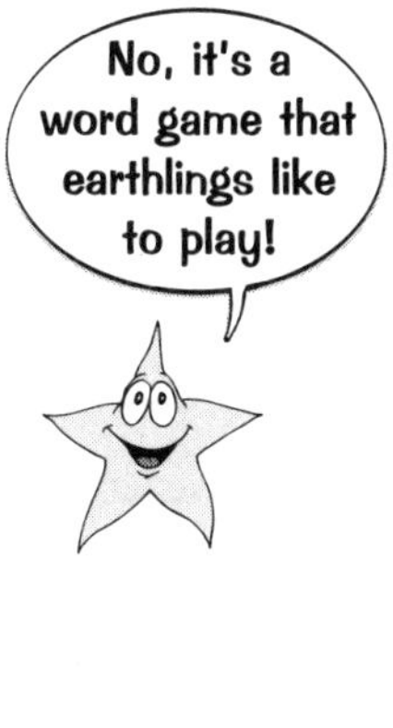
No, it's a word game that earthlings like to play!

Meet Two Young Canadian Authors

The author of this story is Rosamund Mosse. Rosie is a student who is now in high school. She wrote this story when she was just three years older than you are. Rosie has written many stories. She thinks that the best way to improve your writing is to keep practicing.

PEOPLE WATCHING

Some days they would laugh and play. Her mom had a laugh that rang like church bells on a spring morning. Other days they would just sit and talk as the calming ocean waves rolled in.

"What's the matter, Liz?"

"How do you know I'm sad, Mama?" Lizzy had asked.

"I can see it in your eyes."

There was a long pause and then. "If you're sad I can tell. Likewise if you're happy. What you are thinking about, what you are feeling...your eyes are the window to your soul. Always be watching, Lizzy. You know, there are some pretty interesting people, pretty interesting stories, out there."

Lizzy sat huddled on the bank ten years later, just watching the ocean as she and her mother would have done.

At first she was annoyed at another presence; but as she looked closer there was something oddly intriguing about the man she was. He turned to look at the tumbling ocean before them. Then he lifted his chin, in one last effort of dignity, before taking off his glasses to wipe the tears from his eyes. He was short and frail, with wisps of white hair that fell out from under his hat. But those eyes! Eyes that, surely, had sparkled blue once but now turned gray with the dull stare that was held beneath them.

The old man's hair flew back and the wind tore at his clothing. He perched the thick glasses back on his nose. The waves roared in, but to Lizzy, the world fell silent. She looked on, captivated by a story in her imagination, a story she seemed to find in the old man's eyes.

...A little boy turned round to display a face with rosy cheeks and a radiant smile. He had bright blue eyes that sparkled like jewels on his fair complexion. As Lizzy watched, the little boy took his mother's hand and they walked together down to the docks. His mother turned and pointed out the ferries coming in and out of the harbour. The little boy took off his glasses and smiled at the way the wind felt on his face...

The story, like the waves of the ocean, unfurled itself.

...A disgruntled youth flew down to the shoreline, throwing himself to the ground as if wanting to be totally engulfed by the wild, passionate ocean. He rolled over and sat up. Tears flowed from his blue-gray eyes. Tears of anger, hurt and confusion. Tears of adolescence. He stood up then, and looked out at the land beyond...

The old man's gaze was fixed on the ferry heading for the dock coming from Nova Scotia. Like the ocean's tide, the story kept breaking on the beach of Lizzy's imagination.

...He stood at attention while his mother checked him over. His uniform had been neatly pressed and his boots were sparkling. He kissed his mother and smiled. But beyond his brave exterior, Lizzy, sitting over 50 years away, could see how scared he was. He was to return from the war, a transparent, broken person. Even his eyes had lost their sparkle and turned almost gray. They had such depth—but somehow they still seemed remarkably hollow....

He sat down, awkwardly, on a log, as if bothered by arthritis. And, as if in a dream, Lizzy walked down, not quite sure why—to sit beside him. They sat like that for some time, just savouring the silence. Finally, he spoke.

"I used to bring my little girl here."

Reflected in his eyes, Lizzy saw flashes of a little girl, playing by the waves. She had a head of golden curls and eyes of brilliant blue that sparkled and danced like the sun. For a moment, only a moment, Lizzy saw the same sparkle in the old man's eye. But then, "She was only four when she died—only four."

He didn't cry then, not for himself, not for his daughter. He just sat, with an expressionless look on his face. Then turning to her he said, "Forgetting is hard, but sometimes remembering can be even harder."

1. Find places where Rosie has compared one thing to something else. Look for the words "like" and "as" to help you find these similes.

child's eyes — sparkled and danced like the sun

_____

_____

_____

_____

_____

2. Why you think Lizzy returned to this special spot alone?

_____

_____

3. What does the author tell you about the man's appearance?

_____

_____

4. Where does this story take place?

_____

_____

5. What makes "People Watching" a good title for this story?

_____

_____

6. What feelings did you have while you read this story?

_____

_____

Jacob Currie wrote this story during the first term in grade 6. He is just a little older than some of you are now. His hobby is HO model trains.

THE TRAIN RUNNERS

"Next stop, Singing Valley," a husky voice cried out from the speaker and echoed through the empty station

I looked around. My first day as an engineer on the Pine Ridge Railroad and, boy was I nervous. My insides felt like a bunch of Mexican jumping beans. No wonder, I was the youngest engineer ever to enter the railroad.

At 18, it was quite an accomplishment. My mother was incredibly proud of me, and had made me a huge lunch, with chicken sandwiches and a slice of cake with all the trappings.

If only I could eat it all without throwing up.

If only my jitters would stop.

This hot weather was really getting to me, but my thoughts were cut short.

"All aboard!" the conductor cried, as he stepped into the rusty green cab. I took a deep breath and stepped up. I stared at the mass of controls spread out before me.

"Whaa…!" I gasped. A deep throaty laugh came from behind me. I whipped around, and a gray man in his mid-40s, wearing worn gray overalls and covered in black dust (coal dust, I assumed), nearly knocked me over as he gave me a hearty whack on the back.

"Welcome to the workforce, son. I hope you're up to the job."

"Me too," I replied. "It looks awful complicated."

"Ah, it's not. Half that bakoozie doesn't do what it's supposed to. The other chap didn't use it at all. And he got along fine. Well,

until he dropped dead the other day. I reckon that's why you've been hired."

This guy seemed a little funked in the head, but I trusted and liked him.

"I'll show you how to do it. You'll learn fast enough."

"Thanks. Well, shouldn't we all be going?" I asked as my stomach lurched.

"Yeah. Push that there green lever and pull that red one."

I did and the train leapt forward.

The man turned out to be the coal man (who shovels coal into the engine), and as time went by I grew to like him more and more. He was named Malachi and had emigrated from Ireland when he was five. We shared our lunches because I could never eat all of mine.

The conductor, Bill, generally stayed in the caboose, where he read the paper. Every day we would go through a tunnel. Where Malachi told me that, according to local lore, there was a man who lived in the tunnel, made the carvings on the tunnel walls and killed people who passed through.

"I just think they were made by some kids trying to scare folks. . . . They succeeded," my friend told me.

Sometimes we saw the big express trains zooming down the main line. Malachi told me that he had a friend who drove one of them.

"Scare all the cattle they do," he remarked.

I eventually learned what all the controls did, but Malachi was right, many of them were completely useless. One of them was supposed to light up the controls, but it, like many others was broken.

Once, an axle broke and we had to have a mechanic fix it. Unfortunately, the new axle was not the same size as the others, and we had to fix that.

One time, Bill did come up to the cab, to announce that the train was full, for the first time in months. We celebrated by taking an early lunch break.

One day, after I had been working on the railroad for several months, Bill ran up to tell me that a lady was having a baby on the train. I headed the train for the hospital (it was on our route), but a snowdrift had blown onto the track.

I stopped the train and ran back. I found the lady, but I had absolutely no confidence that I could deliver a baby. I closed my eyes, yelled "PUSH" and, amazingly, the baby fell into my arms.

It turned out that the lady was the wife of the Pine Ridge mayor. Because of this, I was awarded a medal reading: "For Railroad Excellence, Awarded to Robert Slater."

They never knew it was for closing my eyes.

———————

1. Who is the main character in the story and what do we know about him?

_____

2. How do we know he was feeling nervous on his first day at work?

_____

3. Name the other two characters and their jobs. _____

_____

4. How did the coal man help the engineer on his first day of work? _____

_____

5. Mark the circle next to the correct answer:
   (a) This story takes place   O over a few days
                                        O over several months
                                        O over more than a year

   (b) The engineer's mother gives him   O just enough for lunch
                                             O not enough for lunch
                                             O too much for lunch

6. Two kinds of trains are described in this story. How do the passenger train and the express train differ? Make two lists. You may add details to your answer that are not in the story.

Robert's passenger train

_____

_____

_____

_____

Express train

_____

_____

_____

_____

How are they the same?

Robert's passenger train

_____

_____

_____

_____

Express train

_____

_____

_____

_____

7. What other words could you use in these sentences for the underlined words?

(a) My mother was <u>incredibly</u> proud of me. _____

(b) I stared at the mass of controls <u>spread out</u> before me. _____

(c) I <u>reckon</u> that's why you've been hired. _____

8. What do you think these expressions mean?

(a) "like a bunch of Mexican jumping beans" _____

(b) "Half that bakoozie" _____

(c) "funked in the head" _____

Tall Tales

Legends about famous people in history and people in your family are often retold many, many times. A good story teller embellishes the story or exaggerates it a little. That's how stories change from the first-hand experience that happened years ago.

Here are the beginnings of some stories that could become tall tales. Add your ideas to make an interesting short story. Draw a sketch to go along with the story.

My friends were always joking around in science class. We didn't think that our science teacher had eyes in the back of his head until one day _____

_____

_____

_____

_____

_____

My uncle Henry told great tall tales.

One Halloween night I saw a rubber bat on the doorstep of my neighbours' house. I stopped to pick it up. I was going to turn and scare my little sister, but _____

_____

_____

_____

_____

I received a strange letter. It was delivered to me in math class. The envelope was black and the writing was silver. I found it in my desk when I sat down. I put it inside my open math textbook and when the teacher wasn't looking I opened it. The letter told me _____

_____

_____

_____

_____

_____

_____

Ask your Mom or Dad to tell you about a tall tale they heard. Retell this tall tale here.

_____

_____

_____

_____

_____

_____

_____

_____

_____

_____

The Great Pretender

Have you ever pretended to be a great singer at one of your school assemblies or talent shows? Perhaps you learned the words of your favourite singer's most popular tune and sang it with some accompaniment. Or maybe you played the song and lip-synched to match the words and the music.

Many performers pay tributes to famous recording stars by singing the songs made famous long ago. Audiences enjoy watching talented singers do these songs in the same style as the artist who first recorded the tunes. Many of the performers your parents or grandparents listened to, like Frank Sinatra and Elvis Presley, are remembered today with the help of impersonators and tribute artists.

Which current singers or groups do you think will be remembered in the future?

_____

Do you know some of their songs by heart? The words to these songs are called the **lyrics**. A lyric is a song-like poem that expresses personal feelings.

Write down some of the lyrics to a tune you really like. You can play the CD, or sometimes you can find the lyrics printed on the inside cover.

_____

_____

_____

_____

_____

_____

_____

_____

_____

_____

_____

Are there any rhyming words included in the selection you chose? _____

If so, list them. _____

_____

When two lines rhyme it is called a COUPLET.

When four lines have two sets of rhyming words it is called a QUATRAIN.

Some songs and poetry are written in free verse. They do not have rhyme or rhythm in the lines of the song.

A BALLAD tells a story from the past. It has several verses. It might have a chorus that is repeated after each verse. It includes four lines with the second and fourth line rhyming. Some of the songs you enjoyed as a younger child were probably ballads.

Try writing a song of your own. It could be about an experience you have had in your life. It could be about a story you have read and want to tell in poetry or song. Read it aloud. You might "borrow" the music from a familiar tune and sing your own words to it.

Someday I want to sing karaoke.

_____

_____

_____

_____

_____

_____

_____

_____

_____

_____

_____

_____

_____

_____

_____

Poetry Favourites

A favourite kind of poetry that many kids write is a cinquain.
Do you remember how they go?

SYLLABLE CINQUAIN

Line 1: Title	2 syllables	*Swimming*
Line 2: Description of title	4 syllables	*Underwater*
Line 3: Action about the title	6 syllables	*Back and forth, side to side*
Line 4: Feeling about the title	8 syllables	*Relaxing, competing or not*
Line 5: Synonym for title	2 syllables	*My sport*

WORD CINQUAIN

Line 1: Title	1 word	*House*
Line 2: Description of title	2 words	*Red building*
Line 3: Action about the title	3 words	*Wide open doors*
Line 4: Feeling about the title	4 words	*Love and family here*
Line 5: Synonym for title	1 word	*Home*

Try some more. Add these to your collection of poetry.

HAIKU is a beautiful kind of poetry based on a Japanese verse form. It is usually about nature and often mentions one of the seasons.

Winter is now here
hate the cold but not the snow
winter has come now
by Gloria Tranby

Irises grow tall
purple waving in the spring
fantastic flowers
by Cathy Da Silva

Which piece of haiku do you prefer? _____

Write your reasons for this choice: _____

_____

_____

To write a haiku, follow this pattern.
Line 1: 5 syllables
Line 2: 7 syllables
Line 3: 5 syllables

Only the first line has a capital letter at the beginning.

Write some haiku of your own. Here are some topics you could use: birds, heat, woods, pets, weather, flowers, campfires, spring, fields, grass, water, snow, trees, clouds, lakes, wildlife.

_____   _____

_____   _____

_____   _____

_____   _____

_____   _____

List Poetry

A poem can sometimes be a list of things. This modern style of poetry doesn't have to rhyme.

Moving Day

Into the moving van
went my bunk beds and dresser,
the dining-room table and chairs,
the television and VCR,
the desk and computer parts,
boxes of clothes and boxes of dishes,
my books and the toys I still use,
my brother's hockey bag and sticks,
and lots more important stuff—
I can't remember it all.

Here's the start of two others. Finish them off!

I like my _____

_____

_____

_____

_____

_____

_____

and I like you!

It's in my backpack with

_____

_____

_____

_____

_____

_____

It must be here somewhere!

I remember the day I moved.

Were you upset?

Are you kidding! The movers dropped his computer and he got a new one from the insurance money!

Capital Consciousness

Ottawa, Ontario, is our nation's capital city. There are capital cities in every province and territory. The people who are elected to the provincial or federal government work in offices in government buildings.

Do you know the provincial and territorial capital cities across Canada?

_____, Newfoundland   _____, Prince Edward Island

_____, Nova Scotia   _____, New Brunswick

_____, Quebec   _____, Ontario

_____, Manitoba   _____, Saskatchewan

_____, Alberta   _____, British Columbia

_____, Nunavut   _____, Northwest Territories

_____, Yukon

You put a capital on the names of the days of the week, the months of the year and the names of cities, provinces and countries. You also need capitals for names of teams, titles of books, personal names and names of organizations, businesses and many products. These are all proper nouns.

Underline all of the nouns in these sentences. Correct the ones that should have a capital letter.

(a) I want to visit the thousand islands near kingston, ontario, in september.

(b) karen and rowan drove to rainy river to visit with jody and morgan.

(c) rob, kieran and david built a treehouse in the oak tree near the end of the road.

(d) They shopped for groceries at _____ and _____ on friday.
(Name some stores near where you live)

(e) The weather was cold and we did not have enough warm clothes when we camped near banff, alberta, last august.

(f) Every year there are collections of clothes and money made by the canadian red cross to help the needy.

(g) bill, fred and jordan were disappointed that they did not meet _____.
(Name a music star)

Invisible Nouns

Some nouns are **CONCRETE NOUNS**. They represent things we know are there with one of our five senses. That means we can see, hear, smell, touch or taste these things.

Underline the concrete nouns in these sentences.

(a) My family has a computer, a television, a VCR, a CD player and three radios.

(b) My two friends will meet me at the movie theatre.

(c) Did you find the baby's quilt in her stroller?

Other nouns are **ABSTRACT NOUNS**. They give a name to things we cannot see. They are the invisible ones.

Nouns like citizenship and happiness are invisible! You can't see them or touch them! Show how these concrete and abstract nouns are related to one another.

(a) You cannot see love, but you can see a heart.

_____*Heart*_____ is a concrete noun and _____ is an abstract noun.

(b) You cannot see joy, but you can see a smile.

_____ is a concrete noun and _____ is an abstract noun.

(c) You cannot see truth, but you can see a correct answer.

_____ is a concrete noun and _____ is an abstract noun.

Can you think of some other abstract nouns? Write them here.

_____   _____

_____   _____

_____   _____

_____   _____

_____   _____

Answer Key

Many of the pages in this workbook contain creative activities and spaces for open-ended responses. Only those that require a correct answer are included in this answer key.

Page 4
time
bottles
peanut butter
boxes
sign
name
clipboard
roster
headline
science
announcements
aloud
buddies
chalkboard
problem

Page 5
schedule
menu
instructions
recipe
profits
DEAR
book
homework
chart
weather
list
score
TV
planner
French
telephone directory

Page 9
3.
short a
Land Rover Volkswagen
Pontiac Subaru
Toyota Cavalier
Caravan Mazda

long a
Blazer

short e
Chevrolet Intrepid
Explorer

long e
Geo Beetle

short i
Jimmy Buick
Civic Intrepid
Buick

long i
Hyundi

short o
Volkswagen Pontiac
Honda

long o
Volkswagen Geo
Toyota Rover

short u
Sunbird Taurus
Hyundi

long u
Subaru Buick

silent vowels
Eagle Dodge

y - long e
Jimmy

y - long i
Hyundi

r-controlled
Sunbird Taurus
Caravan Blazer
Rover Cavalier
Explorer

special vowel sounds
Toyota Chevrolet
Pontiac

Pages 10 and 11
1. kid, cat, chorus, kit, clip
2. choir, crush, cot, kite, kill
3. Christmas, Kevin, cup cabin, coffee
4. track, leak, sick, bake, duck
5. spark, joke, make, week, hulk
6. brisk, brick, deck, bike, fake
7. mark, cake, sulk, choke, truck
8. break, take, steak, crack, neck
9. yoke, buck, pack, quake, bark
10. like, peak, kick, tick-tock, rake
11. quiet
12. box, wax
13. tax, quilt
14. quick, fox
15. quake
16. quite. quiz
17. fix
18. mix

Adjectives
vertical physical
musical practical

Nouns
uncle bicycle
article miracle

Pages 12 and 13
Sample answers:
unison: when everyone does something at the same time.
We all sang in unison.

universal: to give the same thing for all people.
We want to have universal access to education.

biceps: muscles in the upper arm.
Your strong biceps help you to lift heavy things.

bilingual: to be able to speak two languages.
My teacher is bilingual in French and English.

bicentennial: 200 years old.
We will celebrate our country's bicentennial in 2067.

triplets: three babies born at the same time.
The triplets were born at St. Joseph's Hospital on July 10.

triangle: a geometric shape with three straight sides and three vertices
A triangle might be seen in a design of a roof.

triplicate: three copies of a paper.
The job application form was filled out in triplicate.

Pages 14 and 15
1. semifinal
2. semidetached
3. semicolon
4. semicircle
5. semiconscious

6. anti-aircraft
7. antidote
8. antisocial
9. antifreeze
10. antiperspirants

11. illegal
12. inexpensive
13. irresponsible
14. immaturity
15. unnecessary

This is an answer check—not an answer cheat!

Answer Key

Page 16

```
C D L L V R O T A T C E P S L U H M F
Z Q E C S L I B R A R I A N H M Y S J
O H V J O P R E P O S I T I O N Z L N
R H Y R G S S E N E R A W A X G O H Y
S J N O I T E N E T D L X Z K M K B G
A N O I X E L P M O C E A N O I R E W
N O I T A N I B M O C L T A F K E X N
C J W G S S E N I L D N E I R F S P O
N O I N I P O U T M O D S I W N E R I
O C C U P A T I O N O Y S P U A A E S
T Z E I O B C L A B O U R E R I R S I
R E U E R L S I G N A T U R E C S V O
U N O F O N O I T I N I F E D I H I E
A R G U M E N T V U U W S J W R E O L
D A C C O M P L I S H M E N T T R N E
J O E R U T X I F P I M D K U C N N T
K P Z K C R O T C E R I D L K E N N J
Y W T I V X Z L F R E E D O M L U N H
R D Y Q A N O I T A L U P O P E M N V
```

aware**ness**	friendl**iness**
free**dom**	wis**dom**
accomplish**ment**	**argument**
electri**cian**	librar**ian**
labou**rer**	resear**cher**
specta**tor**	direc**tor**
fix**ture**	signa**ture**
opin**ion**	comple**xion**
expres**sion**	televi**sion**
deten**tion**	popula**tion**
combina**tion**	occupa**tion**
defini**tion**	preposi**tion**

Page 17

1. apologize
2. flexible
3. imaginary
4. infectious
5. excellence
6. merchandise
7. greenery, entrance
8. continuous
9. significant
10. unbelievable
11. contradictory
12. resident

Page 18

2-letter: ad Al
3-letter: red eel
4-letter: care read real clad reel reed lard
5-letter: clear Clare
7-letter: declare

2-letter: us
3-letter: act tar sub bus bar tab car
4-letter: crab tart acts bars star cars tabs stab
5-letter: crabs tarts tracts
8-letter: subtract

Pages 23 and 24

1. tensile strength: very strong—will not break under tension
2. split ends: the ends of each strand of hair are split in two
3. lost his grip: to let go of what he was holding
4. kind of picky: to be fussy about something
5. paced and pondered: walked back and forth while thinking
6. prosperous life: successful life
7. delightful children: well-behaved and pleasant kids

Advantages: Walkman, large TV, carpeting, fridge with snack food, (others including peace and quiet).

Disadvantages: loneliness, men climbing up her hair, no good jokes.

8. Rapunzel didn't choose Harold of Burgundy because he fell down when climbing her hair and blamed her for the accident.
9. Rapunzel thought that a prince should be smart. (She also liked a sense of humour.)
10. Rapunzel tied her Walkman headphones together to make a kind of rope. Using that, she lowered herself from the castle and met the prince on the ground.

Page 29

1. 4: Alex saw a bank of controls with labels.
   8: Alex tricked the computer into revealing the secret.
   1: The spaceship careened out of control.
   9: Alex lunged for the red handle.
   3: The ship was being run by its master computer.
   2: Everyone but Alex was unconscious.
   5: Alex decided that the engines had to be disabled.
   6: Alex spoke to the voice activated computer.
   7: The computer refused to shut down the engines.
2. People on the ship were not able to breathe, eat or move without the computer.
4. Both the computer and Alex seem to be able to think. The computer cannot solve problems the way Alex's brain is able to.
5. frightened, worried, concerned, doubtful, confident...

Page 34

1. Child's eyes—sparkled and danced like the sun
   Mom's laugh—rang like a bell
   Bright blue eyes—sparkled like jewels
   The story—like the waves of the ocean
   The story—like the ocean's tide
3. She describes his eyes, hair, glasses, stiff legs
4. Nova Scotia beside the Atlantic Ocean.

Pages 36 and 37

1. Robert Slater: lives with his mother, 18 years old, is a train engineer—the youngest ever to work there, won an award from the town of Pine Ridge.
2.
3. Bill: the train conductor, he takes the tickets from the customers—reads a paper in the caboose
   Malachi: came from Ireland when he was five—works as coal man—coal keeps the engine going—knows the two most important levers on the train. In his 40s now, covered in coal dust.
4. He was friendly and encouraged the young engineer.
5. (a) over several months
   (b) too much for lunch
7. (a) very
   (b) arranged
   (c) think
8. (a) not able to stay still
   (b) an expression for most of the stuff...not a real word
   (c) not thinking clearly

Page 45

St. John's Newfoundland
Charlottetown, Prince Edward Island
Halifax, Nova Scotia
Fredericton, New Brunswick
Quebec City, Quebec
Toronto, Ontario
Winnipeg, Manitoba

Answer Key

Regina, Saskatchewan
Edmonton, Alberta
Victoria, British Columbia
Iqaluit, Nunavut
Yellowknife, Northwest Territories
Whitehorse, Yukon

(a) Thousand Islands, Kingston,
Ontario, September
(b) Karen, Rowan, Rainy, River
Jody, Morgan

(c) Rob, Kieran, David

(d) (Store Names), Friday

(e) Banff, Alberta, August

(f) Canadian Red Cross

(g) Bill, Fred, Jordan, (music star)

Page 46
heart, love
smile, joy
answer, truth

promise, friendship, health,
weather, kindness, wealth

Page 51
1. beliefs   chiefs
   dwarfs   giraffes
   handkerchiefs   roofs
   scarfs   sheriffs
   wharfs
2. calves   elves
   halves   knives
   wolves   lives
   loaves   shelves
   thieves   wives

Page 52
1. pianos   radios   studios
   tacos   videos   rodeos
   banjos   patios   memos
   photos   zeros   dynamos
2. dominoes tomatoes potatoes
   echoes   heroes   vetoes

Page 53
Sample answers:
Her white cat is a Persian.
We all feel tired.
Today, there were two babies in the park.

should/must
should/must
could/might
will/did

Page 54
children/searched
Jeanne/found
Dimitri/looked
Mom/came
all/carried
they/went
It/contained
cobwebs/dirtied

Page 55
go went
find found
come came

Across:
3. caught   5. ate
6. swore   8. threw
11. took   12. blew
14. wore

Down:
1. ran   2. shrank
4. froze   6. stole
9. hung   10. wrote
11. were

Page 57
Samples:
(a) across the playground
(b) from my neighbourhood
(c) until ten o'clock
(d) beside the teacher
(e) with sunscreen
(f) before it finished
(g) at camp
(h) during the storm

Page 58
1. end → last
   thin → slim
   plot → plan
   tug → pull
   stumble → trip
   aid → help
   cut → clip
2. strike → punch
   fasten → bind
   bump → lump
   crash → smash

even → flat
fall → plunge
repair → mend
3. blend
   plump
   spend
   prompt
   tired
   unlock

Page 64
baby's face and angel
classroom and hot oven
grounded kid and a prisoner
Yonge Street and heart
Lake Superior's waves and
wild activity

Page 65
1. pancake
2. sly
3. slow
4. black
5. baby
6. silk
7. wind
8. hawk
9. merry-go-round
10. new
11. bone
12. shoe
13. glove
14. bug

Page 66
on cloud nine
by the skin of our teeth
were held up
once in a blue moon
the apple of her eye
the spitting image
it's raining cats and dogs
has the cat got your tongue
the cat's meow

Page 67
someone loves you and is proud
of you
it's raining very hard
why are you so quiet
I just got here in time
this happens very rarely
they were very excited

Answer Key

Pages 68 and 69

1. (a) fall: drop, autumn
   (b) hard: difficult/challenging, frozen
   (c) tie: make, necktie
   (d) threw: sent, hurled
      through: out of
   (e) weak: tired, not strong
      week: seven days
   (f) allowed: permitted
      aloud: out loud
   (g) chili: a bean stew
      chilly: cold, drafty, shivery
   (h) fair: justified
      fare: cost
   (i) sea: ocean
      see: vision
2. (a) vein vain
   (b) heard herd
   (c) died dyed
   (d) scene seen
   (e) two to too
   (f) wait weight
   (g) their there they're

Pages 74 and 75

On our holiday, we went to Upper Canada Village in Morrisburg, Ontario. We saw the way the Canadian pioneers lived when they settled here. We visited in many old homes where there were only candles or gaslights for the people to use when they were cooking or weaving.
3 smaller sentences
Answers to page 75 will vary.

Pages 76 and 77

1. yelled shouted called
3. "What do you want?" Ravi asked.

His sister Gita replied, "I need a new marker for this project. Do you have one?"

"Not me," Ravi told her with a shrug. "Go look in the kitchen."

"Where," she shouted, "should I look?"

Ravi shook his head. "You are really hopeless," he sighed as he

pointed to the marker in Gita's pencil case.

5. Kerry asked, "Did you enjoy reading your new book?"

"Oh yes," answered Paula. "It was even better than the movie. I saw it last year."

"Sometimes I am disappointed," commented Jennifer, "when I see the movie version after I have read a good book."

"I wonder if authors are pleased with movie versions of their stories?" thought Paula.

She turned to her friends and said, "Let's survey the kids in our class and see if they preferred the movie or the book."

"Great idea!" remarked Kerry and Jennifer. "Let's do it this afternoon."

"Do you think Ms. Phillips will let us?" Paula asked.

"No problem, Jennifer replied. "She's cool!"

Page 78

Are you sure?
Be our friend
Gramps' taxi
Paid for
I'm for fun
Love you forever
You are too close

Page 79

(a) Ont.	(b) Ont.	(c) Que.
(d) Sask.	(e) N.B.	(f) B.C.
(g) B.C.	(h) P.E.I.	(i) NU
(j) N.S.	(k) Alta.	(l) Que
(m) Alta.	(n) N.B.	(o) Nfdl.
(p) Man.	(q) N.S.	(r) Yukon
(s) Royal Canadian Mounted Police		

Page 80

(a) false
(b) true

(c) false
(d) false
(e) true
(f) false
(g) false

Page 83

2. (a) necessity: something that is required for you to live
   (b) adopt: to legally take the responsibility of caring for
   (c) replacement: something that is used instead of something else
   (d) eligible: if you meet certain requirements you are allowed to have something special
   (e) distract: to cause an animal or a person to lose their concentration

Page 85

1. Map of Canada—province of Nova Scotia—south-west shore
2. (a) maybe
   (b) yes
   (c) no
   (d) yes
   (e) yes
   (f) no
   (g) yes
   (h) maybe
3. speculate: to guess, to create a hypothesis
   tablet: piece of stone with writing on it
   exhausted: tired
   severed: cut off
   legendary: stories had been told about
   deliberately: on purpose
4. (a) bottom of a tree—keeps the tree anchored
   (b) beginnings—history

Page 87

2. Douglas fir, silver birch, red oak, sugar maple, red cedar, jack pine
5. (a) false
   (b) true
   (c) true
   (d) opinion
   (e) fact
6. objects and artifacts donated and donation

Maple Leaves

The Maple Leafs are an NHL hockey team.
They are not the Maple Leaves. This team name
does not make a change from an "f" to a "v"
when it becomes plural because it is a proper name.

The maple leaf is
one of your national symbols
in Canada. On my planet,
it's the foozbah flower.

1. Show the plural for each of these words. Simply add an "s" to each word.

belief ___beliefs___   chief _____

dwarf _____   giraffe _____

handkerchief _____   roof _____

scarf _____   sheriff _____

wharf _____

2. These words are exceptions. Here you make the plural by changing "f" to "v"
and adding "es."

calf ___calves___   elf _____

half _____   knife _____

wolf _____   life _____

loaf _____   shelf _____

thief _____   wife _____

Sometimes the dictionary will show you two ways to spell the plural. The first one is
the preferred or most common way. For example, dwarfs and dwarves, wharfs and
wharves, or scarfs and scarves.

3. Use two of the words from each section above in a complete sentence.

_____

_____

_____

_____

_____

Singalong

You say potătoes and I say potătoes!

You say tomătoes and I say tomătoes!

These are the opening lines of an old song. Perhaps one of your parents or grandparents could sing part of it to you. It is about different pronunciations that people have for words. It also helps you remember two exceptions to the rule below.

To make most words that end in an "o" into the plural, just add an "s," not an "es".

1. Make these words into their plural form:

piano _____   radio _____   studio _____

taco _____   video _____   rodeo _____

banjo _____   patio _____   memo _____

photo _____   zero _____   dynamo _____

2. These are exceptions and require "es":

domino _____   tomato _____   potato _____

echo _____   hero _____   veto _____

3. Some words that come from Latin keep their Latin plural form. Choose two of these words and look up their meaning in the dictionary. Write the definition.

analysis	analyses	_____
crisis	crises	_____
criterion	criteria	_____
datum	data	_____
hypothesis	hypotheses	_____
die	dice	_____
phenomenon	phenomena	_____

An Assistant, Please!

LINKING VERBS
These words join or link the subject to another noun or adjective in the predicate.

Subject   Predicate
My old car is rusty.   (The word "is" works as a linking verb.)

Use one of these linking verbs in the sentences below when you see LV.

look, smell, feel, seem, become, turn, taste, appear, be, is, are, was, were, am, been

Hint: You might want to change the tense for some of the words before you use them.

Add nouns and adjectives where they are marked.

Her _____ cat _____ a _____.
     ADJECTIVE   LV   NOUN

We all _____ _____.
         LV   ADJECTIVE

Today, there _____ two _____ in the park.
               LV   NOUN

HELPING VERBS
These words come just before the main verb and help it to show an action.

I will write the postcard tonight.

The word **will** is a helping verb that helps tell that the action will take place in the future.

I have been writing a journal every night.

These words **have been** act as helping verbs to let us know that this is a continuing action.

Use one of these words to help the main verb in the following sentences. Sometimes there will be more than one word that will work.

shall, will, could, would, should, might, must, can, may, do, did, have, had, has

I _____ be home before ten o'clock because the stores close at 9:30.

I know that I _____ study for the test for several days.

There are two ways we _____ take to visit my grandparents.

They _____ not come with us tonight.

In the Attic

Everyone likes to hear stories from the past. If they could talk, many attics could tell stories of children now grown up. The old toys, old clothes, school books and report cards tucked away in boxes, trunks and cupboards are reminders of times past. When you know about people in your past you find out a little something about your own history, too.

When something has happened at a time before the present, we say that it happened in the past. Verbs can be present, past or future tense. (In other languages there are even more tenses.)

They are always the predicate (action) portion of the sentence.

Divide these sentences into subject and predicate and choose a verb that will make sense in these sentences.

went	found	looked	searched	dirtied
carried	contained	opened	came	

$\quad$ S $\quad\quad\quad\quad\quad\quad$ P

The third floor attic was rarely _opened_____.

The children _____ for clues about their family in the attic.

Mary and Jeanne _____ their Mom's wedding dress.

George and Dimitri _____ at the old notebooks from fifty years ago.

Mom _____ upstairs to have a look too.

They all _____ something downstairs for a better look.

They _____ back the next day to see what was in the old black trunk.

It _____ old holiday decorations and lights.

The cobwebs _____ every corner of the attic.

Some of the verbs you used on page 54 are irregular verbs. That means you do not add "ed" to the main verb. The word changes. What are the present tenses, for these three verbs?

Present	Past
_go_	went
_____	found
_____	came

Now, write the past tense of these irregular verbs in the sentences and then put them in the crossword puzzle.

ACROSS

3. We __caught__ seven fish at Lake Sturgeon. **(catch)**

5. They _____ fish for dinner. **(eat)**

6. The dog _____ after a swim in the lake. **(shake)**

7. We _____ that it was hotter this year than last year. **(swear)**

8. Are you the one who _____ my towel in the lake? **(throw)**

11. She _____ everyone in to have ice cream. **(take)**

12. After they _____ the whistle, the race started. **(blow)**

14. We _____ old clothes when we went camping in Algonquin Park. **(wear)**

DOWN

1. They _____ until they got out of the rain. **(run)**

2. Her new sweater _____ when it was wet. **(shrink)**

4. They all _____ inside the air-conditioned store. **(freeze)**

6. He claimed that someone _____ his new jacket. **(steal)**

9. It was _____ next to the red one on the last hook. **(hang)**

10. He always _____ cheques to pay the rent on the first day of the month. **(write)**

13. They _____ beside me when the show started. **(are)**

I Need Company

Everyone needs company some of the time, but most people enjoy some time alone. What do you like to do with others, and when you are by yourself? Brainstorm a list of these things. Give yourself a time limit of four minutes, two for each!

With others	By myself

These words are all prepositions. They must have company to do their job!

on	in	beside	of	below	behind
across	toward	with	within	over	above
before	until	beyond	from	during	after
at	against				

When you see a preposition and some words that follow it, you are reading a prepositional phrase. These words tell you more information about the subjects or verbs of your sentence.

A prepositional phrase can work like an <u>adjective</u> if it describes a noun.

My shoes <u>with the silver stars</u> are packed.

or

It can work like an <u>adverb</u> if it connects with the verb in the sentence.

They are packed <u>in my brown suitcase</u>.

Proposition Prepositions

Finish these sentences with a prepositional phrase that makes sense:

(a) There were 10 of my friends *across the playground* .

(b) The children were all _____.

(c) Some of them could stay out _____.

(d) They sat _____.

(e) The kids _____ didn't get a sunburn.

(f) We decided to go home _____.

(g) The parents _____ were all visiting.

(h) _____ we all stayed together.

Prepositions give you a position!

That is so corny!

Now write a short journal entry for today with at least three prepositional phrases!

This morning _____

_____

_____

_____

_____

_____

_____

_____

_____

_____

_____

_____

_____

_____

_____

It's a Match!

Words that are well matched mean the same thing. They are called SYNONYMS.

1. Match the words in the left column with the synonym in the right column.

Why do we have so many words for the same thing?

end	trip
thin	pull
plot	clip
tug	last
stumble	plan
aid	help
cut	slim

2. Try another set!

Because English is a rich language.

strike	bind
fasten	mend
bump	plunge
crash	flat
even	punch
fall	lump
repair	smash

3. Choose the word that does not belong in each set of three words.

divide	separate	blend
slim	plump	slender
keep	save	spend
tardy	late	prompt
happy	pleased	tired
secure	unlock	safe

Boom! Bang! Crash!

The words in the title sound as though a little kid has opened the cupboard in the kitchen and pulled out a pot. Then several more are falling all around the first one. Then WAAA!

or

It could be the sound of an accident on the highway as one car hits another in a fender bender!

or

Write your idea here.

_____

_____

_____

Some words help to make visual pictures in your mind. Some words make a special sound that helps you to think about what they mean. This is called ONOMATOPOEIA.

Here are some examples:

boom	buzz	crash	crunch	fizz
growl	howl	meow	moan	moo
pitter-patter	pop	purr	quack	roar
rustle	scream	sizzle	slap	smash
splash	splat	whisper	yell	zoom

Choose eight of these words and write a sentence for each. You might want to add word endings to some of the words.

(sizzle) The sizzling hamburgers on the barbecue made me feel hungry.

_____

_____

_____

_____

_____

_____

_____

_____

Tongue Twisters

Peter Piper picked a peck of pickled peppers. If Peter Piper picked a peck of pickled peppers, where's the peck of pickled peppers Peter Piper picked?

Can you finish these tongue twisters?

She sells sea shells _____.

How much wood would a woodchuck chuck if _____

Did you learn these three tongue twisters when you were little? _____

How fast can you say them now without tripping on your tongue?

When most of the words in a verse or a sentence start with the same sound or letter it is called alliteration. Tongue twisters are a good example of alliteration. The same consonant sound is repeated many times and makes it hard to pronounce the words.

Try to make a sentence or a verse with many of these words. You might want to add different endings to some of them.

radish	raspberry	railroad
rascal	rodent	rapid
ruin	reach	red
rush	refuse	real
r_____	r_____	r_____

Ron the rodent _____

_____

_____

Try again with another letter or sound.

_____

_____

_____

_____

_____

_____

Here's one I made up: Edgar eats elegant eggplant!

Look in magazines and newspapers to see if you find any examples of alliteration. Often advertisers use alliteration in parts of their ads.

See what you can find. Write any that you find here, or make up some of your own.

Helpful Heroes Halt Runaway Honda

RUGBY RULES AT RUNNYMEDE

HURRICANE HURLS HAIL

_____

_____

_____

_____

_____

_____

Make a magazine ad for "Luscious Lemon Lollipops." Remember to use pictures as well as words.

We're Connected Somehow!

A *Venn diagram* is used to compare and contrast two or more things. If you compare a house and a trailer for example, you will put words that tell how they are the same into the overlapping part. The characteristics that only belong to the house will go into one large part of one circle and the characteristics that only belong to the trailer will go into the large part of the other circle.

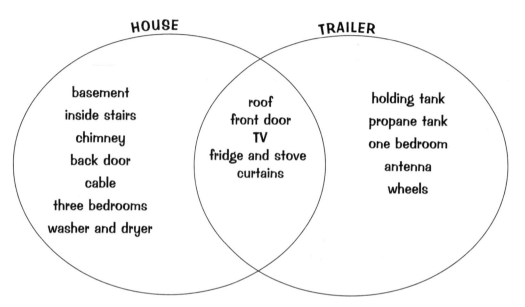

HOUSE

TRAILER

basement
inside stairs
chimney
back door
cable
three bedrooms
washer and dryer

roof
front door
TV
fridge and stove
curtains

holding tank
propane tank
one bedroom
antenna
wheels

Add two more things that you think belong in each section of the Venn diagram.

Now make two more Venn diagrams for each one of these comparisons:
• yourself to your brother, sister or a friend
• two movies that are popular

Hey, there's not enough room here!

So get another piece of paper, Freddie.

Now let's interpret this information with words. Use three of these words to write a sentence about how the things are the same.

similarly   as   also   like   likewise   in the same way   both

A house has a front door with a screen door. A trailer has a front door with a screen door on one side of the trailer. This is the front of the trailer when it is parked.

_____

_____

_____

_____

_____

_____

Use three of these words to write a sentence about how they are different.

but   however   otherwise   yet   on the other hand   still   although   even

_____

_____

_____

_____

_____

_____

_____

Painting Pictures

A description of an event or a place can be made more interesting by painting word pictures. Just the right adjective or adverb can be enough to create a picture in readers' minds. But when you want to tell someone about something special, you can also use **metaphors** or **similes**.

If you say, "The class was a zoo," you mean that the kids were loud and not following the plans for the day. "Zoo" is a metaphor for people who are out of control.

What comparisons are being made in these sentences?

1. The baby has an angel's face.

The baby's face is compared to the face of an angel.

2. It is so hot! Our classroom is an oven.

_____

3. I'm grounded this week! I'm a prisoner in my own home.

_____

4. Yonge Street is the heart of Toronto.

_____

5. Lake Superior is wild tonight.

_____

If you say, "Fred is as quiet as a mouse when he leaves for work," you know that he doesn't make a sound when he moves around getting ready to leave. "As quiet as a mouse" is a simile. The word "like" is also used in similes.

Use these words to complete the similes in the following sentences.

wind	black	silk	hawk	sly
glove	slow	bug	shoe	baby
new	bone	pancake	merry-go-round	

1. In the book *Flat Stanley*, Stanley was as flat as a _____.

2. Everyone thought the salesperson was as _____ as a fox.

3. It took so long for them to be ready. They were as _____ as molasses in January.

4. Late at night, the water at the lake was as _____ as ink.

5. I slept like a _____ last night.

6. The baby's hair feels as smooth as _____.

7. The new pony can run like the _____.

8. They had to watch their new kitten like a _____.

9. I feel like we are on a _____.

10. My watch was repaired and now it's as good as _____.

I'm as happy as a clam.

11. They are as happy as a dog with a good _____.

12. This bike is as comfortable as an old _____.

13. The suit is perfect. It fits me like a _____.

14. She is as snug as a _____ in a rug.

Try some similes of your own. Some of them might be exaggerations.

Are clams happy?

1. My friend is as tall as the _____.

2. My friend looks like _____.

3. It's so crowded. There are as many people here as _____.

4. My school is like a _____.

Time Flies When You're Having Fun

The kids were all on cloud nine. Tonight was the night they had been waiting for, the school's Education Week concert. This year the choir was performing two selections. Both were pieces they would enter in the upcoming Kiwanis Music Festival.

When Ms Sarcee lined the choir up to walk on stage, one person was missing. Within seconds, Joey ran in, all out of breath. His father was right behind him.

"We just got here by the skin of our teeth," Mr. Simonetti said. "There was an accident at the corner and we were held up!"

"That's OK," replied Ms Sarcee. "At least you're here now. It's only once in a blue moon that the mayor is able to attend the concert. Tonight she's here. I'm so glad that all the grade five and six students are present."

"Do your best now!" Dad said, looking at Joey. "Your grandmother will be in the audience and you know that you are the apple of her eye!"

The concert was over in no time at all.

After the concert the students met up with families and friends in the front foyer of the school. Joey's grandmother came up to him and gave him a big hug. "You were the cat's meow, Joey," she said, "just like your dad when he was in the choir. I always said you were the spitting image of your Dad—and just imagine, you can sing even better than he could at your age!"

On the drive home it started to pour. Joey's mother commented, "It's raining cats and dogs. We're lucky that the rain held off until the end of the night."

Joey and his brother started to giggle. When Grandmother asked them what was so funny, they both looked at each other and laughed even harder. Next when she said to them, "What's the matter, has the cat got your tongue?" they laughed so hard it was like

_____ .

A FIGURE OF SPEECH is an exaggerated expression that is used to describe something.

Underline any figures of speech—old or new—that you see in the story. Then add one more to finish it.

Have you noticed that sometimes older people say phrases that are difficult for you to understand? Joey's parents and grandmother use some strange expressions to add colour to what they say. They're speaking English but sometimes the words just don't sound like they make any sense at all. This is because they are using IDIOMS.

Find these idioms in the story. Now try to tell what they mean. Draw a funny picture to go with each one.

You are the apple of my eye.

I think this means _someone loves_
you a lot and is proud of you.

It's raining cats and dogs

I think this means _____

_____

Has the cat got your tongue?

I think this means _____

_____

I got here by the skin of my teeth.

I think this means _____

_____

It's only once in a blue moon.

I think this means _____

_____

They were on cloud nine.

I think this means _____

_____

Double Meanings

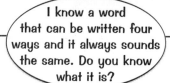

I know a word that can be written four ways and it always sounds the same. Do you know what it is?

HOMOPHONES are words that sound the same but have different meanings.

1. Change ONE of the underlined homophones in these sentences.
You might need to use a dictionary or thesaurus to help you.
You may use just one word or a phrase that makes sense.

(a) Leaves <u>fall</u> from the trees in the <u>fall</u>.

_____

(b) It's too <u>hard</u> to plant seeds in the winter when the ground is <u>hard</u>.

_____

(c) It is easier to <u>tie</u> a knot in the <u>tie</u> before you put it on.

_____

(d) Guy and David <u>threw</u> their airplanes <u>through</u> the upstairs window.

_____

(e) She told the doctor she had been feeling <u>weak</u> for at least a <u>week</u>.

_____

(f) He was <u>allowed</u> to have the questions read <u>aloud</u> to him for the tests.

_____

(g) Many people like to eat some hot <u>chili</u> for dinner on a <u>chilly</u> night.

_____

(h) It wasn't <u>fair</u> that he had to pay the <u>fare</u> on the bus for all of us.

_____

(i) The <u>sea</u> goes on as far as I can <u>see</u>.

_____

2. Just for fun, we'll make silly sentences by using homophones. Show that you know which one is the correct word by using it in the right part of the sentence.

(a) The doctor needed to put a needle into a _____ in my arm to do a blood test. He tried in _____ on my left arm and had to use my right arm. **(vein, vain)**

(b) Have you _____ that there will be a new _____ of buffalo at the national park next year? **(herd, heard)**

(c) She said that she almost _____ from surprise when she saw the colour her friend had _____ her hair. **(died, dyed)**

(d) They went back to see the _____ of the accident. They said that they had _____ a car swerving carelessly from one lane to another. **(seen, scene)**

(e) My _____ brothers will be going away _____ camp. I wish I could go, _____. **(to, too, two)**

(f) The postal clerk said, "Please _____ , I'll check the _____ on that parcel when I finish with this customer." **(wait, weight)**

Did you guess these four words— pair, pear, pare, and pere!

(g) They will play the game where everyone puts _____ shoes in a pile over _____ and then races to find the right pair. When _____ finished everyone must run back to the line. The first back wearing their own shoes is the winner. **(their, they're, there)**

3. Use these words correctly in a sentence:

pried _____

pride _____

flee _____

flea _____

board _____

bored _____

Visit a Fortune Teller

Have you ever made one of these before?

1. Cut out the square on the opposite page.

2. Fold on all of the dotted lines.

3. Print one pair of antonyms on opposite corners of the outside square. Print the other pair on the other two corners. You remember that antonyms are opposite words, don't you?

4. Repeat step 3 on the inside square with new word pairs.

5. Put your two thumbs and two forefingers into the open flaps (they look like little tents).

6. Ask your friend to choose one of the four words. Spell the word by moving the flaps together for the first letter and apart for the second letter, together for the third letter, and apart again for the fourth letter. Repeat this pattern until the last letter is done.

7. Now ask your friend to choose one of the two new words. Again, spell this word and move the flaps for each letter.

8. When this word is finished, ask your friend to make one last choice.

9. Then lift the flap and read your friend's fortune out loud.

Here are two pairs of antonyms for the first square:

inside	outside
under	over

Think of two pairs for the second round.

Here are some ideas for fortunes!

- You will be rich!
- You will have a job with computers.
- You will be in show business.
- You will be a famous author.
- You will live to be 100.
- You will always be happy.
- You will visit another planet.

After you do this one, find a blank piece of paper and make some more antonym fortune tellers.

You will make two kinds of folds.

1. Fold up or toward you when you see lines like this ---------

2. Fold down or away from you when you see lines like like this ....

3. Follow the alphabetical order A–H when you make the folds.

4. Fold and reopen on lines I–L.

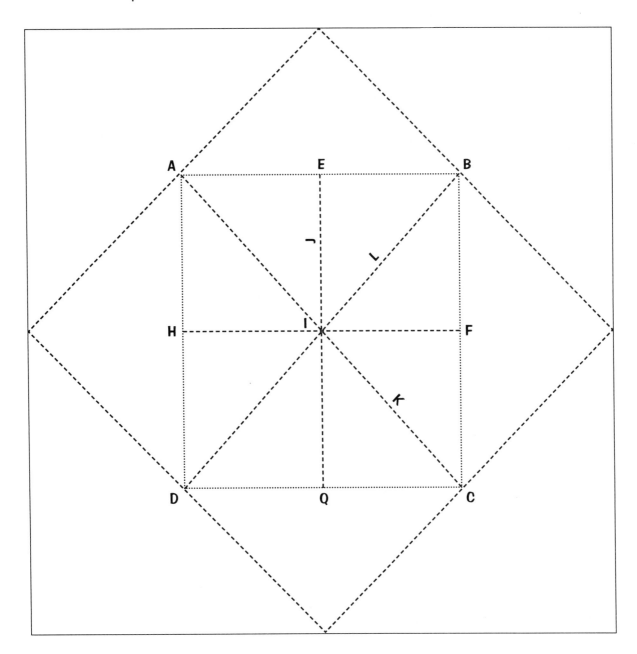

Smileys, Not Similes

If you have sent or received any e-mail you probably know what "smileys" are. When you hear someone talking, you can get an idea about their mood by the tone of their voice. With e-mail and letters you can't. Someone decided that a fun way to communicate a person's mood would be with a new form of punctuation that can be arranged to make faces.

Bend your head over onto your left shoulder and what do you see?

:)   ;)   : (

I thought the "e" in e-mail stood for Edgar!

The first guy could be saying, "I'm happy to be talking to you."

The guy who is winking might be saying, "Do you get my joke?"

What do you think the last smiley is saying? _____

_____

Write a message to three friends. End each one with a smiley to show what you are feeling.

_____

_____

_____

_____

_____

_____

_____

_____

_____

Rambling Roads

When we ramble along on a road, we are out for a sightseeing drive. When we ramble on a holiday it doesn't really matter where we are going. That might be OK for a trip when you want to see interesting things and discover the local points of interest, but it is not OK when you write or read something.

Rambling sentences are sometimes called run-on sentences. Usually they have too many small sentences joined together incorrectly. When you were younger, you probably wrote some rambling sentences by putting too many "ands" and "thens" in your work.

Try to fix up these rambling or run-on sentences that might be found in your younger brother's or sister's journal.

My mother is interested in collecting cups and saucers from older people like her aunts who used to play tea party with her when she was a child.

My mother is interested in collecting cups and saucers. She likes to get them from her aunts and other older people. She remembers having tea parties with her aunts when she was a child.

I made one run-on sentence into ___*three*___ smaller sentences.

On our holiday, we went to Upper Canada Village in Morrisburg, Ontario, where we saw the way the Canadian pioneers lived when they settled here and we visited in many old homes where there were only candles or gaslights for the people to use when they were cooking or weaving.

_____

_____

_____

_____

_____

_____

I made one run-on sentence into _____ smaller sentences.

I'll never ramble on.

Last week there were so many good things to watch on television that I couldn't decide what to watch because I just love sports and since the Pan American games were televised I wanted to watch many of the events with my parents who also love to watch these competitions.

_____

_____

_____

_____

_____

I made one run-on sentence into _____ smaller sentences.

We went to my cousin George's wedding last Saturday in Calgary, Alberta, but before the wedding we had time to visit Heritage Park where we rode an old train pulled by a steam engine all around the old-fashioned village.

_____

_____

_____

_____

_____

I made one run-on sentence into _____ smaller sentences.

Tonight I will go to my second karate class at the community centre with my friend Jacob whose brother is one of the instructors because he got his black belt and took some special classes about how to teach kids karate and how to do it safely.

_____

_____

_____

_____

I made one run-on sentence into _____ smaller sentences.

May I Quote You on That?

When the speaker's name is at the BEGINNING, quotation marks are used like this:

> Helena yelled to her friend, "Stay away from the edge of the dock!"

When the speakers name is in the MIDDLE, use quotation marks like this:

> "Maura," Helena shouted, "you should stay away from the edge!"

When the speaker's name comes at the END, use quotation marks this way:

> "Stay away from the edge of the dock! It is slippery and the water is deep there," called Helena.

---

1. What words are used instead of the word "said" in the three examples above?

_____ _____ _____

2. Brainstorm twelve other words that could be used to replace the word "said" in a sentence that includes a quotation.

_____ _____ _____

_____ _____ _____

_____ _____ _____

_____ _____ _____

3. Add the missing quotation marks.

What do you want? Ravi asked.

His sister Gita replied, I need a new marker for this project. Do you have one?

Not me, Ravi told her with a shrug. Go look in the kitchen.

Where, she shouted, should I look?

Ravi shook his head. You are really hopeless, he sighed as he pointed to the

marker in Gita's pencil case.

4. Make these sentences into direct quotations. Add a speaker to each. The first word in a direct quote will have a capital.

_____ _____ Do you know when they will be home from camp?

I don't know. _____ _____. Ask her!

Let's go on the subway. _____ _____.

I've been waiting all week to see this movie. _____ _____.

So have I! _____ _____, I hear it is great!

5. Place quotation marks, commas and ending marks in the following sentences.

Kerry asked Did you enjoy reading your new book

Oh yes answered Paula it was even better than the movie I saw it last year

Sometimes I am disappointed commented Jennifer when I see the movie version after I have read the book

I wonder if authors are pleased with movie versions of their stories thought Paula

She turned to her friends and said let's survey the kids in our class and see if they preferred the movie or the book

Great idea remarked Kerry and Jennifer Let's do it this afternoon

Do you think Ms Phillips will let us Paula asked

No problem Jennifer replied She's cool

I'm 4 Fun

Imagine you are older and have bought the car of your dreams.
If you were registering this new car and needed to buy licence plates, would you take the next ones in the regular sequence, or do you think you would order personalized licence plates? _____

If you wanted personalized ones, what would you want yours to say?

_____

Some people have used their own initials and the initials of their partner.
Some people have used the name of their business or profession.
Some people take a favourite word and then make it into a very short sentence.

What do you think these licence plates mean?
Put in periods to mark the abbreviations on the ones that need them.
Some extra punctuation may help the meaning of some.

Some numbers might change into words.

IMA DR

RU SURE

I'm a Doctor

GRAMPS TXI

BR FRIEND

PAID 4

IM4 FUN

LU4EVR

UR2 CLOSE

Make up some funny licence plates of your own.

Keep It Short

Some abbreviations are standardized so that everyone knows what they mean. Canada Post wants us to use special abbreviations for the provinces on mail we send. Each province is represented by two capital letters. There is another abbreviated form that you will see in some of your text books. You need to know both.

	Standard form	Postal form
Nunavut	(no abbreviation)	NU
Northwest Territories	N.W.T	NT
Yukon	Y.T.	YK
British Columbia	B.C.	BC
Alberta	Alta.	AB
Saskatchewan	Sask.	SK
Manitoba	Man.	MB
Ontario	Ont.	ON
Quebec	Que.	QC
New Brunswick	N.B.	NB
Nova Scotia	N.S.	NS
Prince Edward Island	P.E.I.	PE
Newfoundland	Nfld.	NF

Do you know the province in which the following tourist sites or cities are located? Write the standard abbreviation for the province on the line following the place name.

(a) The Mint, Ottawa, _____

(b) Baffin Island, _____

(c) Museum of Civilization, Hull, _____

(d) King's Landing, _____

(e) Stanley Park, Vancouver, _____

(f) Red River, _____

(g) Queen Charlotte Islands, _____

(h) Green Gables, _____

(i) Ontario Place, Toronto, _____

(j) Cape Breton Island, _____

(k) West Edmonton Mall, Edmonton, _____

(l) Walled Old Town, _____

(m) Banff, Lake Louise and Jasper, _____

(n) The Citadel, _____

(o) Longest Covered Bridge, Hartford, _____

(p) Cape Spear Lighthouse, _____

(q) R.C.M.P. Museum, Regina, _____

(r) Whitehorse, _____

(s) R.C.M.P. is the abbreviation for _____ _____

_____ _____ .

Just Because

We have **Velcro** because an engineer's pet dog was bothered by burrs stuck in his fur. The animal and his owner had returned from a walk and the burrs were attached everywhere. Burrs have little hooks which grab on to anything passing by. These help seeds to be carried to a new location. The idea to make some fasteners with tiny hooks came to Georges de Mestral, a Swiss engineer, who then created Velcro. Today, before children learn to tie up shoelaces, many have shoes fastened with Velcro. Some backpacks and notebooks are fastened this way too.

We have **Frisbees** because Yale University students used to toss empty pie tins by flicking their wrists in just the right way. The pie tins came from the Frisbie Pie Company. The game was made safer when plastic discs, shaped like flying pie tins, were manufactured by Walter Morrison in 1918. The name Frisbee is almost the same as the original Frisbie Pie Company.

My spaceship looks like a frisbee!

Each of these inventions was created because an inventor connected something he saw with an idea for something useful to people. Both of these inventions have become popular. Anyone can be an inventor! It doesn't matter how old you are or how long you have been in school.

Do you know why we have **sandwiches**? The story goes that many years ago, the Earl of Sandwich enjoyed gambling so much that he didn't want to leave the tables to eat. The meal prepared for him to eat with his hands was made of bread and meat. We now call a meal between two pieces of bread a sandwich, after the Earl who liked gambling so much! Almost anything can go between two pieces of bread.

Now try these true and false questions:

(a) Burrs are not part of a plant.   true   false

(b) Velcro is used on shoes.   true   false

(c) A pie plate has a spherical shape.   true   false

(d) Frisbees are made at a bakery.   true   false

(e) Inventors need to be creative.   true   false

(f) Inventors must be well educated.   true   false

(g) Sandwiches are all the same.   true   false

Let's imagine some situations and think of what caused them. In some others, you will need to think of what the effect might be. There are not any right answers. Be creative with your ideas. The **effect** tells you **what** happened. The **cause** tells you **why** it happened.

Cause: Your parents' car ran out of gas on a busy road.

Effect: _____

Cause: You spent your allowance at the candy store.

Effect: _____

Cause: _____

Effect: Your brother shouted at you, "Go away!"

Cause: _____

Effect: The plane was an hour late leaving.

Cause: You fell out of the tree.

Effect: _____

Cause: Your dog was sprayed by a skunk last night.

Effect: _____

Cause: _____

Effect: The visiting author signed my copy of her book.

Cause: _____

Effect: He watched the reports of the space flight on television.

Cause: The fireworks display was incredible!

Effect: _____

A Sign of the Times

= NO SERVICE

NO PETS ALLOWED
Seeing-eye dogs are welcome

These are signs found on many restaurant doors. They spells out some of the laws that restaurant owners must follow. Some laws are made by the health department and some of them are designed to protect human rights.

The use of a seeing-eye dog is important for someone who is blind or has limited vision. Seeing-eye dogs are working dogs and must be allowed to enter buildings where other animals are kept out. The dog's vision become the replacement eyes for his owner. These days, the dogs are also called guide dogs.

A guide dog begins training as a young puppy. It is adopted by a family and raised to be obedient, just like any family pet. The dog also is trained by the family to do special tasks. The dog may be taken in to a shopping mall while undergoing its training. It must learn how to wait while its trainer is eating or shopping. It is also trained to watch for danger. A special note is carried by the trainer to explain why the dog is in a building where pets are not usually allowed.

Some dogs are not successful in their training as guide dogs. Perhaps they grow too big or do not have the right temperament to be a working dog. These animals still make wonderful pets and may be adopted by a family.

When training is about halfway through, the guide dog is matched with a blind person who is eligible for a dog. When they are comfortable with each other, both return home to begin the business of daily living. This might include going to work in an office building downtown, riding a bus, visiting friends and going to a place of worship.

It is important for everyone to remember that when a guide dog is in a harness, it is working. You shouldn't stop and pet the dog or distract it from its work. When you see a guide dog at work, watch it and notice how it watches for traffic. It's wonderful how it guides its owner safely across streets, through crowds and around obstacles. A seeing-eye dog is a special treasure!

1. Explain why you think the sign says: No shoes-No shirts-No service.

_____

_____

_____

_____

2. What is the meaning of these words:

(a) necessity _____

(b) adopt _____

(c) replacement _____

(d) eligible _____

(e) distract _____

3. What question might you ask the owner of a guide dog?

_____

_____

_____

4. Besides seeing-eye dogs, there are special dogs trained to help people who are deaf. There are also some horses trained for people with physical disabilities to ride for enjoyment.

Finish this sentence with your own thoughts.

Animals can be valuable to people with disabilities because _____

_____

_____

_____

_____

Pirates, Tricksters or Maybe Knights

One of the most exciting tales of mystery has its roots on Oak Island in Nova Scotia. Many facts are known about this place but even more questions are left unanswered. It has been named the Money Pit. People speculate that there is treasure buried deep underground. This treasure would have been put there deliberately in the fifteenth century. Many attempts to retrieve the treasure have been unsuccessful. Six people have died in these attempts. Underground photography through a borehole showed chests and a severed human hand. Even today, no one knows what the treasure is or when it will be discovered.

Three teenaged boys were the first to explore this area in 1795. One of the boys, Daniel McGinnis, had seen a suspicious saucer-shaped hollow in the ground under a large old oak tree that had a broken limb. He brought his friends back with shovels to search the area. Tales of the legendary pirates Blackbeard and Captain Kidd who roamed the Atlantic Ocean were probably familiar to them. Perhaps they thought that these pirates had come ashore and buried their treasure for safekeeping.

The boys found a number of peculiar things as they dug further into the clay. They worked steadily for several weeks. Just a half metre below the surface, they found a layer of flagstone that was not available in that part of the country. A bit farther down they found a four-metre round shaft that was filled with loose, sandy soil. They found oak platforms at the depths of three, six and nine metres. They only gave up when sea water rushed in to fill in the areas where they had dug. They realized that the people who had built this hiding place had gone to a great deal of trouble to keep something hidden—even building a booby trap to protect it!

Over the last 200 years, many people have explored Oak Island. There have been several companies interested in discovering the secrets of the Money Pit. Engineers have studied the structure and decided that there must have been a pressure seal that was broken when the boys were first digging. Discoveries have been made of many underground tunnels that lead away from the main shaft. Water levels were carefully controlled by these tunnels.

Several artifacts have been discovered in the shafts and nearby area. These include a pair of Spanish-American scissors, some parchment and a tablet found 27 metres below the surface, with the message *Forty feet below, two million pounds are buried.*

Theories about the reasons for this booby trap are many. Some suggest that the lost treasure of the Templar Knights is there. Another theory is that aliens and UFOs might be responsible for this mystery. What's certain is that whoever built the hideaway did not return.

You might be able to find out more information about Oak Island by doing a search on the Internet.

1. In an atlas, where would you look for Oak Island? _____

2. Did the following events happen? Fill in the correct circle.

   (a) Treasure was buried on Oak Island.   ○ Yes   ○ No   ○ Maybe

   (b) Daniel McGinnis found a strange   ○ Yes   ○ No   ○ Maybe
        depression in the land under an oak tree.   ○ Yes   ○ No   ○ Maybe

   (c) Pirates killed six people.   ○ Yes   ○ No   ○ Maybe

   (d) Millions of dollars have been spent   ○ Yes   ○ No   ○ Maybe
        exploring Oak Island.

   (e) Oak platforms were found at   ○ Yes   ○ No   ○ Maybe
        three-metre intervals.

   (f) Only local material was used in the pit.   ○ Yes   ○ No   ○ Maybe

   (g) The builders never returned for the treasure.   ○ Yes   ○ No   ○ Maybe

   (h) Someday we may hear about a discovery   ○ Yes   ○ No   ○ Maybe
        on Oak Island.

3. What is the definition of these words:

   speculate _____

   tablet _____

   exhausted _____

   severed _____

   legendary _____

   deliberately _____

4. What are two meanings of the word "roots?"

   (a) _____

   (b) _____

   Which one is used in the first paragraph? _____

5. If the treasure on Oak Island is discovered, who do you think the rightful owners should be?

   _____

6. What do you think might be found in the pit?

   _____

Once Upon a Tree

A Halifax artist by the name of Tyler Aspin has created a wonderful way to collect stories from across Canada. His sculpture, the Canada Tree, is a 10-metre tall, two-tonne model of a tree. Tyler designed this tree to help all Canadians tell their stories.

There are many wooden artifacts embedded in the trunk and branches of the tree. Each of these objects was donated by an interested citizen of our country. A fascinating story comes along with each item. The more than 600 donations include two wooden paddles from Ernie Coombs, which were used by Casey and Finnegan on the TV show *Mr. Dressup*, a piece of a hockey stick autographed by Wayne Gretzky, shingles from Green Gables in Prince Edward Island, toys donated by many children and even an acorn picked up from the lawn of the Governor General's official residence in Ottawa.

The history of some important Canadian events is included in the stories that the tree can tell. A cross section of a Douglas fir tells the story of the annual gift to the city of Boston of a Christmas tree. This is done to commemorate the help that the citizens of Boston gave to the people of Halifax after the explosion on the morning of December 6, 1917. A small piece of wood from a wooden casement window placed in our federal parliament buildings in 1910 is now part of the tree. There are also many items that are rarely in use today. These include wooden spools for thread, wooden button hooks and wooden fishing tools.

The materials used in the Canada Tree are from every province and territory in this country. There is red oak from Prince Edward Island, red cedar from British Columbia, silver birch from Saskatchewan, sugar maple from Quebec and jack pine from the Northwest Territories.

The Canada Tree has travelled across Canada and will also be displayed in other countries. It is taken apart in sections to be packed safely for travel. Stories of ordinary Canadians are joined together in this tribute to our country. People of different ages, cultures and religions find bits of personal and national history collected in the Canada Tree.

1. Draw a picture of what you think the Canada Tree looks like. If you have seen the tree, you can draw it from your memory.

You can see pictures of the Canada Tree, Tyler Aspin and many of the artifacts at the Canada Tree Web site: www.canadatree.com

2. List six kinds of wood that we know are part of the Canada Tree sculpture.

_____   _____

_____   _____

_____   _____

3. What other kinds of wood might be included in the tree?

_____   _____

_____   _____

4. Think of something made of wood that is special in your family.
Tell a story about this object.

_____

_____

_____

_____

_____

5. Circle the correct answers:

(a) The Canada Tree is a living tree.	True	False
(b) Tyler Aspin is a sculptor who carves wood.	True	False
(c) Green Gables is a tourist spot in P.E.I.	True	False
(d) Wayne Gretzky's autograph is an important part of the Canada Tree.	Fact	Opinion
(e) The Canada tree is 10 metres tall.	Fact	Opinion

6. Find two synonyms for the word "item."

_____ and _____

Find two words that come from the base word "donate."

_____ and _____

The Daily News

What is your favourite section of your local newspaper. _____

What about your parents? Mom's: _____ Dad's: _____

There is a part of every newspaper called the editorial section. This is where the editor of the paper makes comments about events in the news or policies that the government is making. These written comments include some facts but also many opinions.

Sometimes the editor wants to convince you and other readers of their side on an issue. You might think that an argument is something you have with your brother or sister. An argument can be a good piece of informational writing.

Let's see about writing two sides to an argument. You need to put in lots of details and facts to support your argument.

These points will help your argument sound convincing:
• Begin with a strong statement that gives the main idea.
• Make up some statistics to help prove one side of the argument or the other.
• Quote some speeches from important people.
• Draw conclusions from the facts you give.

Write an editorial about having year-round schools. These are schools where kids would not have a two-month summer vacation but a number of smaller vacations through the year.

FOR

Introduction—Main point

_____

_____

Reasons

_____

_____

_____

Conclusion

_____

_____

AGAINST

Introduction—Main point

_____

_____

Reasons

_____

_____

_____

Conclusion

_____

_____

When you read about an issue like this, there are many different opinions. That makes it a controversial issue. After the is in the paper, readers write letters to the editor to agree or disagree with what was published. It is interesting to see whether more are in favour of the opinion in the paper or not in favour.

You could conduct a survey to check with the kids in your class about the year-round school issue. First, carefully word your question so that you will get a definite answer to it.

How would you ask the question? _____

Now tally your answers.

What do the greatest number of people think? _____

For this workbook, it's OK to make up some statistics.

But for school, nothing beats real research.

10-9-8-7-6-5-4-3-2-1-Blast Off!

When Edgar is ready to return home to the mysterious planet from which he came, he invites you to come along for just 48 hours. You accept his invitation.

Draw a picture of the Earth as it looks from the spacecraft.

Draw a picture of your spacecraft.

What did the aliens look like? Compare them to Edgar.

_____

_____

How did Edgar communicate with his family and friends?

_____

_____

How did you communicate with them?

_____

_____

Tell about any habits they have that are different from ours.

_____

_____

What did they ask you about life on Earth?

_____

_____

What did you eat while you were there?

_____

_____

Did you find out the name of their planet? What was it?

_____

_____

What did you like most about your trip?

_____

_____

What did you miss most about Earth?

_____

_____

Why do you think you were chosen to travel and see Edgar's home?

_____

_____

_____

A Special Magazine

You and your friends might have lots of fun creating a magazine of your own. What name would you consider calling it? _____

What do you think you might put in the first issue? Think of columns and articles that would appeal to kids your age.

_____

_____

_____

_____

_____

_____

Will you accept advertisements from companies to help pay for the production of the magazine? If so, which ones?

_____

_____

_____

_____

_____

You can submit letters and pictures to kids' magazines right now. Look over your writing portfolio and send something away. Each magazine usually has an address near the beginning where all the contributors are listed. Sometimes there is a special request for particular kinds of work and then the address will be listed on that page.

Here are the addresses of two popular kids' magazines in Canadian schools:

Kids World Magazine
108-93 Lombard Ave
Winnipeg MB R3B 3B1

Owl Magazine
500–179 John St
Toronto ON M5T 3G5

Writing contests are fun to enter.

ADDRESSING THE ENVELOPE

This is the way Canada post office prefers us to address an envelope.
It is a new system and not the same one your parents learned in school.

Remember these things:
- put the return address on top left side and stamp on top right
- place the full name and address of the person receiving the letter slightly to the left of the middle of the envelope
- don't use any punctuation
- use the two-letter abbreviation for provinces and states
- only print the country's name if it is a different one from Canada

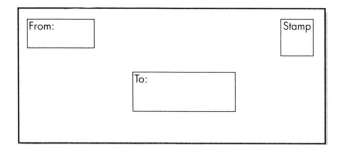

Don't just send your story or picture in the envelope. You must include a business letter with anything you submit. It should be short and to the point. You need to have a clear message. This is one format for a business letter.

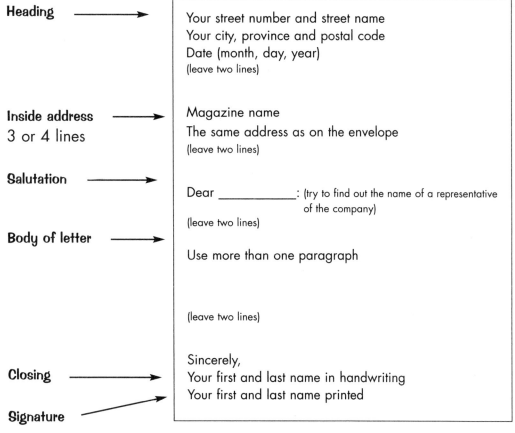

Heading ⟶	Your street number and street name Your city, province and postal code Date (month, day, year) (leave two lines)
Inside address ⟶ 3 or 4 lines	Magazine name The same address as on the envelope (leave two lines)
Salutation ⟶	Dear _____: (try to find out the name of a representative of the company) (leave two lines)
Body of letter ⟶	Use more than one paragraph (leave two lines)
Closing ⟶ **Signature** ⟶	Sincerely, Your first and last name in handwriting Your first and last name printed

Let's Be Pen Pals

A friendly letter is a great way to keep in touch with someone. It's a little more formal than an e-mail, but many older people prefer a "real" letter.

When you write a friendly letter, it follows a different format from a business letter. Here are the parts you need:

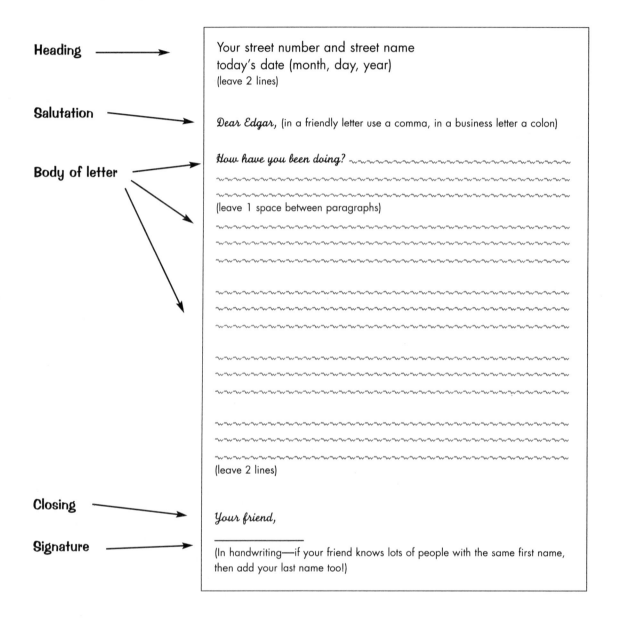

Heading ——————→ Your street number and street name
today's date (month, day, year)
(leave 2 lines)

Salutation ——————→ *Dear Edgar,* (in a friendly letter use a comma, in a business letter a colon)

Body of letter ——————→ *How have you been doing?* ～～～～～～～～～～～～～～～
～～～～～～～～～～～～～～～～～～～～～～～～～～～～～
～～～～～～～～～～～～～～～～～～～～～～～～～～～～～
(leave 1 space between paragraphs)
～～～～～～～～～～～～～～～～～～～～～～～～～～～～～
～～～～～～～～～～～～～～～～～～～～～～～～～～～～～
～～～～～～～～～～～～～～～～～～～～～～～～～～～～～

～～～～～～～～～～～～～～～～～～～～～～～～～～～～～

～～～～～～～～～～～～～～～～～～～～～～～～～～～～～
～～～～～～～～～～～～～～～～～～～～～～～～～～～～～
～～～～～～～～～～～～～～～～～～～～～～～～～～～～～
(leave 2 lines)

Closing ——————→ *Your friend,*
_____
Signature ——————→ (In handwriting—if your friend knows lots of people with the same first name, then add your last name too!)

Now write a friendly letter to an aunt or uncle. You can tell them about finishing this workbook.

After I move back home, let's write to each other.

Here is a letter from Edgar to you. Just fill in the blanks to make it your own.

DGAR THE ALIEN
Hovering 200 Metres Up
Etobicoke, ON   M9W 1C1
_____

_____
(Your first name and last name)

_____
(Your street)

_____
(Your city, province, postal code)

Dear _____,
(Your first name)

Congratulations. You've come a long way in this workbook. I hope you learned a lot about reading, thinking and language arts.

One thing I learned on Earth is how important it is to think about your work. You really have to know what you do well and where you need help. For instance, I'm really good at spaceship repair and languages, but I have a hard time with avoiding comets and doing tough math.

I have a hunch that you're especially good at _____ and _____. You probably need to work harder at _____ and _____.

I'm really glad that I landed in Canada when I came to Earth. I think your country has the best of everything. You have exciting big cities like Vancouver, Toronto and Montreal. You have two wonderful oceans (and one very cold one). You have rich prairie land in Saskatchewan and Manitoba, wonderful mountains in Alberta and British Columbia, and beautiful scenery in Newfoundland and the Maritime provinces. You even have polar bears in Nunavut and the Northwest Territories!

I hope you get to visit my planet when your technology gets more advanced. We have two very nice moons, several suns and fabulous pools of methane gas that my friends just love to play in. Unfortunately, the ground is a bit rocky, but that doesn't matter because we all fly around in spaceships. You'd learn how in no time.

Your friend,

Edgar

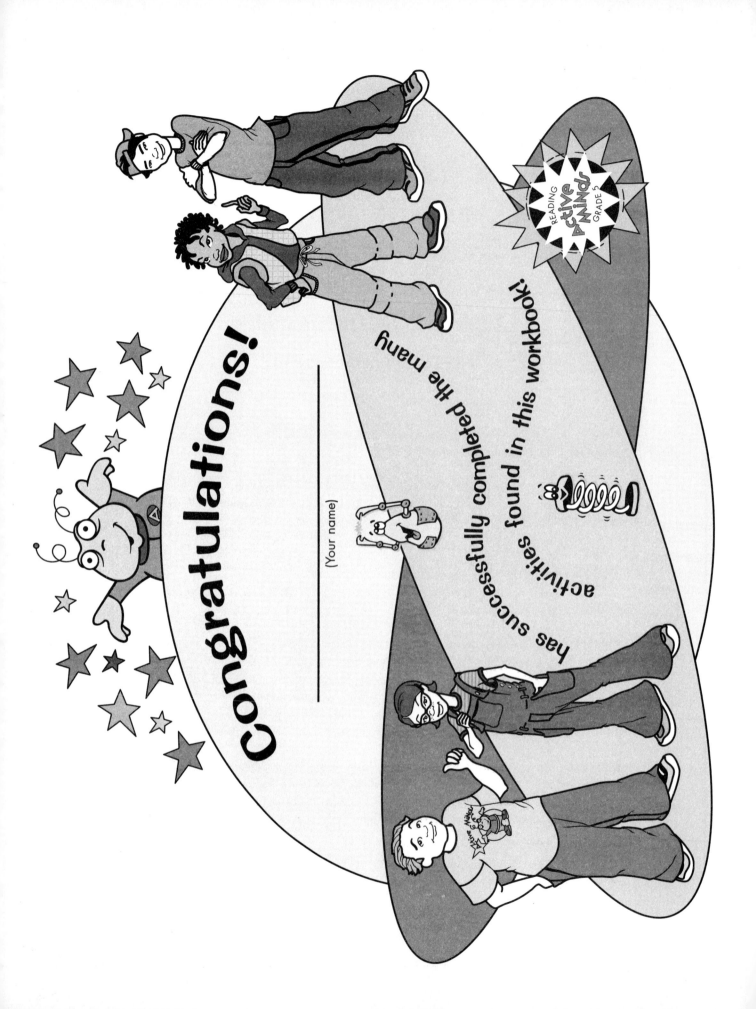

Mathematics
Grade 5

This workbook belongs to:

_____

Table of Contents

Where Are You At?

Let's see how you are doing with your Grade 5 math. Answer the following questions.

1.
```
  9 254
+ 1 706
```
2.
```
  72 146
−  8 437
```
3.
```
   58
× 43
```
4.
```
   94
× 27
```
5. 8)529

6. Name the value of each of these circled digits.

(a) 4 ③51 _____

(b) 3⑨ 825 _____

(c) ②6 714 _____

(d) 90 ④58 _____

(e) 78 5②1 _____

7. What is the perimeter of these figures?

(a)

(b)

(c)

(d)

(e)

_____   _____   _____   _____   _____

8. Continue the following patterns.

(a) 5   3   6   4   7   5   ___ ___ ___ ___

(b) 3   6   9   12   15   18   ___ ___ ___ ___

(c) 21   19   17   15   13   11   ___ ___ ___ ___

(d) 1   5   9   13   17   21   ___ ___ ___ ___

9. Write the following numbers in written form.

(a) 3 256 _____

(b) 6 178 _____

(c) 2 365 _____

(d) 6 187 _____

10.
```
  5 372
+ 4 845
```
11.
```
  13 490
−  2 576
```
12.
```
   76
× 41
```
13.
```
   34
× 85
```
14. 4)256

You're All Right!

You get to be the teacher today! One of your students has just handed in his homework and you need to mark it. Look at each answer and mark a 'check' for correct answers, an 'x' for incorrect answers, and write down the correct answer beside the 'x' to help out your student. Good luck, teacher!

1. $8 \times 7 = 56$ ✓   **2.** $48 \div 4 = \enclose{circle}{11}$ ✗ *12*   **3.** $5 \times 7 = 37$ **4.** $9 \times 4 = 36$

5. $6 \times 8 = 46$ **6.** $54 \div 9 = 5$ **7.** $3 \times 8 = 24$ **8.** $15 \div 15 = 0$

9. $3 \times 9 = 27$ **10.** $7 \times 7 = 51$ **11.** $8 \times 5 = 50$ **12.** $32 \div 4 = 8$

13. $6 \times 7 = 42$ **14.** $9 \times 12 = 109$ **15.** $132 \div 11 = 11$ **16.** $11 \times 8 = 88$

17.
$$\begin{array}{r} 12 \\ \times\ 12 \\ \hline 144 \end{array}$$

18.
$$\begin{array}{r} 70 \\ \times\ 2 \\ \hline 140 \end{array}$$

19.
$$\begin{array}{r} 25 \\ \times\ 5 \\ \hline 150 \end{array}$$

20.
$$\begin{array}{r} 100 \\ \times\ 8 \\ \hline 880 \end{array}$$

How did your student do?

Answers correct: _____
Total number of questions: 20

Here's a Trick!

To remember your 9x tables, just use your head, but even more, use your fingers!
1. Place your hands out on a table (or on your lap) with your fingers outstretched.
2. Take the number by which you are multiplying the 9. For example, if the question is 3 x 9, you take the number 3.
3. Counting from the left, locate your third finger and hide it under your palm like this:

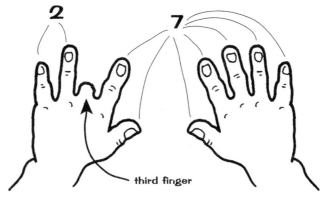

4. Look at what fingers are left and use them for each digit.
   So, your answer for this question is 27.

Hidden Numbers

Answer these questions and then find your answers in the number find below. The answers in the square will always be straight, but they could be forwards, backwards, or diagonal.

(a) 672
    + 258
    —————
     930

(b) 942
    – 538

(c) 456
    + 671

(d) 275
    – 188

(e) 827
    + 342

(f) 759
    – 374

(g) 431
    + 814

(h) 451
    – 174

(i) 627
    + 503

(j) 530
    – 98

(k) 710
    + 97

(l) 1036
    – 945

(m) 581
    + 412

(n) 524
    – 436

(o) 2461
    + 4528

(p) 5108
    – 4736

(q) 3762
    + 1560

(r) 4819
    – 4306

(s) 1865
    + 9536

(t) 7307
    – 3859

(u) 8341
    + 974

9	8	9	6	1	2	4	5
3	4	4	8	8	0	7	3
1	2	9	3	4	4	3	7
5	4	3	0	3	8	5	2
5	4	0	3	2	5	3	9
1	0	4	1	1	8	2	9
9	6	1	1	2	7	2	3

After finishing your addition and subtraction and finding the answers in the number find, check to see what numbers are left over. Write these numbers down below in order starting from the top of the grid, working left to right and top to bottom.

What is the pattern with these numbers?

Numbers not circled: ____ ____ ____ ____ ____ ____ ____ ____

Describe Pattern: _____

What would the next numbers be? ____ ____ ____ ____ ____ ____ ____ ____

Place Value Bingo

1. Cut out the bingo cards on the left side of the page, as well as the smaller boxes with numbers on the right side. Keep your cards together in an envelope so that you don't lose them.
2. Hand out the bingo cards. You can play with 1, 2, 3, or 4 players.
3. Find some pennies, pegs, or whatever you think will make a suitable marker.
4. Choose someone who will pick numbers from the envelope. We will call this person the caller.
5. The caller picks a number and announces the number.
6. The players try to find the place value square for that number and place a marker on the appropriate square.
7. The winner is the first person to get one whole line marked.

Example:

Caller pulls 0.9 and says, "Under the _____tenths_____, _____nine tenths_____."

Place a marker on _____0.9_____.

Another example:

Caller pulls 40 000 and says, "Under the _____ten thousands_____, _____forty thousand_____."

Place a marker on _____40 000_____.

100 000	10 000	1 000	100	10	1	0.1	0.01
200 000	30 000	5 000	100	30	3	0.2	0.07
400 000	60 000	7 000	400	90	5	0.9	0.05
100 000	40 000	1 000	200	40	1	0.8	0.06
800 000	90 000	2 000	700	80	2	0.5	0.03
700 000	10 000	8 000	900	20	6	0.6	0.09

100 000	700 000	40 000
200 000	800 000	50 000
300 000	900 000	60 000
400 000	10 000	70 000
500 000	20 000	80 000
600 000	30 000	90 000

100 000	10 000	1 000	100	10	1	0.1	0.01
400 000	60 000	3 000	900	20	1	0.9	0.04
700 000	10 000	8 000	800	60	3	0.7	0.05
800 000	20 000	5 000	300	10	6	0.2	0.08
500 000	80 000	4 000	500	70	2	0.3	0.02
300 000	90 000	1 000	700	80	8	0.5	0.01

1 000	7 000	400
2 000	8 000	500
3 000	9 000	600
4 000	100	700
5 000	200	800
6 000	300	900

100 000	10 000	1 000	100	10	1	0.1	0.01
900 000	40 000	6 000	300	20	8	0.5	0.02
200 000	70 000	1 000	900	10	9	0.8	0.03
500 000	50 000	3 000	800	40	5	0.9	0.08
400 000	30 000	2 000	500	80	3	0.4	0.07
800 000	90 000	9 000	700	60	6	0.7	0.05

10	70	4
20	80	5
30	90	6
40	1	7
50	2	8
60	3	9

100 000	10 000	1 000	100	10	1	0.1	0.01
700 000	10 000	4 000	600	40	2	0.3	0.01
300 000	30 000	9 000	200	90	1	0.8	0.03
200 000	60 000	1 000	300	80	4	0.4	0.05
400 000	80 000	2 000	500	60	6	0.2	0.02
800 000	90 000	7 000	800	30	8	0.9	0.08

0.1	0.7	0.04
0.2	0.8	0.05
0.3	0.9	0.06
0.4	0.01	0.07
0.5	0.02	0.08
0.6	0.03	0.09

100 000	10 000	1 000	100	10	1	0.1	0.01
600 000	50 000	2 000	100	50	9	0.1	0.03
900 000	80 000	3 000	900	40	7	0.3	0.05
200 000	20 000	7 000	200	30	5	0.2	0.08
800 000	30 000	1 000	800	60	3	0.4	0.02
500 000	50 000	8 000	300	70	1	0.5	0.09

100 000 = hundred thousands
10 000 = ten thousands
1 000 = thousands
100 = hundreds
10 = tens
1 = ones
0.1 = tenths
0.01 = hundreths

Don't forget your place value columns.

Successful in Fractions

Draw and colour in the following fractions.

$\frac{1}{2}$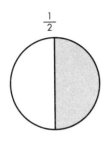

$\frac{2}{2}$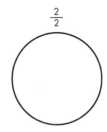

$\frac{2}{4}$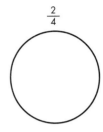

$\frac{1}{3}$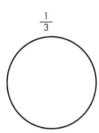

$\frac{2}{3}$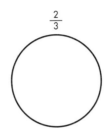

$\frac{1}{4}$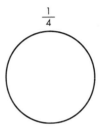

$\frac{1}{3}$ ☐

$\frac{1}{5}$ ☐

$\frac{3}{4}$ ☐

$\frac{2}{4}$ ☐

Students Are Highly Successful After Completing Grade Five Math Workbook!

Read this headline. How many A's are in the headline? _____4_____

How many letters altogether are there in the headline? _____63_____

The fraction that tells us the number of A's in the headline compared to the number of letters in the headline is $\frac{4}{63}$. We can then say that $\frac{4}{63}$ rds of the letters are A's.

Write out the fractions comparing the number of these letters to all the letters of the headline.

$s = \dfrac{}{63}$ $t = \dfrac{}{\quad}$ $o = \dfrac{}{\quad}$ $v = \dfrac{}{\quad}$

The number on the top is the NUMERATOR.
The number on the bottom is the DENOMINATOR.
Write the numerators of the fractions above.

$\dfrac{4}{63}$ = numerator
      = denominator

s _____   t _____   o _____   v _____

All Fractured Up!

Hey there, doc! You just got a new patient and you need to decode what the patient is trying to tell you. To get the patient's message below, answer each fraction question and place the letters down below, like this:

1. First $\frac{1}{2}$ of body $\dfrac{b}{}$ $\dfrac{o}{11}$

2. Middle $\frac{1}{5}$ of heart $\dfrac{}{5}$

3. Last $\frac{1}{2}$ of muscle $\dfrac{}{12}$ — —

4. First $\frac{1}{3}$ of intestine   — — $\dfrac{}{6}$

5. Last $\frac{1}{5}$ of bones $\dfrac{}{7}$

6. First $\frac{1}{2}$ of health $\dfrac{}{4}$ — —

7. Middle $\frac{1}{3}$ of growth   — $\dfrac{}{3}$

8. First $\frac{1}{3}$ of digestion $\dfrac{}{10}$ — —

9. Last $\frac{1}{5}$ of cerebellum $\dfrac{}{1}$ —

10. Last $\frac{1}{2}$ of stomach   — — $\dfrac{}{2}$ —

11. First $\frac{2}{5}$ of pulse $\dfrac{}{9}$ $\dfrac{}{8}$

Decode your patient's message here:

$\dfrac{}{1}$ $\dfrac{}{2}$, $\dfrac{}{3}$ $\dfrac{}{4}$ $\dfrac{}{5}$ $\dfrac{}{6}$ $\dfrac{}{7}$ $\dfrac{}{8}$ $\dfrac{}{9}$ $\dfrac{}{10}$ $\dfrac{o}{11}$ $\dfrac{}{12}$?

For extra practice:
There are a lot of fractions around your own home.
- Practice reading fractions when somebody at your house is trying a new recipe.
- Try to calculate what fraction of the house your bedroom takes up.
- What fraction of a day do you spend doing school work? watching TV?

I spend $\frac{1}{8}$ of my day eating!

Strategize While You Exercise

Don't let a problem get you down. In fact, don't let it be a problem.
Here are some tips to help.

- **Be sure you understand the question.**
  Read it over a few times to be sure you understand.
- **Eliminate any extra information that you do not need.**
- **Underline the information that is important.**
- **Try various methods to solve it.**
- **Check to see if your answer is correct.**

METHODS FOR FINDING SOLUTIONS TO YOUR QUESTION

You can use any number of these methods for any question. One might work better,
you might use two or three before you get the answer, or you might just end up using
them all!

- **Trial and Error (or Guess and Check)**
  Here you simply try something out that you think might work, then check to see if it
  does. If not, you try again, using the information that you gained from the first try.
- **Draw a Picture, Graph, or Chart**
  These are often helpful if you like to see what the question actually looks like.
- **Use Objects to Help**
  Sometimes actual objects, like game pieces, toothpicks, counters, and so on help to
  work out a question.
- **Work Backwards**
  Don't actually sit backwards! Read the question, working through it from the last bit
  of information to the first.

Here's a quick question to try out your new strategies.

Mrs. Underhill is making her seating plan for her new Grade 5 class. For her front
row she has 5 students: Emiko, Zachry, Ravi, Jake and Marcel. Marcel must be seated
closest to the door. Zachry likes to talk to Marcel too much so he shouldn't be seated
beside him. Jakes needs to be in the middle to see the board, and Ravi cannot be
next to Jake. What does Mrs. Underhill's plan look like?

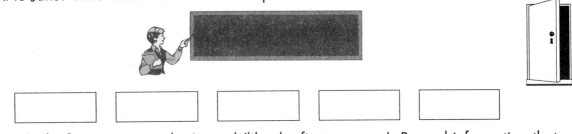

Get rid of information you don't need (like the first sentence). Reread information that
is important (like the information about each student). This question would definitely
work well with a drawing or graph, as shown above.

No Problem!

Try out your new strategies on these problems questions.

1. The pizza at Indian Road Crescent School's special lunch days costs $1.00. Find some different ways that the students could pay for this pizza using nickels, dimes, quarters, and loonies.

   for example: 5¢ + 5¢ +5¢ + 10¢+ 25¢+ 25¢+ 25¢

2. Jehan and Jason have just released their latest compact disc with their very best songs. In January, they sold 500 CDs. In February, they sold 580. Each month they manage to sell 80 more than the last month. How many CDs will they sell in the month of August? What will their total be at the end of the year?

3. Mrs. Shisko is planning to take her class to the Ryerson Theater and she needs to organize the transportation of her class. The cars can take 3 students and the vans can take 5 students. Mrs. Shisko has 26 students. How many different ways could she take her students? What is the most efficient way that uses the exact number of seats for the 26 students?

4. Altogether, Mike, Dave, and Tim have 120 mystery books. Mike has 15 more than Dave. Tim has 30 less than Mike. How many mystery books does each have?

Measure Pleasure!

Measure each line of these letters in millimetres.

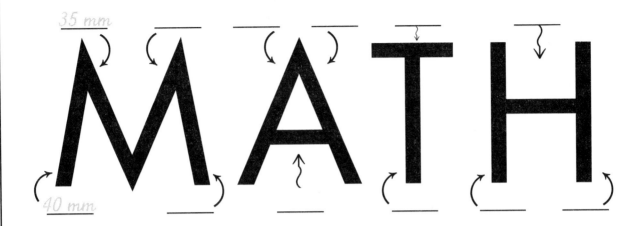

35 mm

40 mm

Now try some letters to spell your own name. Use a ruler to draw the straight lines. If you want to try measuring curvy letters, use a piece of string.

Don't forget to write the unit of measurement (for example 16 cm).

Find these things in your house and see how many centimetres in length they are.

pencil _____   fork _____   toothbrush _____   book _____

eraser _____   shoe _____   dinner table _____   envelope _____

BE CAREFUL
When you are measuring be sure to start at the zero. Some rulers have the zero at the very end, but others do not.

Do You Measure Up?

Estimate before you measure. Then see if you were close.

Did you know that there are interesting ratios to your body?
Measure these parts of your body and then we'll see.

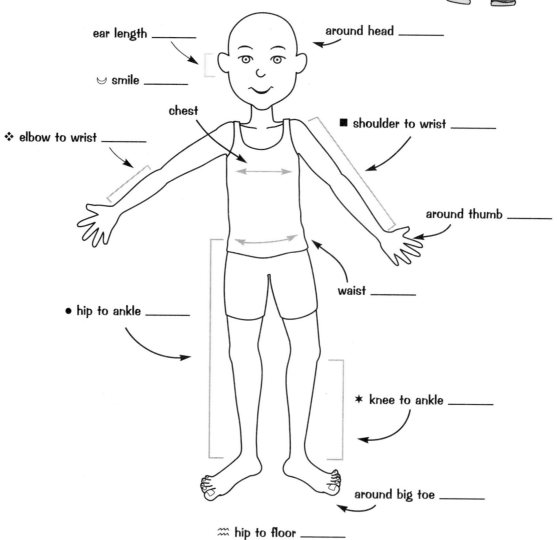

⇕ height head to floor _____

ear length _____

around head _____

⌣ smile _____

chest

■ shoulder to wrist _____

❖ elbow to wrist _____

around thumb _____

waist _____

● hip to ankle _____

✳ knee to ankle _____

around big toe _____

〰 hip to floor _____

Compare the following parts in ratios.

Calculate the decimals if you have a calculator.

	ratios	decimals
1. $\dfrac{❖}{■}$ =	_____	= _____
2. $\dfrac{✳}{●}$ =	_____	= _____
3. $\dfrac{〰}{⇕}$ =	_____	= _____

Around and Around We Go!

PERIMETER is the measurement around a space, like the distance of a fence around a yard.

Using a ruler, measure around these shapes to answer this riddle:

What goes around and around and around and never stops?

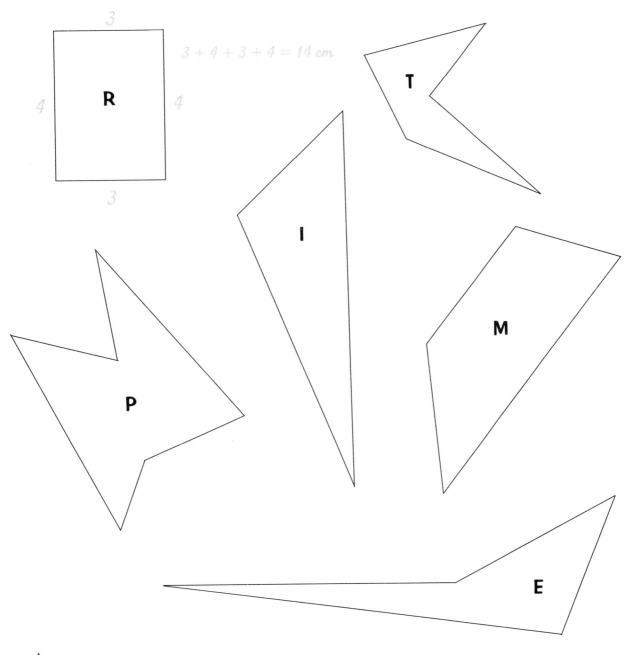

Answer:

Fill in letters here: ___ ___ ___ ___ ___ ___ ___ ___ ___
(Perimeters from above) 25 mm   280 mm   14 cm   22 cm   19 cm   280 mm   165 mm   280 mm   14 cm

More to Get Around

Find the perimeter of these figures.
Then write your answer in words in the crossword puzzle.

ACROSS

1

2

3

4

DOWN

1

5

3

3

2

4

2 + 3 + 3 + 4 = 12

6

Each Square Counts

Someone has just baked your favourite dessert! Hot cross buns! Yum! Yum! The pan has already been cut into squares and each square counts. Before you get to eat your hot cross buns, you must find the areas.

AREA is the measure of how much surface space something takes up.

This is the surface space taken up by 1 cm².

This is the surface space taken up by 2 cm².

Now to dessert! Just count the squared centimetres in the pan and you have the area. Find the area of the treats below.

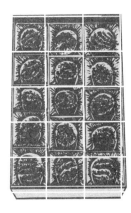

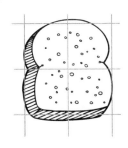

_____ cm²   _____ cm²   _____ cm²

Now it is your turn to make the proper area in the space below.

1. 9 cm²   **2.** 14 cm²   **3.** 11 cm²

4. 3 cm²   **5.** 5 cm²   **5.** 10 cm²

Dream Room

Here's your chance to design the bedroom you've always dreamed of having. Take a look at this one to help you decide what kind of neat things to add to your room. When you're done, estimate the area that some of the objects take up.

Sample Bedroom Plan   **Your Bedroom Plan**

Bed

Computers

Pool Table

Dresser

Hot Tub

TV/Stereo   Closet

Each unit represents 1 square metre (m²).

Object	Area (in m²)	Your Objects	Area (in m²)
Bed	6 m²		
Pool Table			
Computer Centre			
Hot Tub			
Dresser			
Closet			
TV/Stereo Cabinet			

Phone Tag

What kind of area do you need to call a friend?
Find out the area of each shape to answer the question.
Fill in the letters below.

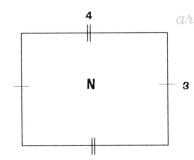

$$area = \ell \times w$$
$$= 4 \times 3$$
$$= 12\ cm^2$$

N — 4, 3

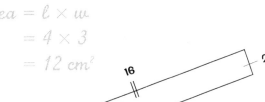

R — 16, 2

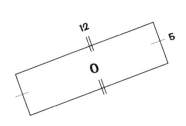

O — 12, 5

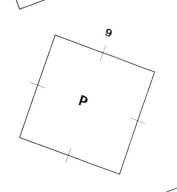

P — 9

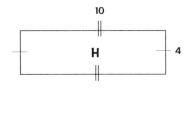

H — 10, 4

A — 7, 4

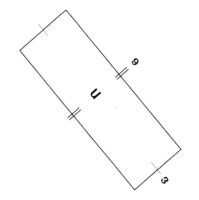

U — 9, 3

M — 5

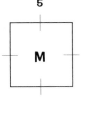

C — 8

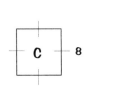

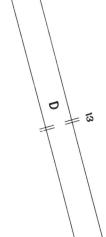

D — 13, 3

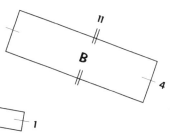

B — 11, 4

E — 14, 1

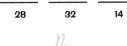

Fill in letters here: ___ ___ ___ ___   ___ ___ ___ ___ &
　　　　　　　　　28　32　14　28　　64　60　39　14

___ ___ ___ ___ ___   ___ ___ ___ ___ ___ ___
81　40　60　12　14　　12　27　25　44　14　32

High Five!

How much area does your hand take up? To estimate the area of an irregular object, count the squares.

For one whole square...  ...count 1 cm²

For about half of the square... 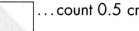 ...count 0.5 cm²

Try this one.

There are 6 almost 1 cm².

There are 4 more about 0.5 cm².

The total is 8 cm².

Trace your hand, spread out, to see approximately how much space it takes up.

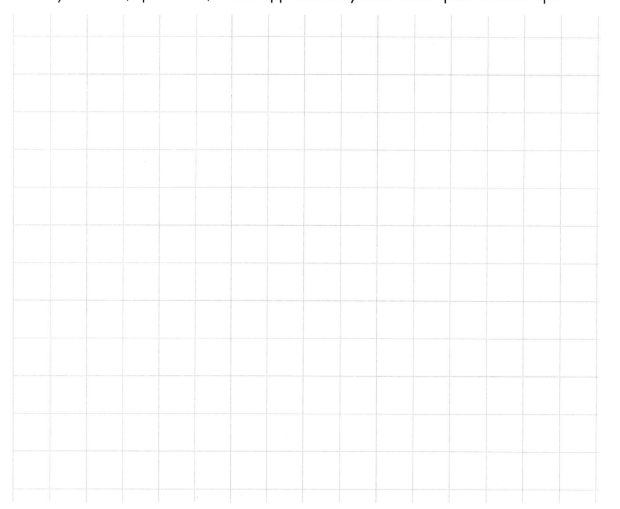

Area of your hand _____

"Polygon on the Side, Please!"

Polygons are simply closed figures!

This is a polygon.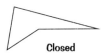
Closed

This is not a polygon.
Open

Polygons can have any number of sides. Try making a few of your own.

3 sides   **4 sides**   **5 sides**   **6 sides**   **7 sides**

Polygons that have 3 sides are called triangles. See if you can decode the names of these triangles, using the alphabet code below. (The pattern for the codes is started, but you must continue it!) Once you have the names, draw a line from the name to the correct triangle.

A B C D E F G H I J K L M N O P Q R S T U V W X Y Z
1 2 3 4 5 6 7 _ _ _ _ _ _ _ _ _ _ _ _ _ _ _ _ _ _ _

___ ___ ___ ___ ___ ___ ___ ___ ___ _A_ ___
 5   17   21   9   12   1   20   5   18   1   12

___ ___ ___ ___ ___ ___ ___ ___ ___
 9   19   15   19   3   5   12   5   19

_C_ _A_ ___ ___ ___ ___ ___
 19   3   1   12   5   14   5

Polygons that have 4 sides are called quadrilaterals.

Write the names of these quadrilaterals, using the code, and draw a line matching the name with the shape.

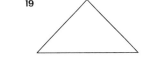

___ ___ ___ ___ ___ ___
 19   17   21   1   18   5

___ ___ ___ ___ ___ ___ ___ ___ ___
 18   5   3   20   1   14   7   12   5

___ ___ ___ ___ ___ ___ ___ ___ ___ ___ ___ ___ ___
 16   1   18   18   1   12   12   5   12   15   7   18   1   13

___ ___ ___ ___ ___ ___ ___
 18   8   15   13   2   21   19

Map It Out!

Coordinates help you to locate a point on a grid. The first number represents the position according the side numbers on the grid (the x-axis). The second number represents the bottom numbers on the grid (the y-axis).

For example, the point (8,2) is already shown for you. Plot out the rest of the points and join them in their order.

Start here
(8, 2)	(4, 4)
(6, 4)	(5, 2)
(8, 6)	(1, 2)
(8, 7)	(1, 1)
(1, 7)	(8, 1)
(1, 6)	(8, 2)
(5, 6)	Done!

What is the shape?

_____

Try to plot out a letter in your own name.

_____ _____

_____ _____

_____ _____

_____ _____

_____ _____

_____ _____

_____ _____

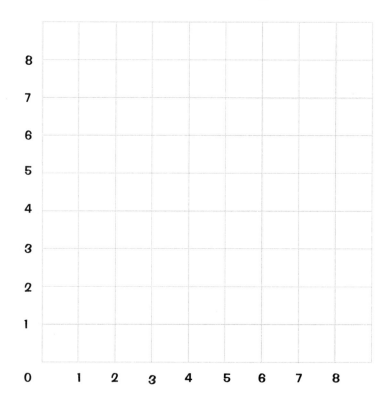

Shape Up!

These are the nets for some very common shapes. When cut and folded, they create three-dimensional solids.

Try to guess what they are before you cut out each one.

A net is a two-dimensional layout for a solid.

Shape Up Some More!

Finally Shaped Out!

Netting Class

Now that you are an expert in 3-D, fill in this chart.

Faces = flat + curved sides
Corners = Points

Draw Solid	Solid Name	Faces	Edges	Corners
Edge Face Face Edge Face	Cylinder	3	2	0
	Rectangular Prism			
	Cube			
	Cone			
	Square-based Pyramid			
	Triangular-based Pyramid			

From where you are sitting right now, look to find as many of these 3-D shapes around you. List them here.

Object	Shape

Can You See the Difference?

When two shapes are exactly alike, they are called congruent.

These two are congruent.

But these two are not congruent.

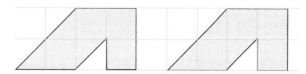

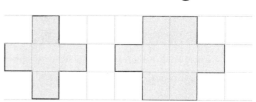

Draw a line connecting the pictures that are congruent.

Then decode the riddle with the leftover non-congruent pictures.

The riddle is: what should you be seeing if things are congruent?

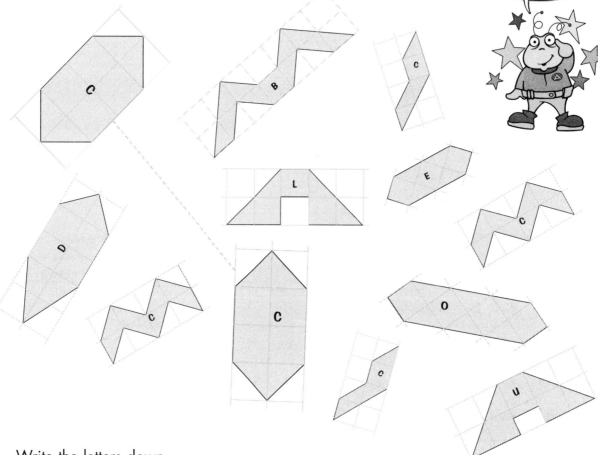

Write the letters down.

_____ _____ _____ _____ _____ _____

Then unscramble them to answer the question.

_____

Pattern Plus

Patterns are everywhere in math. In the 100-chart below, you can see that a pattern has started. Continue this pattern by colouring the multiples of 2.

1	2	3	4	5	6	7	8	9	10
11	12	13	14	15	16	17	18	19	20
21	22	23	24	25	26	27	28	29	30
31	32	33	34	35	36	37	38	39	40
41	42	43	44	45	46	47	48	49	50
51	52	53	54	55	56	57	58	59	60
61	62	63	64	65	66	67	68	69	70
71	72	73	74	75	76	77	78	79	80
81	82	83	84	85	86	87	88	89	90
91	92	93	94	95	96	97	98	99	100

Now see the pattern you make by colouring the multiples of 3.

1	2	3	4	5	6	7	8	9	10
11	12	13	14	15	16	17	18	19	20
21	22	23	24	25	26	27	28	29	30
31	32	33	34	35	36	37	38	39	40
41	42	43	44	45	46	47	48	49	50
51	52	53	54	55	56	57	58	59	60
61	62	63	64	65	66	67	68	69	70
71	72	73	74	75	76	77	78	79	80
81	82	83	84	85	86	87	88	89	90
91	92	93	94	95	96	97	98	99	100

There are patterns without numbers, too, like those in carpets, wallpaper, and even in the weather.

You can guess what to do with this one! Time for the 4s!

1	2	3	4	5	6	7	8	9	10
11	12	13	14	15	16	17	18	19	20
21	22	23	24	25	26	27	28	29	30
31	32	33	34	35	36	37	38	39	40
41	42	43	44	45	46	47	48	49	50
51	52	53	54	55	56	57	58	59	60
61	62	63	64	65	66	67	68	69	70
71	72	73	74	75	76	77	78	79	80
81	82	83	84	85	86	87	88	89	90
91	92	93	94	95	96	97	98	99	100

Look at each pattern. Check out the spaces, the lines and the direction of the pattern. Then see the differences in each chart.

Look at the chart and you can just imagine the 5s. They're too easy. Let's pass onto the multiples of 6.

1	2	3	4	5	6	7	8	9	10
11	12	13	14	15	16	17	18	19	20
21	22	23	24	25	26	27	28	29	30
31	32	33	34	35	36	37	38	39	40
41	42	43	44	45	46	47	48	49	50
51	52	53	54	55	56	57	58	59	60
61	62	63	64	65	66	67	68	69	70
71	72	73	74	75	76	77	78	79	80
81	82	83	84	85	86	87	88	89	90
91	92	93	94	95	96	97	98	99	100

Seventh heaven

1	2	3	4	5	6	7	8	9	10
11	12	13	14	15	16	17	18	19	20
21	22	23	24	25	26	27	28	29	30
31	32	33	34	35	36	37	38	39	40
41	42	43	44	45	46	47	48	49	50
51	52	53	54	55	56	57	58	59	60
61	62	63	64	65	66	67	68	69	70
71	72	73	74	75	76	77	78	79	80
81	82	83	84	85	86	87	88	89	90
91	92	93	94	95	96	97	98	99	100

Eight is great!

1	2	3	4	5	6	7	8	9	10
11	12	13	14	15	16	17	18	19	20
21	22	23	24	25	26	27	28	29	30
31	32	33	34	35	36	37	38	39	40
41	42	43	44	45	46	47	48	49	50
51	52	53	54	55	56	57	58	59	60
61	62	63	64	65	66	67	68	69	70
71	72	73	74	75	76	77	78	79	80
81	82	83	84	85	86	87	88	89	90
91	92	93	94	95	96	97	98	99	100

Notice the last digit
in your 8 chart.
8   48
16   56
24   64
32   72
40   80
This might help you.

Unit 4 • Patterning of tables

Nine lives—colour them in.

1	2	3	4	5	6	7	8	9	10
11	12	13	14	15	16	17	18	19	20
21	22	23	24	25	26	27	28	29	30
31	32	33	34	35	36	37	38	39	40
41	42	43	44	45	46	47	48	49	50
51	52	53	54	55	56	57	58	59	60
61	62	63	64	65	66	67	68	69	70
71	72	73	74	75	76	77	78	79	80
81	82	83	84	85	86	87	88	89	90
91	92	93	94	95	96	97	98	99	100

Just like the 5s, you can imagine the 10s and 11s.
Try colouring in your multiples of 12 now.

1	2	3	4	5	6	7	8	9	10
11	12	13	14	15	16	17	18	19	20
21	22	23	24	25	26	27	28	29	30
31	32	33	34	35	36	37	38	39	40
41	42	43	44	45	46	47	48	49	50
51	52	53	54	55	56	57	58	59	60
61	62	63	64	65	66	67	68	69	70
71	72	73	74	75	76	77	78	79	80
81	82	83	84	85	86	87	88	89	90
91	92	93	94	95	96	97	98	99	100

These patterning charts should help you with your multiplication tables.

Hundreds of Patterns

1	2	3	4	5	6	7	8	9	10
11	12	13	14	15	16	17	18	19	20
21	22	23	24	25	26	27	28	29	30
31	32	33	34	35	36	37	38	39	40
41	42	43	44	45	46	47	48	49	50
51	52	53	54	55	56	57	58	59	60
61	62	63	64	65	66	67	68	69	70
71	72	73	74	75	76	77	78	79	80
81	82	83	84	85	86	87	88	89	90
91	92	93	94	95	96	97	98	99	100

Circle all the different patterns that you can find in this 100-chart and write them down. By the way, don't just look at the ones you have already found in the last pages. There are tonnes more!

Example: diagonally down from the 1 to 12 to 23 to 34 to 45 and so on

_____

_____

_____

_____

_____

Try to fill in the following patterns:

(a) 4   7   10   _____ _____ _____ _____ _____ _____

(b) 99   88   77   _____ _____ _____ _____ _____ _____

(c) 2   4   3   5   4   _____ _____ _____ _____

(d) 6   7   8   7   8   9   8   _____ _____ _____

Pitter Pattern

Find the pattern in these sets of numbers.
Just look to see how much is added or subtracted.

1. 6 $\xrightarrow{+2}$ 8 $\xrightarrow{+2}$ 10 $\xrightarrow{+2}$ 12 $\xrightarrow{+2}$ 14 $\xrightarrow{+2}$ 16

2. 20 $\xrightarrow{-3}$ 17 $\xrightarrow{-3}$ 14 $\xrightarrow{-3}$ ___ ___ ___

3. 5 $\xrightarrow{+5}$ 10 $\xrightarrow{+5}$ 15 ___ ___ ___

Now look for both addition and subtraction in each set of numbers.

4. 2 $\xrightarrow{+3}$ 5 $\xrightarrow{-2}$ 3 $\xrightarrow{+3}$ 6 $\xrightarrow{-2}$ 4 $\xrightarrow{+3}$ 7

5. 15 $\xrightarrow{-1}$ 14 $\xrightarrow{+6}$ 20 $\xrightarrow{-1}$ 19 ___ ___

6. 2 7 5 10 ___ ___

Here are other kinds of patterns. Give them a try.

7. 1 2 4 8 _____ _____

8. 3 9 27 _____ _____

9. 1 3 5 7 11 13 _____ _____

10. 5 10 20 35 _____ _____

> Rules! Rules! Rules!
> Patterns always have a rule.
> For example, in #1 the rule is
> to add 2. So what you're
> really doing on this page is
> finding rules.

It's School Time

Here's a schedule of the week as your teacher has prepared it.

Time	Monday	Tuesday	Wednesday	Thursday	Friday
9:00	Writing	Writing	Writing	Writing	Writing
9:40	Reading	Reading	Library	Reading	Reading
10:30	Recess	Recess	Recess	Recess	Recess
10:45	Math	Math	Math	Math	Math
11:20	Gym	Science	Science	Gym	Science
12:00	Lunch	Lunch	Lunch	Lunch	Lunch
1:00	Spelling	Spelling	Spelling	Spelling	Spelling
1:50	French	French	French	French	French
2:30	Recess	Recess	Recess	Recess	Recess
2:45	Art	Social Studies	Music	Social Studies	Drama
3:40	Go Home	Go Home	Go Home	Go Home	Go Home

How many minutes per week do you have:

French? _____

Writing? _____

Gym? _____

Recess? _____

Do you have more of:

Gym or Library? _____

Science or Reading? _____

Art or Social Studies? _____

Math or French? _____

What can you tell after reading the chart?

_____

_____

_____

_____

Make a chart comparing the number of minutes for each subject.

Subject	Minutes per Week
Writing	200

Lace Them Up!

Make one of your own by looking around. Find at least 10 to 15 pairs of shoes.

Let's make an easy chart of how many shoes have laces and how many do not have laces. Start with a quick tally that might look like this:

Shoes with Laces	Shoes without Laces
IIII	HHL II

Shoes with Laces	Shoes without Laces

Now we need to make these into charts.

Do yours here.

Laces	No laces
4	7

Laces	No laces

What about a bar graph? Easy.

Your bar graph.

8
7
6
5
4
3
2
1

Laces   No laces

8
7
6
5
4
3
2
1

Laces   No laces

Shoes for the summer at Palmerston school

	5	10	15	20	25	30	35	40
Running Shoes								
Sandals								
Regular Shoes								

According to this chart, how many people wear

sandals in the summer?   _____

running shoes in the summer?   _____

regular shoes in the summer?   _____

Use < (less than), = (equal to), or > (more than) for the following:

running shoes _____ regular shoes

sandals _____ running shoes and regular shoes

regular shoes _____ sandals

I've Lost My Head

1. Katie and Kirsten are taking a summer trip in their car. They quickly pass by a farm where they see horses and chickens. They were going quickly and could not get the whole count of what they saw. Katie counted 5 heads and Kirsten counted 14 legs. How many chickens and horses were there?

   Use pictures, graphs, charts, or drawings to help you. Here's one idea.

   ○ ○ ○ ○ ○
   |||| |||| || || ||

   Chickens ___3___   Horses ___3___

2. Later they pass by another farm. This farm has ducks and cows. Katie counted 10 heads and Kirsten counted 28 legs. How many ducks and cows were there?

   Ducks _____   Cows _____

3. The next farm was a little different. This time there were farmers who wore hats, and some dogs and geese who didn't. (Dogs and geese aren't fond of hats!) They saw 13 heads (of which 5 had hats) and 30 legs. How many dogs, geese, and farmers with hats were there?

   Farmers with Hats _____   Geese _____   Dogs _____

They finally made it to their destination: the circus. In the circus ring, Katie and Kirsten saw elephants, horses, clowns with red noses, and acrobats walking on wooden stilts. Katie counted 34 legs (of which 4 were wooden). Kirsten counted 5 red noses, 13 heads, and 4 trunks. How many elephants, horses, clowns, and stilt-walking acrobats were there?

Elephants _____   Horses _____   Clowns _____   Acrobats _____

Survey Says...

You've just taken a survey in your class to see who has long hair, who has medium length hair, and who has short hair. Here are your findings.

Long hair ~~||||~~ | Medium hair ~~||||~~ ||| Short hair ~~||||~~ ~~||||~~ ~~||||~~

Your teacher asks you to present your findings in as many different ways as possible. Here are four. They are incomplete, so you need to finish them off.

First, a simple

CHART

Students with long hair	6
Students with medium hair	
Students with short hair	

Label with titles and numbers.

Then a
BAR GRAPH

Fill in the rest.

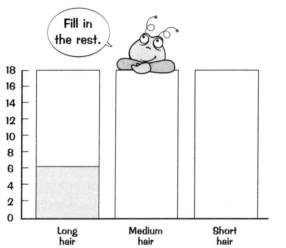

and a
PIE GRAPH

Long: 6

Finally, you need a pictograph. Have fun drawing. We'll start it off for you.

Students with long hair	😊😊😊😊😊😊
Students with medium hair	
Students with short hair	

Unfortunately, I don't have any hair.

There are many ways to give information. Do your own survey. Try to find some more ways of presenting your data. Here are some ideas.

- What animals do people keep as pets in their homes?
- How many children in your class take music lessons?
- What percentage of commercials in 30 minutes are advertising food?
- Who enjoys Coke most, Pepsi most, or both equally?
- How many hours of TV do most people watch per day?

It's a Match! Yes or No?

MATCH GAME #1

- Cut these squares out to use them as pieces. (Use counters, beads, or other game pieces if you don't want to cut the page.)
- Now find a paper bag. (If you don't have one, use a baseball cap, or something to hold your pieces.)

Here's how you play:
- Place 3 pieces in the bag: 1 white and 2 greys.
- Pull two pieces out of the bag. Give yourself a point if the pieces match.
- Replace them in the bag, then continue. If it does not match, give a point to "No Match."
- Play for at least 20 turns.

Before you start:
Do you think there will be more in the "Match" column or more in the "No Match"? Why?_____

Tally your points here:

Match	
No Match	

What are your chances of getting a match? Well, here are the possible draws you could make.

> If you pull a white and a grey, the point goes to "No Match."

white and grey   grey and white   grey & grey

So you have a better chance of winning if you are "No Match."

MATCH GAME #2
Play game 1, but this time with 2 whites and 2 greys.

Before you start:
Do you think there will be more in the Match column or more in the "No Match"? Why?_____

Tally your points here:

Match	
No Match	

What are your chances of getting a match? Calculate the possible draws you could make.

Alphabet Probability

Read one page of a novel or a short story that you have handy. You could also use the newspaper or a comic book. What are the chances of coming across the various letters in the alphabet? Well, let's see.

First you need to tally the letters on the page (or pages that you have just read.)

For example, if you read this sentence, you would count every single letter, like this.

The children are becoming experts at probability.

for "The"–1t, 1h, 1e

Continue the tally with your letters.

A	B	C	D	E	F	G	H	I	J	K	L	M

N	O	P	Q	R	S	T	U	V	W	X	Y	Z

What letter appeared the most? _____
What letters appeared the least? _____
Is there a greater chance of reading a vowel or a consonant? _____
Which vowel appeared the most? _____
Did the most frequent vowel appear more or less than the most frequent consonant? _____

Use the greater than (>), equal to (=), and less than (<) symbols to complete the following questions.

What are the chances of coming across these letters?

s (>) u   g ( ) l   p ( ) o   t ( ) c   x ( ) f

g ( ) m   b ( ) q   e ( ) a   u ( ) k   d ( ) q

Is a computer keyboard set up so that the most frequently used letters are in a convenient spot? (Take a look at one if you are able to.)

_____
_____
_____

Fun With Dice

If you are rolling a die, what are your chances of landing on the following set? (Colour in the fraction.)

Four

Three

An even number

An odd number

If you have an 8-sided die, what are your chances of landing on the following:

Five

Number smaller than five

Number greater than six

An even number

Dice Game

Difference means how much is between the numbers. You **SUBTRACT** when you are looking for the **DIFFERENCE.**

Figure out whether it would be better to be Player #1 or Player #2.

How to play:
- Take turns rolling two 6-sided dice.
- Player #1 gets a point if the difference between the two dice is 0, 1, or 2.
- Player #2 gets a point for all other differences.

For example:

Rolled Dice: 4 & 5→The difference between the two dice is only 1, so player #1 scores.

2 & 6→The difference between the two dice is 4, so player #2 scores.

Which do you think would be the better choice? _____

Tally your points here: Player #1 _____ Player #2 _____

Now, let's figure out in a chart who has the better chance of winning.

Dice Rolled		Difference
1	1	0
1	2	1
1	3	2
1	4	
1	5	
1	6	
2	2	
2	3	
2	4	
2	5	
2	6	

Dice Rolled		Difference
3	3	
3	4	
3	5	
3	6	
4	4	
4	5	
4	6	
5	5	
5	6	
6	6	

Who is most likely to win?

_____

Answer Key

Many of the pages in this workbook contain creative activities and spaces for open-ended responses. Only those that require a correct answer are included in this answer key.

Page 2
1. 10 960   2. 63 709   3. 2 494
4. 2 538   5. 66 R1
6. (a) 300   (b) 9 000   (c) 20 000
   (d) 400   (e) 20
7. (a) 12   (b) 8   (c) 14
   (d) 28   (e) 16
8. (a) 8, 6, 9, 7   (b) 21, 24, 27, 30
   (c) 9, 7, 5, 3   (d) 25, 29, 33, 37
9. (a) three thousand two hundred fifty six
   (b) six thousand one hundred seventy-eight
   (c) two thousand three hundred sixty-five
   (d) six thousand one hundred eighty-seven
10. 10 217   11. 10 914
12. 3 116   13. 2 890
14. 64

Page 3
1. ✓   2. × 12
3. × 35   4. ✓
5. × 48   6. × 6
7. ✓   8. × 1
9. ✓   10. × 49
11. × 40   12. ✓
13. ✓   14. × 108
15. × 12   16. ✓
17. ✓   18. ✓
19. × 125   20. × 800   TOTAL: 9/20

Page 4
(a) 930   (b) 404   (c) 1 127
(d) 87   (e) 1 169   (f) 385
(g) 1 245   (h) 277   (i) 1 130
(j) 432   (k) 807   (l) 91
(m) 993   (n) 88   (o) 6 989
(p) 372   (q) 5 322   (r) 513
(s) 11 401   (t) 3 448   (u) 9 315

Not Circled: 2, 3, 4, 3, 4, 5, 4, 5
Pattern: −1, +1, +1, −1
Next: 6, 5, 6, 7, 6, 7, 8, 7

Page 9
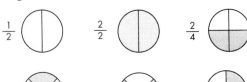
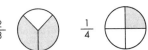

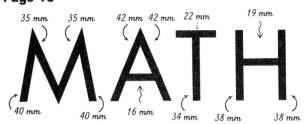

$\frac{1}{3}$

$\frac{1}{5}$

$\frac{3}{4}$

$\frac{2}{4}$

$s = \frac{5}{63}$ $t = \frac{4}{63}$

$o = \frac{4}{63}$ $v = \frac{1}{63}$

$s = 5, t = 4, o = 4, v = 1$

Page 10
1. bo   2. a   3. cle
4. int   5. s   6. hea
7. ow   8. dig   9. um
10. ache   11. pu

Decoded message: Uh, what's up doc?

Page 11
Mrs. Underhill's seating:
Ravi, Zachry, Jake, Emiko, Marcel

Page 12
2. August: 1 060
   End of year: 11 280
3. Various Answers
   Most efficient:
   4 vans, 2 cars = 26
4. Mike = 55, Dave = 40, Tim = 25

Page 13

Page 14
Ratios 1, 2, 3 should each be approximately = 0.5

Page 15
P = 25 mm   E = 280 mm
R = 14 cm   I = 22 cm
M = 19 cm   T = 165 mm
Answer: Perimeter

There are 30 fish on the cover.

Answer Key

Page 16

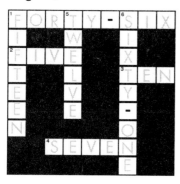

Page 17

Hot cross buns = 6 cm²
Chocolates = 15 cm²
Sandwich = 4 cm²

Page 18

Bed = 6 m²
Pool Table = 8 m²
Computer Centre = 5 m²
Hot Tub = 4 m²
Dresser = 3 m²
Closet = 2 m²
TV/Stereo = 4.5 m²

Page 19

A = 28	B = 44	C = 64
D = 39	E = 14	H = 40
M = 25	N = 12	O = 60
P = 81	R = 36	U = 27

Answer: Area code & phone number

Page 21

Equilateral

Isosceles

Scalene

Square

Rectangle

Parallelogram

Rhombus

Page 22

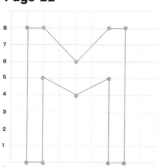

Page 29

Draw Solid	Solid Name	Faces	Edges	Corners
Edge Face Face Edge Face	Cylinder	3	2	0
	Rectangular Prism	6	12	8
	Cube	6	12	8
	Cone	2	1	0
	Square-based Pyramid	5	8	5
	Triangular-based Pyramid	4	6	4

Page 30

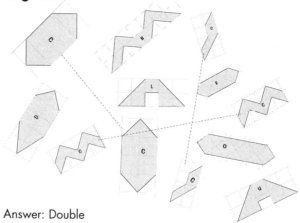

Answer: Double

Page 31 to 34

Multiples of 2

Multiples of 3

Answer Key

Multiples of 4

1	2	3	4	5	6	7	8	9	10
11	12	13	14	15	16	17	18	19	20
21	22	23	24	25	26	27	28	29	30
31	32	33	34	35	36	37	38	39	40
41	42	43	44	45	46	47	48	49	50
51	52	53	54	55	56	57	58	59	60
61	62	63	64	65	66	67	68	69	70
71	72	73	74	75	76	77	78	79	80
81	82	83	84	85	86	87	88	89	90
91	92	93	94	95	96	97	98	99	100

Multiples of 6

1	2	3	4	5	6	7	8	9	10
11	12	13	14	15	16	17	18	19	20
21	22	23	24	25	26	27	28	29	30
31	32	33	34	35	36	37	38	39	40
41	42	43	44	45	46	47	48	49	50
51	52	53	54	55	56	57	58	59	60
61	62	63	64	65	66	67	68	69	70
71	72	73	74	75	76	77	78	79	80
81	82	83	84	85	86	87	88	89	90
91	92	93	94	95	96	97	98	99	100

Multiples of 7

1	2	3	4	5	6	7	8	9	10
11	12	13	14	15	16	17	18	19	20
21	22	23	24	25	26	27	28	29	30
31	32	33	34	35	36	37	38	39	40
41	42	43	44	45	46	47	48	49	50
51	52	53	54	55	56	57	58	59	60
61	62	63	64	65	66	67	68	69	70
71	72	73	74	75	76	77	78	79	80
81	82	83	84	85	86	87	88	89	90
91	92	93	94	95	96	97	98	99	100

Multiples of 8

1	2	3	4	5	6	7	8	9	10
11	12	13	14	15	16	17	18	19	20
21	22	23	24	25	26	27	28	29	30
31	32	33	34	35	36	37	38	39	40
41	42	43	44	45	46	47	48	49	50
51	52	53	54	55	56	57	58	59	60
61	62	63	64	65	66	67	68	69	70
71	72	73	74	75	76	77	78	79	80
81	82	83	84	85	86	87	88	89	90
91	92	93	94	95	96	97	98	99	100

Multiples of 9

1	2	3	4	5	6	7	8	9	10
11	12	13	14	15	16	17	18	19	20
21	22	23	24	25	26	27	28	29	30
31	32	33	34	35	36	37	38	39	40
41	42	43	44	45	46	47	48	49	50
51	52	53	54	55	56	57	58	59	60
61	62	63	64	65	66	67	68	69	70
71	72	73	74	75	76	77	78	79	80
81	82	83	84	85	86	87	88	89	90
91	92	93	94	95	96	97	98	99	100

Multiples of 12

1	2	3	4	5	6	7	8	9	10
11	12	13	14	15	16	17	18	19	20
21	22	23	24	25	26	27	28	29	30
31	32	33	34	35	36	37	38	39	40
41	42	43	44	45	46	47	48	49	50
51	52	53	54	55	56	57	58	59	60
61	62	63	64	65	66	67	68	69	70
71	72	73	74	75	76	77	78	79	80
81	82	83	84	85	86	87	88	89	90
91	92	93	94	95	96	97	98	99	100

Subject	Minutes per Week
Writing	200
Reading	200
Library	50
Math	175
Gym	80
Science	120
Spelling	250
French	200
Art	55
Music	55
Drama	55
Social Studies	110

Page 35
(a) 13, 16, 19, 22, 25, 28
(b) 66, 55, 44, 33, 22, 11
(c) 6, 5, 7, 6, 8
(d) 9, 10, 9, 10

Page 36

Answers	Rules
2. 11, 8, 5	(− 3)
3. 20, 25, 30	(+ 5)
5. 25, 24	(− 1, + 6)
6. 8, 13	(+ 5, − 2)
7. 16, 32	(× 2)
8. 81, 243	(× 3)
9. 17, 19	(prime numbers)
10. 55, 80	(+5, +10, +15, etc.)

Page 37
French = 200 minutes   Writing = 200 minutes
Gym = 80 minutes   Recess = 150 minutes
More of Gym   More Reading
More Social Studies   More French

Page 38
Sandals = 35
Running Shoes = 20
Regular Shoes = 10
Running > Regular
Sandals > Running and Regular
Regular < Sandals

Page 39
2. 6 ducks, 4 cows
3. 5 farmers, 6 geese, 2 dogs
Challenge: 4 elephants, 4 horses, 5 clowns, 2 acrobats

Page 40

Students with long hair	6
Students with medium hair	8
Students with short hair	15

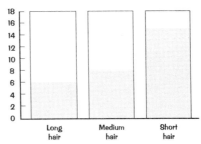

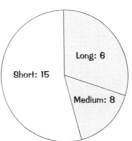

Answer Key

Page 44

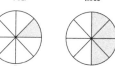

Four   Three   An even number   An odd number

Five   Number smaller than five   Number greater than six   An even number

Dice Rolled		Difference
1	1	0
1	2	1
1	3	2
1	4	3
1	5	4
1	6	5
2	2	0
2	3	1
2	4	2
2	5	3
2	6	4

Dice Rolled		Difference
3	3	0
3	4	1
3	5	2
3	6	3
4	4	0
4	5	1
4	6	2
5	5	0
5	6	1
6	6	0

Player #1 has advantage.

Page 53

Chance of landing on a...

red = $\frac{1}{2}$

orange = $\frac{1}{4}$

yellow = $\frac{1}{4}$

of landing on a...

red = $\frac{1}{6}$

orange = $\frac{1}{2}$

yellow = $\frac{1}{3}$

Page 54

Player #1

Number Landed On	Points
1 (× 3)	3
2 (× 3)	6
3 (× 3)	9
4 (× 3)	12
5 (× 3)	15
6 (× 3)	18
7 (× 3)	21
8 (× 3)	24

Player #2

Number Landed On	Points
1 (+ 8)	9
2 (+ 8)	10
3 (+ 8)	11
4 (+ 8)	12
5 (+ 8)	13
6 (+ 8)	14
7 (+ 8)	15
8 (+ 8)	16

Total point: 108   Total point: 100

Player #1 had a better chance of winning.

Player #1

Number Landed On	Points
1 (× 2)	2
2 (× 2)	4
3 (× 2)	6
4 (× 2)	8
5 (× 2)	10
6 (× 2)	12
7 (× 2)	14
8 (× 2)	16

Player #2

Number Landed On	Points
1 (+ 4)	5
2 (+ 4)	6
3 (+ 4)	7
4 (+ 4)	8
5 (+ 4)	9
6 (+ 4)	10
7 (+ 4)	11
8 (+ 4)	12

Total point: 72   Total point: 68

Player #1 had a better chance of winning.

Page 55

	Smallest	2 096
		2 781
		5 028
		5 348
		8 064
		19 453
		34 961
		40 703
	Largest	62 091

Page 56

1. 2 166
2. 1 495
3. 1 598
4. 2 448
5. 962
6. 1 008
7. 2 204
8. 2 142
9. 1 121
10. 1 645
11. 648
12. 2 814

Page 57

(c) 56
(d) 81
(l) 13
(o) 15
(u) 62
(s) 48
(k) 73

Answer: Sucks Blood

Page 58

$249.72 = 2 CD ($34.90) + 3 sweaters ($89.37) + watch ($125.45)

$89.90 = 2 pairs of jeans

$64.69 = sweater ($29.79) + 2 CD ($34.90)

$329.98 = shirt ($14.89) + rollerblades ($189.64) + watch ($125.45)

$154.25 = one hundred fifty-four dollars twenty-five cents

$125.45 = one hundred twenty-five dollars forty-five cents

$79.10 = seventy-nine dollars ten cents

$44.95 = forty-four dollars ninety-five cents

$29.79 = twenty-nine dollars seventy-nine cents

$17.45 = seventeen dollars forty-five cents

$14.89 = fourteen dollars eighty-nine cents

Page 59

Prices	Hundreds	Tens	Ones	Tenths
$189.64	$200	$190	$190	$189.60
$154.25	$200	$150	$154	$154.30
$125.45	$100	$130	$125	$125.50
$79.10	$100	$80	$79	$79.10
$44.95	$0	$40	$45	$45.00
$29.79	$0	$30	$30	$29.80
$17.45	$0	$20	$17	$17.50
$14.89	$0	$10	$15	$14.90

Answer Key

Items	Price	Nearest Dollar
Chips and pop for party	$5.80	$6
Pen set	$9.15	$9
Stickers	$7.55	$8
Computer game	$42.68	$43
Sunglasses	$11.25	$11
Sweater	$26.50	$27
Books	$14.95	$15
New video games	$65.55	$66

1	4	6	1
5	3	6	1
8	2	7	9

Page 60

(a) 428
   four hundred twenty-eight
(b) 853
   eight hundred fifty-three
(c) 3 437
   three thousand four hundred thirty-seven
(d) 269
   two hundred sixty-nine
(e) 709
   seven hundred nine
(f) 1 048
   one thousand forty-eight

Page 61

1. (a) (b) (c) (d) (e) (f) (g) (h) *[Egyptian numeral symbols]*

2.

Hundred thousands	Ten thousands	Thousands	Hundreds	Tens	Ones
[symbol]	*[symbol]*	*[symbol]*	*[symbol]*	*[symbol]*	*[symbol]*

3. (a) (b) (c) (d) (e) (f) (g) (h) *[Egyptian numeral symbols]*

4. (a) 42   (b) 1 006   (c) 30 013
   (d) 321

Page 62

1. $2.40   2. $37.50   3. $36.00
4. 11   5. 256   6. 13
7. $35.50   8. 14   9. 260

Page 63

T   c = 150   d = 50   r = 25
I   c = 25   d = 6   r = 3
D   c = 110   d = 35   r = 18
R   c = 250   d = 80   r = 40
E   c = 165   d = 50   r = 25
M   c = 90   d = 25   r = 12.5
Answer: Diameter

Page 64

Destinations	Your clock	24-hour digital clock
Paris, France	7:30 a.m.	07:30
Cairo, Egypt	5:48 p.m.	17:48
Vancouver, B.C.	2:35 p.m.	14:35
Istanbul, Turkey	1:10 a.m.	01:10
Cape Town, S. Africa	10:52 p.m.	22:52
Quito, Ecuador	12:10 p.m.	12:10

Destinations	Your watch time	Time difference	New watch time for trip
Paris, France	9:25	6 hours ahead	15:25
Cairo, Egypt	12:56	7 hours ahead	19:56
Vancouver, B.C.	5:15	3 hours behind	02:15
Istanbul, Turkey	3:20	8 hours ahead	11:20
Cape Town, S. Africa	11:37	7 hours ahead	18:37
Quito, Ecuador	2:43	1 hours behind	01:43

Answer Key

Page 65
1. 2 000 mL
2. 7 000 mL
3. 25 000 mL
4. 3 700 mL
5. 6 830 mL
6. 94 000 mL
7. 4 180 mL
8. 130 000 mL
9. 4 750 mL
10. 2 L
11. 4 L
12. 7.6 L
13. 0.4 L
14. 33 L
15. 5.2 L
16. 0.85 L
17. 3.25 L
18. 28.5 L

Page 66
1. Area = approx. 29 units^2
2. Area = approx. 21 units^2
3. Area = approx. 26 units^2
4. Area = approx. 15 units^2
5. Area = approx. 15 units^2
6. Area = approx. 33 units^2

Page 67
1. 8 cm^3
2. 96 cm^3
3. 24 cm^3
V. 2 cm^3
O. 3 cm^3
L. 8 cm^3
U. 8 cm^3
M. 1 cm^2
E. 10 cm^3

Page 68
Down
1. $3 \times 3 \times 1 = 9$ cm^3
2. $5 \times 2 \times 3 = 30$ cm^3

Across
2. $2 \times 2 \times 3 = 12$ cm^3
3. $2 \times 1 \times 4 = 8$ cm^3
4. $2 \times 2 \times 8 = 32$ cm^3

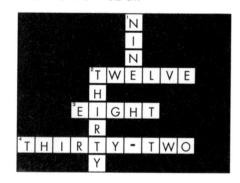

Page 69
(a) 30 cm^3
(b) 84 cm^3
(c) 16 cm^3
(d) 72 cm^3
(e) 20 cm^3
(f) 60 cm^3

Page 71
Mirror, mirror, on the wall,
who's the fairest of them all?

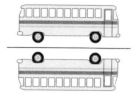

Pages 72 and 73
∠JAM   obtuse
∠BED   right
∠YES   obtuse
∠FUN   acute
∠GYM   right
∠YOU   acute

1. ∠HOT = 120° = obtuse
2. ∠BUD =   93° = obtuse
3. ∠MAT =   75° = acute
4. ∠PEN =   90° = right
5. ∠HOP = 155° = obtuse
6. ∠CAT =   60° = acute
7. ∠PAL =   35° = acute
8. ∠DOG =   90° = right

Page 74
2. Correct   Not correct   Not correct

3.

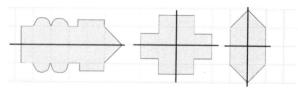

Page 76

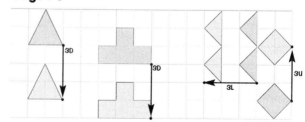

Answer Key

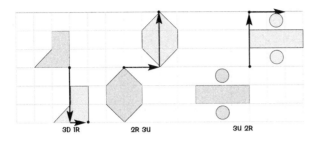

3D 1R   2R 3U   3U 2R

Page 77

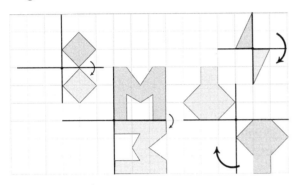

Page 79

How many toothpicks for...
1 square?	4
2 squares?	7
3 squares?	10

1	2	3	4	5	6	7
4	7	10	13	16	19	22

# of triangles	1	2	3	4	5	6	7
# of toothpicks	3	5	7	9	11	13	15

How many toothpicks for...
8 triangles?	17
10 triangles?	21
11 triangles?	23
15 triangles?	31
20 triangles?	41

Page 80

Rhombus #	1	2	3	4	5	6	7
Units of Perimeter	4	8	12	16	20	24	28

Square #	1	2	3	4	5	6	7
Units of Perimeter	4	6	8	10	12	14	16

Page 81

Pattern to 18 blocks:
4 green blocks
6 red blocks
10 red and yellow blocks

Pattern to 29 blocks:
12 red and green blocks
7 blue blocks
13 blue and yellow blocks
30th blue

Page 82

1 family = 1 window, 8 bricks
2 families = 2 windows, 13 bricks
3 families = 3 windows, 18 bricks

# of families	1	2	3	4	5	6	7
# of windows	1	2	3	4	5	6	7
# of bricks	8	13	18	23	28	33	38

10 families: 53, 10
15 families: 78, 15
20 families: 103, 20

Folds	Sections
1	2
2	4
3	8
4	16
5	32
6	64

Page 83

Rule	-2
8	6
5	3
4	2
2	0
7	5
3	1
6	4

1.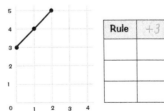

Rule	+3

2.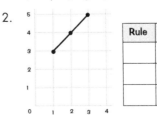

Rule	+2

Answer Key

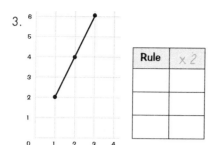

3.

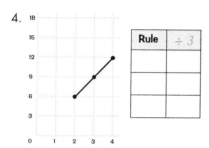

4.

Page 84
1. I love Math = $175.00
2. I love Mathematics = $262.50
3. I love Mathematics = $99.00

Page 87
Total = 30
Average = 6 hours

Page 88
4 000	700
90	3

1. 8 000	2. 9 000	3. 50
4. 7	5. 200	6. 300
7. 6	8. 2 000	9. 10
10. 60 000		

1. 50 000 + 3 000 + 700 + 8
   = fifty-three thousand seven hundred eight
2. 90 000 + 1 000 + 200 + 40 + 5
   = ninety-one thousand two hundred forty-five
3. 40 000 + 6 000 + 300 + 20
   = forty-six thousand three hundred twenty
4. 70 000 + 4 000 + 800 + 30 + 6
   = seventy-four thousand eight hundred thirty-six

Page 89
1. 288	2. 200
3. 371	4. 152
5. 492	6. 245
7. 243	8. 141

1. 224	2. 273
3. 240	4. 546
5. 216	

Page 90
Across
1. 41 R4	2. 69 R3	3. 90 R1
4. 38 R9	5. 96 R7	6. 7 R10

Down
1. 31 R5	2. 71 R2	7. 42 R8
5. 65 R7	8. 12 R11	

Page 91
1. $2 \times 5 \times 2 \times 5$
2. $3 \times 11 \times 3$
3. $2 \times 5 \times 2 \times 3$
4. $2 \times 2 \times 2 \times 2 \times 2$
5. $2 \times 5 \times 3 \times 3$
6. $2 \times 2 \times 3 \times 7$
7. $2 \times 13 \times 2 \times 2$
8. $2 \times 17 \times 2 \times 2$
9. $3 \times 3 \times 3 \times 2$

Prime numbers:
1, 2, 3, 5, 7, 11, 13, 17, 19, 23, 29, 31, 37, 41, 43

Page 92

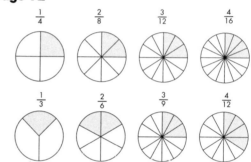

(a) $\frac{3}{4} = \frac{6}{8} = \frac{9}{12} = \frac{12}{16} = \frac{15}{20}$
(b) $\frac{2}{5} = \frac{4}{10} = \frac{6}{15} = \frac{8}{20} = \frac{20}{50}$

(c) $\frac{2}{3} = \frac{4}{6} = \frac{6}{9} = \frac{8}{12} = \frac{20}{30}$
(d) $\frac{5}{8} = \frac{10}{16} = \frac{40}{64} = \frac{50}{80} = \frac{60}{96}$

(e) $\frac{2}{7} = \frac{4}{14} = \frac{6}{21} = \frac{14}{49} = \frac{20}{70}$
(f) $\frac{4}{9} = \frac{8}{18} = \frac{16}{36} = \frac{32}{72} = \frac{36}{81}$

(g) $\frac{3}{11} = \frac{6}{22} = \frac{9}{33} = \frac{18}{66} = \frac{24}{88}$
(h) $\frac{7}{10} = \frac{14}{20} = \frac{21}{30} = \frac{35}{50} = \frac{56}{80}$

Page 93
(a) >	(b) >	(c) >	(d) =	(e) <
(f) >	(g) =	(h) >	(i) <	(j) >

Page 95
1. 0.42	2. 0.07	3. 0.84

4. $\frac{40}{50} = \frac{80}{100}$ 5. $\frac{31}{50} = \frac{62}{100}$ 6. $\frac{12}{20} = \frac{60}{100}$

7. $\frac{4}{25} = \frac{16}{100}$ 8. $\frac{3}{50} = \frac{6}{100}$ 9. $\frac{6}{10} = \frac{60}{100}$

10. $\frac{24}{25} = \frac{96}{100}$ 11. $\frac{17}{20} = \frac{85}{100}$

4. 0.8	5. 0.62	6. 0.6	7. 0.16
8. 0.06	9. 0.6	10. 0.96	11. 0.85

$\frac{22}{25} = \frac{88}{100} = 0.88$

Spin

- Find a pencil and a paper clip.
- Using the spinner provided, place the pencil in the middle of the circle with the paper clip looped around the pencil.
- Spin your paper clip spinner at least 40 times to see where it lands.

Before you play:

What colour do you think you will land on the most? _____

What colour do you think you will land on the least? _____

Now get spinning! As you play, keep track of your results on this graph.

Red	Orange	Yellow

Colour in each section of the spinner.

What are the chances of landing on the:

red? _____

orange? _____

yellow? _____

Here's another spinner to try.

BE CAREFUL!
Even though it may look as if the red is 1 colour out of 3 colours, the chances of getting red is not 1 out of 3. The red takes up half of the spinner, so the chance is half.

Before you play:

What colour do you think you will land on the most? _____

What colour do you think you will land on the least? _____

Red	Orange	Yellow

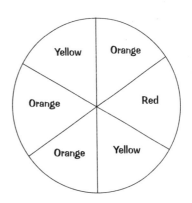

What are the chances of landing on the:

red? _____

orange? _____

yellow? _____

More Spinning Around

For this spinning game, you will need to use a pencil and paper clip.

How to play:
- Place your pencil in the middle of the spinner with the paper clip wrapped around.
- Take turns spinning.
- Player #1 must multiply the number it lands on by 3. The answer is Player 1's points.
- Player #2 must add 8 to the number it lands on. The answer is Player 2's points.

For example:

Player #1: lands on 3   Player #2: lands on 3
$3 \times 3 = 9$ $3 + 8 = 11$
9 points   11 points

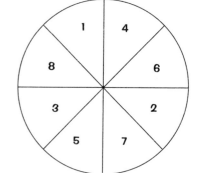

Before you start:
Who do you think will win? Player #1 or Player #2? Why?

_____

Tally your points here: Player #1 _____   Player #2 _____

To find out which player you should choose to be, let's look at your chances of winning for each possibility. You need to chart the possibilities below.

Number landed on	Points
1 (× 3)	3
2 (× 3)	6
3 (× 3)	9
4 (× 3)	
5 (× 3)	
6 (× 3)	
7 (× 3)	
8 (× 3)	

Player #1

Number landed on	Points
1 (+ 8)	9
2 (+ 8)	10
3 (+ 8)	11
4 (+ 8)	
5 (+ 8)	
6 (+ 8)	
7 (+ 8)	
8 (+ 8)	

Player #2

Now add the points. Who has the better chance of winning? _____

What would happen if Player #1 multiplied the spinner number by 2 and Player #2 added 4 to the spinner number? Who do you think would win? Make a chart to find out.

Number landed on	Points

Player #1

Number landed on	Points

Player #2

Numbers Cross

First read the numbers below and write the numbers using digits. (The first one is already done for you.) Place each number in the Number Cross below.

Then place the numbers in order from smallest to largest.

ACROSS

1. five thousand three hundred forty-eight

2. sixty-two thousand ninety-one

3. forty thousand seven hundred three

4. five thousand twenty-eight

5. eight thousand sixty-four

DOWN

6. thirty-four thousand nine hundred sixty-one

7. nineteen thousand four hundred fifty-three

8. two thousand seven hundred eighty-one

9. two thousand ninety-six

Place numbers in order from smallest to largest

(smallest) _____2 096_____

_____

_____

_____

_____

_____

_____

_____

(largest) _____

Be careful with numbers that may have ZEROS!

Twenty-twenty Vision

Twenty-twenty is one assessment of perfect vision.
Let's see if you have "twenty-twenty" multiplication.

Steps to remember:

1. Always work from right to left.

2. Circle the number you are working with.

3. When you are done with the first number, stroke it out.

4. Stroke out the carry-over work, and place a zero in the ones column to prepare for the tens.

5. Continue with the next number.

6. Add the two numbers together.

```
    46        46        46        46        46        46
  × 93      × 93      × 93      × 93      × 93      × 93
            138       138       138       138       138
                                  0      4230      4230
                                                   4368
```

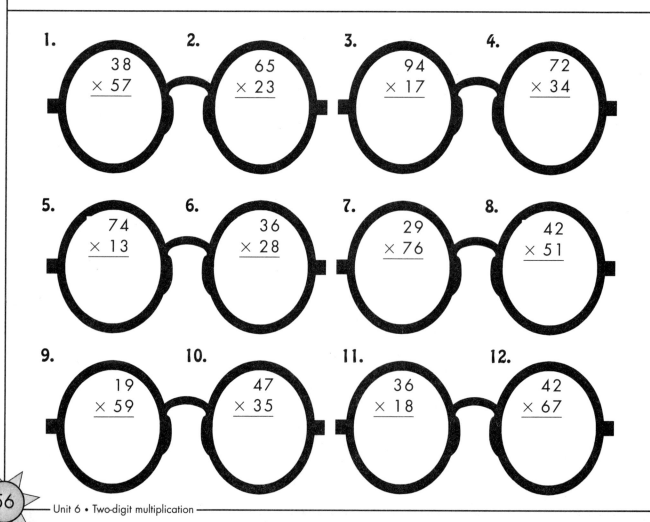

1.
```
  38
× 57
```

2.
```
  65
× 23
```

3.
```
  94
× 17
```

4.
```
  72
× 34
```

5.
```
  74
× 13
```

6.
```
  36
× 28
```

7.
```
  29
× 76
```

8.
```
  42
× 51
```

9.
```
  19
× 59
```

10.
```
  47
× 35
```

11.
```
  36
× 18
```

12.
```
  42
× 67
```

Divide, Multiply, Subtract, Bring Down...and Conquer!

DMSB is all you need to remember. It may seem complicated at first, but just remember these letters and you'll be great!

First, you must know the names.

$$23 \rightarrow \text{quotient (answer)}$$

$$\text{divisor} \leftarrow 4)\overline{92} \rightarrow \text{dividend (what you're dividing into)}$$

Now, you can get to the fun stuff.

D Divide the divisor into the first number of the dividend. See how many times it can fit in.

$4)\overline{92}$ "4 can fit into 9 2 times"

M Place the number on top (quotient) and multiply it with the divisor.

$\begin{array}{r} 2 \\ 4)\overline{92} \\ 8 \end{array}$ "2 times 4 is 8"

S Subtract the difference.

B Bring down the next number.

$\begin{array}{r} 2 \\ 4)\overline{92} \\ 8\downarrow \\ \hline 12 \end{array}$

Time for you to answer this riddle with your new skills. Finish these questions. The answer for each represents a letter below. Look for the answer below and place the appropriate letter from the question.

(b) $\begin{array}{r} 23 \\ 4)\overline{92} \\ 8\downarrow \\ \hline 12 \\ 12 \\ \hline 0 \end{array}$ (c) $2)\overline{112}$ (d) $3)\overline{243}$ (k) $8)\overline{584}$

(l) $7)\overline{91}$ (o) $7)\overline{105}$ (s) $5)\overline{240}$ (u) $4)\overline{248}$

> Use whatever you can think of to help you remember DMSB. One way is to think of Dracula's Mother.

What does Dracula's Mother do that will help you remember how to divide?

Answer:

48	62	56	73	48
_b_				
23	13	15	15	81

Shopping Spree

It's your lucky day! You have the opportunity to go shopping AND you'll be given money to spend.

What items can you buy that would bring your total as close as possible to...
(You may buy more than 1 of each item.) Use the second line to do the math work.

$100.00 _Jeans + CD + CD + CD_

TOTAL _$49.95 + $17.95 + $17.95 + $17.95 = $98.80_

$250.00 _____

TOTAL _____

$90.00 _____

TOTAL _____

$65.00 _____

TOTAL _____

$330.00 _____

TOTAL _____

Write each price in words.

$189.64 _one hundred eighty-nine dollars sixty-four cents_

$154.25 _____

$125.45 _____

$79.10 _____

$44.95 _____

$29.79 _____

$17.45 _____

$14.89 _____

Round 'em Up!

Round each of the prices to the nearest...

Prices	Hundreds	Tens	Ones	Tenths
$189.64	$200	$190	$190	$189.60
$154.25				
$125.45				
$79.10				
$44.95				
$29.79				
$17.45				
$14.89				

Estimate these items by rounding them to the nearest unit (dollar).

Items	Price	Nearest Dollar
Chips and pop for party	$5.80	$6
Pen set	$9.15	
Stickers	$7.55	
Computer game	$42.68	
Sunglasses	$11.25	
Sweater	$26.50	
Books	$14.95	
Video games	$65.55	

Find the rounded prices above in this number find.

1	4	6	1
5	3	6	1
8	2	7	9

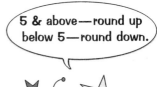

5 & above—round up
below 5—round down.

Bases Loaded, Adders Up!

Use these base ten blocks to fill in the blanks with numbers and words.

(a)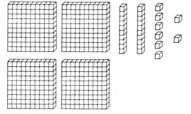

428

four hundred twenty-eight

(b)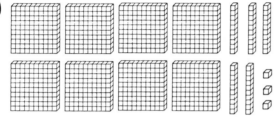

_____

_____

(c)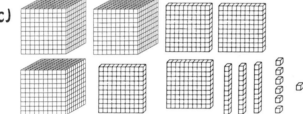

_____

_____

(d)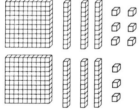

_____

_____

(e)

_____

_____

(f)

_____

_____

Write Like an Egyptian!

Ancient Egyptian numerals are pictographs. They looked very different from the numbers we know today.

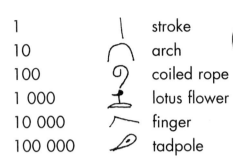

1	\	stroke
10	arch	arch
100	coiled rope	coiled rope
1 000	lotus flower	lotus flower
10 000	finger	finger
100 000	tadpole	tadpole

Instead of having numbers for 2 through to 9, Egyptians simply used the stroke like this: 3 = III, 6 = IIIIII And so on.

1. Give the Egyptian symbol for each of the following numerals.

(a) 1 \ _____

(b) 2 || _____

(c) 40 ∩∩∩∩ _____

(d) 700 _____

(e) 1 000 _____

(f) 90 000 _____

(g) 200 _____

(h) 500 000 _____

2. Name the Egyptian place value columns in the spaces provided.

Hundred thousands	Ten thousands	Thousands	Hundreds	Tens	Ones
tadpole					

3. Give the Egyptian symbol for each.

(a) 7 ||||||| _____

(b) 720 234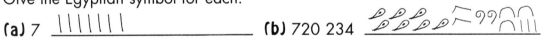

(c) 66 _____

(d) 200 931 _____

(e) 25 _____

(f) 4 321 _____

(g) 30 _____

(h) 1 111 _____

4. Change the following Egyptian numeral to our numerals.

(a) ∩∩∩ || _____

(b) lotus ||| || || _____

(c) finger finger ∩ ||| _____

(d) coiled rope coiled rope coiled rope ∩∩ | _____

Problems! Problems! Problems!
Get Rid of Them!

The answers to these problems are in one of the bubbles on the page. Find the answer and cross out the bubble, and write the answer inside the appropriate bubble beside the question.

1. Stamps costs 48 cents. Jason bought 5 stamps and it cost him ◯.

2. Nicole goes to the market each week to spend her $7.50 earnings on candy. She spends ◯ after 5 weeks.

3. Scott is buying a birthday gift bag for his 24 friends that he has invited over. Each bag costs $1.50, so Scott's total cost is ◯.

4. Katrina has a novel that she must finish in the next 14 days. There are 154 pages left to read. Reading the same amount each night to finish on time, Katrina should read ◯ pages per day.

5. Room 207 is going on a big science field trip. Their subway tokens cost $1.00 per student. The admission price for the science centre is $4.50, and the lunch and movie in the afternoon costs $2.50 each. With 32 students in the class, it will cost ◯ dollars for the whole class to go .

6. Starting with 1 as the first prime number, 3 as the second prime number, and so on, the sixth prime number will be ◯ .

7. Paul decides to go to the movies with 4 other friends. They each buy a movie ticket for $3.75, a pop for $1.25, and a medium-sized popcorn for $2.10. The total amount for all five is ◯ .

8. Ann is counting groups of coins. Her first group has 8 coins, the second group has 6. The third group has 10, the next has 8. Following is a group a 12, and then a group of 10. Looking at the pattern that Ann is making, the number of coins in the next group will be ◯.

9. The grade five class at Palmerston is presenting an art display this week. They have been doing an art piece each week for the last 13 weeks. With 20 students in the class and each student presenting all works during the week, there will be a total of ◯ art works at the show.

Around We Go

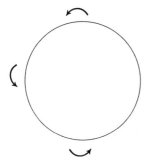

Circumference
(distance around)

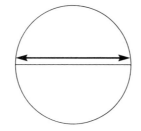

Diameter
(distance cutting across
through the centre)

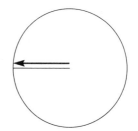

Radius
(outside to the centre)

Use some yarn or string to measure around these circles. Then use your ruler to see how long the piece of yarn was to get all around the circle. You will then have found the circumference! Measure the diameter and radius, even though your clues for the riddle are found only in the circumference. Use your answers to solve this riddle:

What is the funeral service called for a ruler?

Dental floss works to measure circumference.

Use mm.

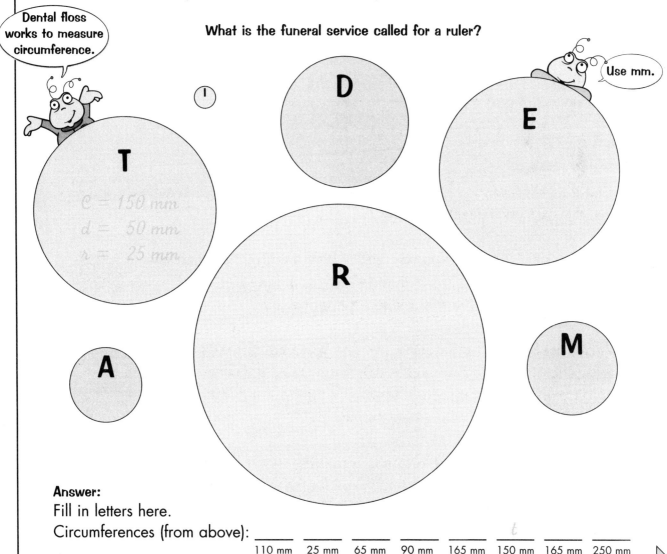

Circle T:
C = 150 mm
d = 50 mm
r = 25 mm

Answer:
Fill in letters here.

Circumferences (from above): ____ ____ ____ ____ ____ ____ ____ ____

110 mm   25 mm   65 mm   90 mm   165 mm   150 mm   165 mm   250 mm

What Time Is It?

It's time for a trip around the world. Yippee!! However, first you have to know how to read a 24-hour clock.

Your Clock

Airport Clock

Remember to add 12 hours only to the times that are in the evening (p.m.).

Check the times that these planes are leaving.
Write the time as it would appear on a 24-hour digital clock.

Destinations	Your clock	24-hour digital clock
Paris, France	7:30 a.m.	07:30
Cairo, Egypt	5:48 p.m.	17:48
Vancouver, B.C.	2:35 p.m.	
Istanbul, Turkey	1:10 a.m.	
Cape Town, S. Africa	10:52 p.m.	
Quito, Ecuador	12:10 p.m.	

Once you get to your destination, you must change your watch because of the time difference. Figure out the difference and change the time.

Destinations	Your watch time	Time difference	New watch time for trip
Paris, France	9:25	6 hours ahead	15:25
Cairo, Egypt	12:56	7 hours ahead	
Vancouver, B.C.	5:15	3 hours behind	
Istanbul, Turkey	3:20	8 hours ahead	
Cape Town, S. Africa	11:37	7 hours ahead	
Quito, Ecuador	2:43	1 hour behind	

Fill It Up!

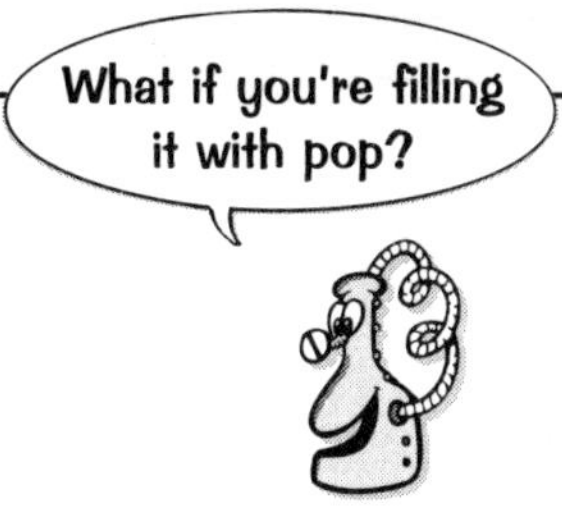

What if you're filling it with pop?

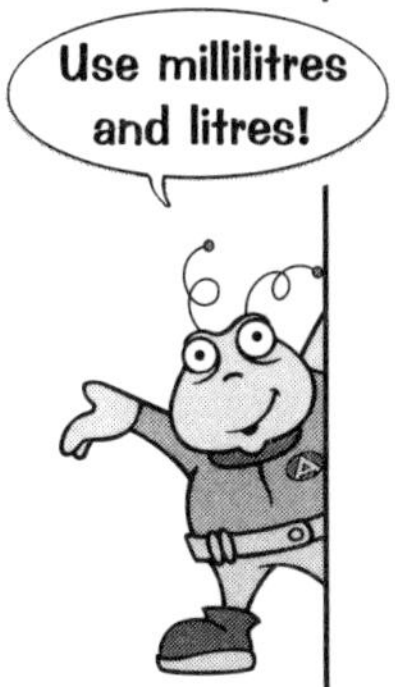

Use millilitres and litres!

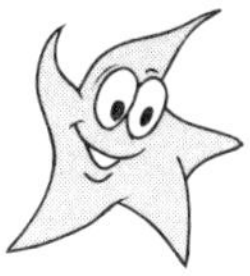

VOLUME calculates the number of 1 cm cubes that could fit into a regular-shaped structure.

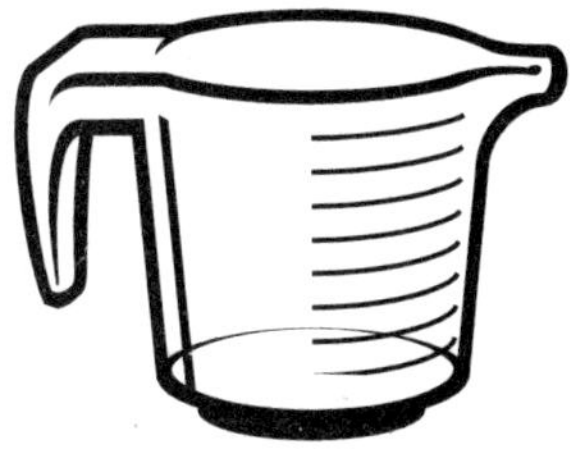
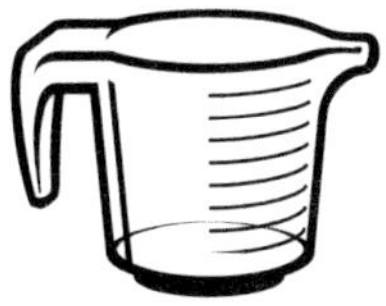
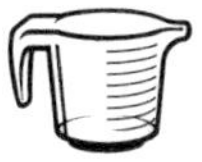

1 L = 1 000 mL **0.5 L = 500 mL** **0.25 L = 250 mL**

Brainstorm the kinds of things you would measure using millilitres and litres. Write them in the VENN diagram.

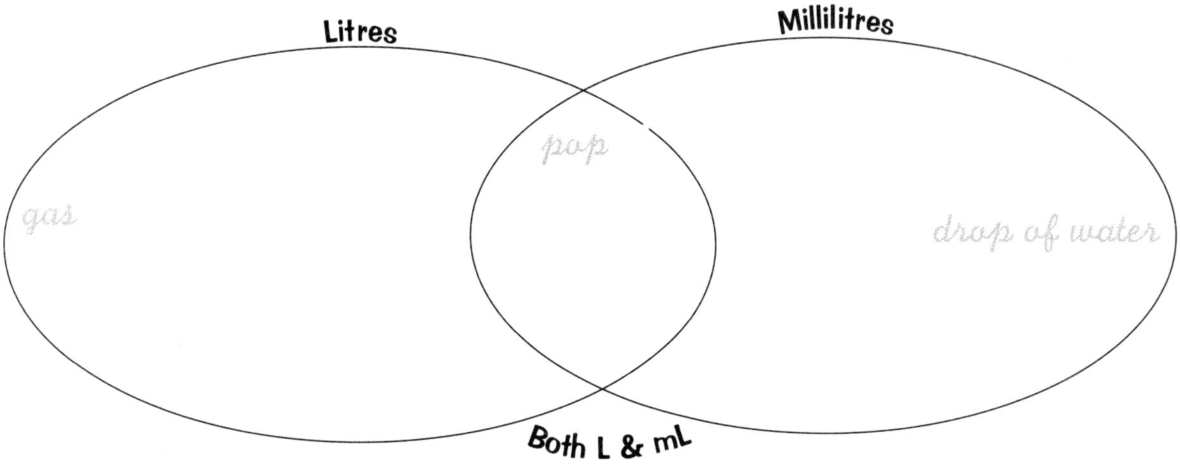

Litres
Millilitres
gas
pop
drop of water
Both L & mL

Remember that 1 L = 1 000 mL and answer these questions.

1. 2 L = ____________mL **2.** 7 L = ____________mL **3.** 25 L = ____________mL

4. 3.7 L = ____________mL **5.** 6.83 L = ____________mL **6.** 94 L = ____________mL

7. 4.18 L = ____________mL **8.** 130 L = ____________mL **9.** 4.75 L = ____________mL

Now remember the reverse, that 1 000 mL = 1 L and answer these questions.

10. 2 000 mL = ________L **11.** 4 000 mL = ________L **12.** 7 600 mL = ________L

13. 400 mL = ________L **14.** 33 000 mL = ________L **15.** 5 200 mL = ________L

16. 850 mL = ________L **17.** 3 250 mL = ________L **18.** 28 500 mL = ________L

Funky Space

Count whole squares first, then add the fractions.

Estimate the area of these fun figures.

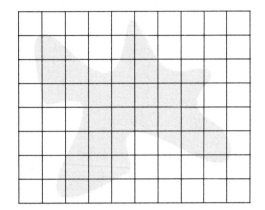

1. Area _____

2. Area _____

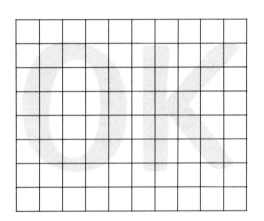

3. Area _____

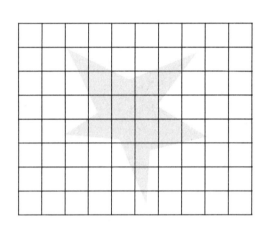

4. Area _____

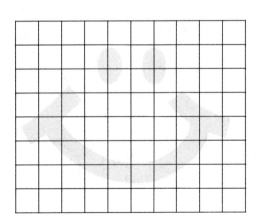

5. Area _____

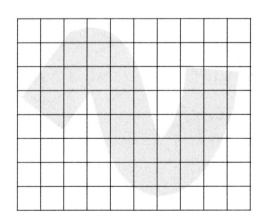

6. Area _____

Turn Up the Volume

LENGTH measures a line.

   The length of this line is ___4___ cm.

AREA measures the number of surface squares.

    The area of this shape is ___6___ cm².

VOLUME measures the amount of space an object takes up in cubes.

    The volume of this structure is ___1___cm³.

The volume of this structure is ___8___cm³.

What is the volume of these structures? Each block represents a cm³.

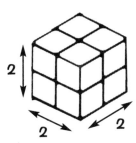   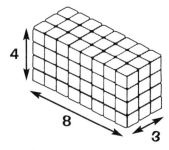   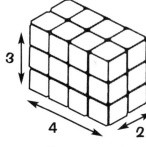

1. _8_ cm³   **2.** ___ cm³   **3.** ___ cm³

Just count the cubes!

Look at the letters below and write the volume that the structure takes up.

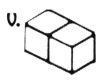   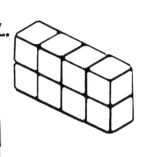

V.   L.   M.

O.   E.

U.

V ___ cm³ O ___ cm L ___ cm³ U ___ cm³ M ___ cm³ E ___ cm³

More Volume, Please!

To calculate the **AREA** of a regular space, remember: **LENGTH x WIDTH.**

length = 2
width = 6

Area = l × w
     = 2 × 6
     = 12 cm²

To calculate the **VOLUME**, remember: **LENGTH × WIDTH × HEIGHT.**

length = 3
width = 4
height = 2

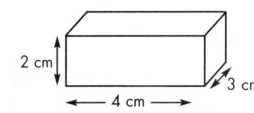

2 cm
4 cm
3 cm

Volume = l × w × h
       = 3 × 4 × 2
       = 24 cm³

Find the area of the following structures and write your answer in the volume crossword.

DOWN

1. l = 3   l × w × h   **2.** l = 5
   w = 3   = 3 × 3 × 1   w = 2
   h = 1   = _____ cm³   h = 3

ACROSS

2. l = 2   **3.** l = 2   **4.** l = 2
   w = 2   w = 1   w = 8
   h = 3   h = 4   h = 2

Cube Fun

The best way to understand volume is to make the solid shape. Using the centimetre grid paper, measure the following half nets, cut them out, and fold them into the appropriate shape.

For example, this first container has the height of 1 cm, the length of 5 cm, and the width of 2 cm.

The net without its top looks like this.

Cut this out and fold up the sides according to the measurements. Now you can see what the volume of 1 cm × 5 cm × 2 cm looks like. You could actually fit 10 small centimetre cubes in your container.

Calculate the volume of the following containers. Then measure and cut to see the actual size of that volume.

	length	height	width	VOLUME		length	height	width	VOLUME
(a)	3	5	2	_____	(b)	7	3	4	_____
(c)	8	1	2	_____	(d)	4	6	3	_____
(e)	5	4	1	_____	(f)	6	2	5	_____

Time to Reflect!

Help me to figure out this coded message. You may use a mirror if you have one close by. The message is a mirrored image, so just reflect what you see!

MI

MIRROR, MIRROR, ON THE WALL,

WHO'S THE FAIREST OF THEM ALL?

Now try your name.   NAME

NAME

How about mirroring these pictures. Give it a shot.

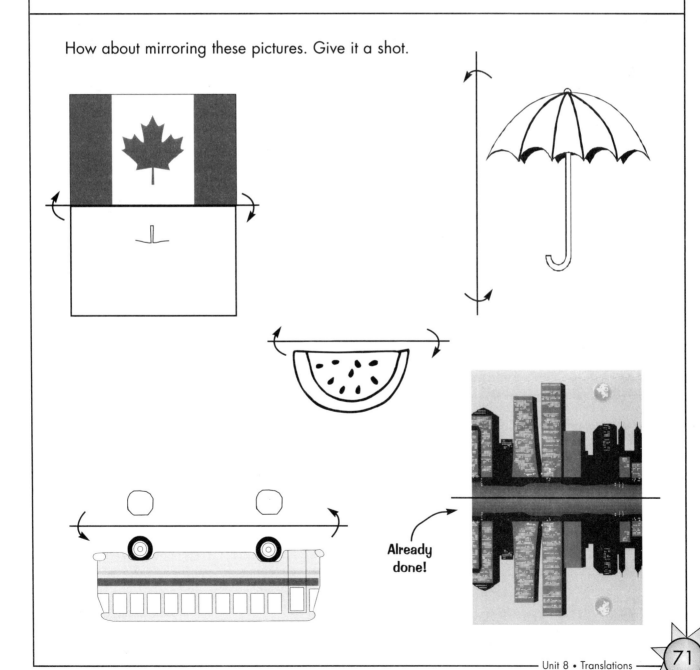

Already
done!

What a Cute Angle!

Angles are all around us. Look at the angle these scissors make. What about the hands on a clock?

Make a list of all the things that you can see right now that have angles.

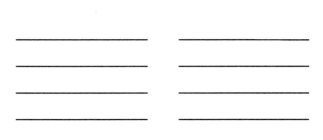

_____ _____

_____ _____

_____ _____

_____ _____ _____

_____ _____ _____

We use an instrument called a protractor to measure angles.

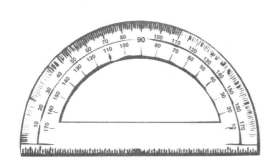

This ∠ABC is 90°.
It is called a RIGHT angle.

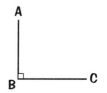

This ∠ABC is less than 90°.
It is called an ACUTE angle.

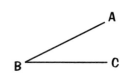

This ∠ABC is more than 90°.
It is called an OBTUSE angle.

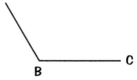

Label the angles below as right, acute, and obtuse.

∠ JAM _____

∠ BED _____

∠ YES _____

∠ FUN _____

∠ GYM _____

∠ YOU _____

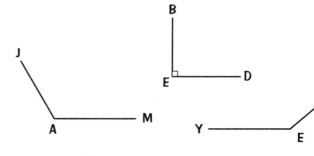

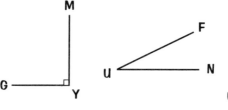

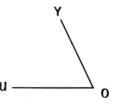

Measure the angles shown and name the angle as right, acute, or obtuse.

1.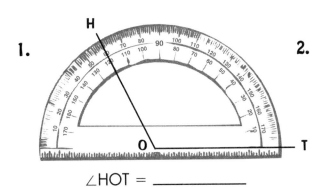

∠HOT = _____

_____

2.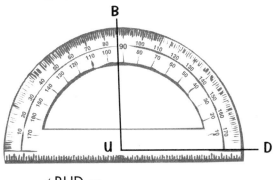

∠BUD = _____

_____

3.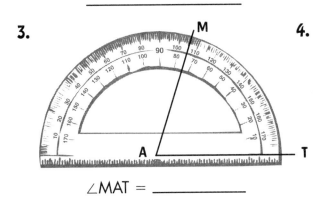

∠MAT = _____

_____

4.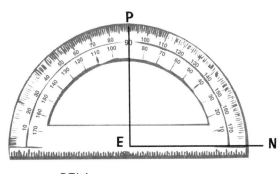

∠PEN = _____

_____

5.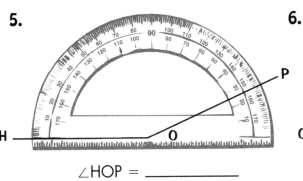

∠HOP = _____

_____

6.

∠CAT = _____

_____

7.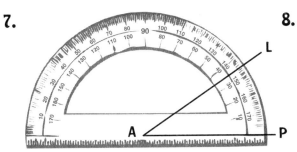

∠PAL = _____

_____

8.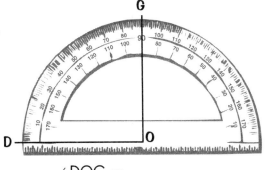

∠DOG = _____

_____

I'm Flipping Out!

SYMMETRY is when things are equal on both sides, like placing a mirror in the middle.

1. These are symmetrical.   These are close, but not quite.

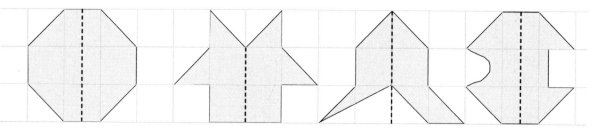

2. Is the line of symmetry in these pictures and shapes correct? Circle your answer. If not, draw the correct line.

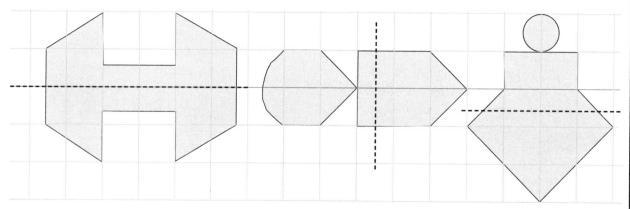

Correct   Not   Correct   Not   Correct   Not

3. Find and draw the line of symmetry for these pictures and shapes.

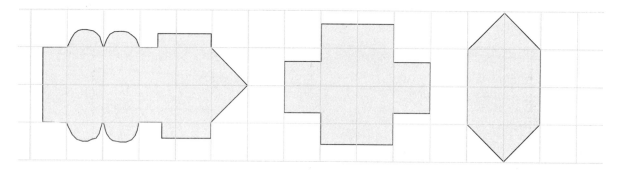

4. Try drawing your own symmetrical shapes using the graph paper.

Here are some examples of some flipped out shapes.

| Shape | Image | Shape | Image | Shape | Image |

Now you try some.

| Shape | Image | Shape | Image | Shape | Image |

| Shape | Image | Shape | Image | Shape | Image |

Slip, Sliding Away

Here are some examples of some slides.

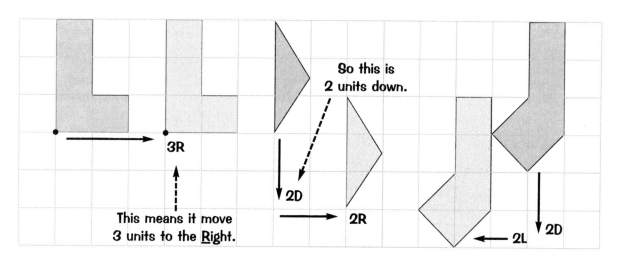

So this is
2 units down.

3R

This means it move
3 units to the Right.

2D

2R

2L

2D

Slide these shapes to their new position. Check where each point of the shape has moved. They each move the same number of squares.

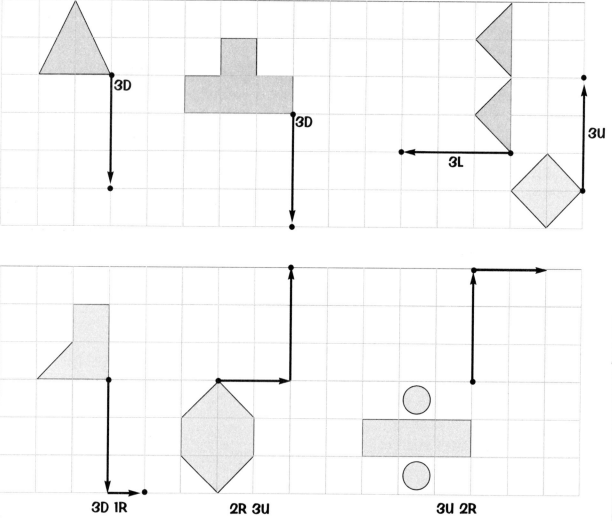

3D

3D

3L

3U

3D 1R

2R 3U

3U 2R

To Everything...Turn, Turn, Turn

These figures have been rotated or turned around at centre point.

These are $\frac{1}{4}$ turns

These are $\frac{1}{2}$ turns

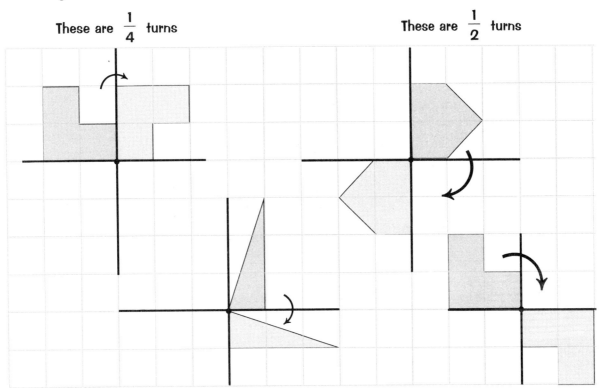

Turn these figures a $\frac{1}{4}$ turn.

Turn these figures a $\frac{1}{2}$ turn.

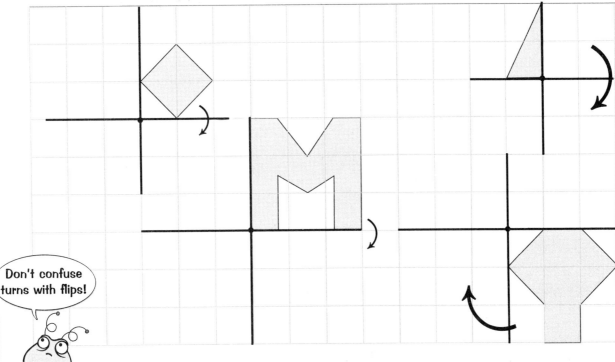

Don't confuse turns with flips!

Test Your Tessellations

TESSELLATIONS are simply combinations of flipping, sliding and turning.

So dance away! Here is an example. Colour it in using 1 colour for triangles and another for squares.

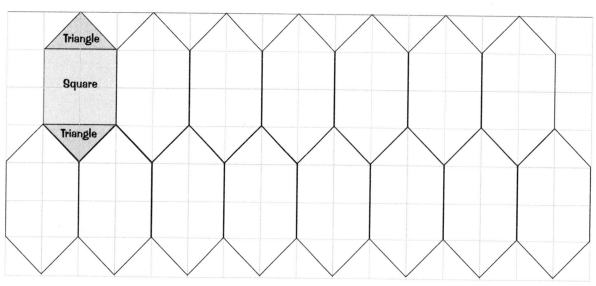

Try your own tessellating patterns with these shapes.

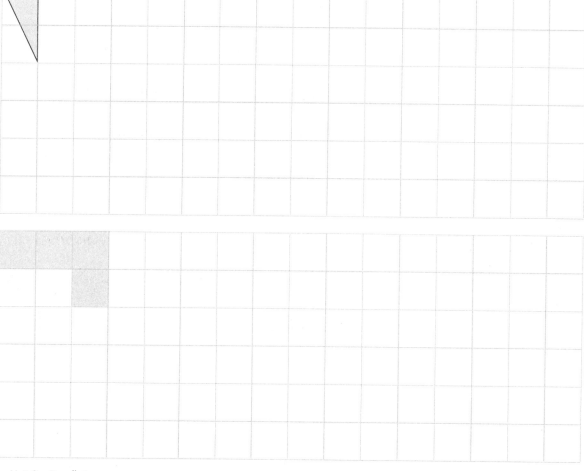

Toothpick Tricks

How many toothpicks does it take to make

1 square? _____

2 squares? _____

3 squares? _____

Continue to fill in this chart to show the ratio of squares to toothpicks.

1	2	3	4	5	6	7
4	7					

Continue this toothpick pattern of triangles.

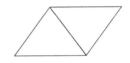

# of triangles	1	2	3	4	5	6	7
# of toothpicks	3	5					

How many toothpicks would you need to make

8 triangles? _____   15 triangles? _____

10 triangles? _____   20 triangles? _____

11 triangles? _____

Try a pattern of your own with toothpicks and draw it here. Then fill in your chart.

# of _____	1	2	3	4	5	6	7
# of toothpicks	3	5					

Get on the Rhombus Bus!

A RHOMBUS is a polygon that looks just like this:

Continue to build 2 more rhombuses on the grid below.

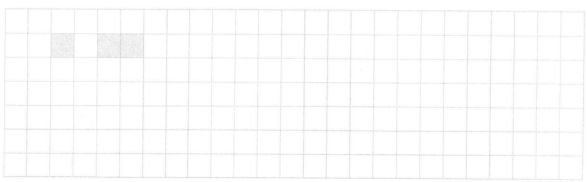

PERIMETER, as you recall, is the measurement around a space.

Fill in the chart below showing the perimeter of each rhombus.
Try to calculate what the perimeter would be for the next 3 rhombuses.

Rhombus #	1	2	3	4	5	6	7
Units of Perimeter	4						

Square It Up!

Continue to build squares in the same way you did above.

Square #	1	2	3	4	5	6	7
Units of Perimeter	4	6					

Don't Go Colour Blind!

Colour these shapes with the appropriate colours (or use whatever colour you have handy).

Red	Blue	Green	Yellow

How many different patterns can you make with the different colours?
List the possibilities below.

> If you have any blocks or other coloured pieces to help you, use them!

For Example: **R B G Y**   (Short forms make it easier. These examples use the first
           B G Y R   letter of each colour. You could also use a coloured dot or line
           Y R B G   showing the actual colours in a pattern.)

Continue with all of the different combinations possible.

_____   _____   _____   _____

_____   _____   _____   _____

_____   _____   _____   _____

_____   _____   _____   _____

Here's a new pattern. Colour it to make it easier to understand.

Red	Red	Green	Green	Blue	Blue	Yellow	Yellow

There are only 8 shapes/blocks now. If we repeat the pattern until there are 18 blocks,
how many green blocks would there be? _____

how many red blocks would there be? _____

how many red and yellow blocks would there be? _____

> You can draw, graph, sketch, or chart this!

If we repeat the pattern until there are 29 blocks,
how many blue blocks would there be? _____

how many red and green blocks would there be altogether? _____

how many blue and yellow blocks would there be altogether? _____

What would the 30th coloured block be? _____

Build It Up!

You are now the manager at a construction site. It is your job to order enough bricks and windows for your buildings.

Here is your first building for 1 family.
You need 1 window and 8 large bricks.

For 2 families, you use ____ windows and ____ bricks.

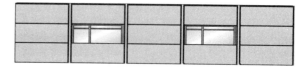

A 3-family building requires ____ windows and ____ bricks.

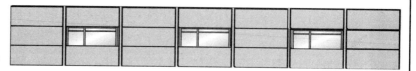

Fill in the following chart based on the pattern above.

# of families	1	2	3	4	5	6	7
# of windows	1						
# of bricks	8						

How many bricks and windows do you think you would need for:

10 families? ____ bricks ____ windows   15 families? ____ bricks ____ windows

20 families? ____ bricks ____ windows

Fold It Up!

It's laundry time. Oh no! With the large linen items, like your bed sheets, you need to fold them a number of times.

After 1 fold, there are 2 sections.

After 2 folds, there are 4 sections.

After 3 folds, there are _____ sections.

(Try this with a scrap piece of paper to help you see this.)

Fill in the chart for your laundry learning.

Folds	Sections
1	
2	
3	
4	
5	
6	

Not Just a Garden Plot

Don't forget that the 1st number is for the left-side axis (the x-axis) and the 2nd number is for the bottom axis (the y-axis).

Plot the following coordinates on the grid.

(8, 6)

(5, 3)

(4, 2)

(2, 0)

Rule	− 2
8	6
5	3
4	2
2	0
7	
3	
6	

If you look at the pattern in the chart, each coordinate has a difference of 2. So you can make a rule that you must subtract 2 from the 1st number in each coordinate. Fill in the rest of the chart, and add the coordinates on the grid.

Give Me Some Rules!

Plot the coordinates in each exercise, fill in the chart, and find the rule for each.

1.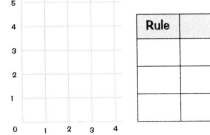

(3, 0)
(4, 1)
(5, 2)

2.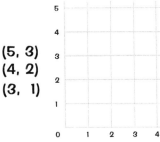

(5, 3)
(4, 2)
(3, 1)

3.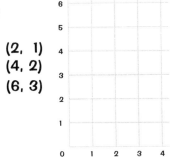

(2, 1)
(4, 2)
(6, 3)

4.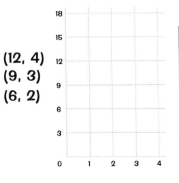

(12, 4)
(9, 3)
(6, 2)

Patterns in Problems

1. If A is worth one dollar, B is worth $2, C is worth $3, and so on, how much is the word MATH worth?

MATH is worth $42!

A = *$1*	B = *$2*	C = *$3*	D = *$4*	E = *$5*	F =	G =
H =	I =	J =	K =	L =	M =	N =
O =	P =	Q =	R =	S =	T =	U =
V =	W =	X =	Y =	Z =		

What is your name worth? _____

What is this sentence worth? I love mathematics! _____

Find a word that is worth $15 _____ $30 _____

$50 _____ $100 _____

What is the most expensive word you can think of? _____

New Value

2. What if the pattern of worth increased by $1.50, as opposed to the $1.00 as above? For example,

A = $1.50	B = $3.00	C = *$4.50*	D =	E =	F =	G =
H =	I =	J =	K =	L =	M =	N =
O =	P =	Q =	R =	S =	T =	U =
V =	W =	X =	Y =	Z =		

What is your name worth now? _____

What is the math sentence above worth now? _____

Jumping Values

3. Look carefully at this pattern and complete it to the end of the alphabet.

A = $2	B = $0	C = $3	D = $1	E = $4	F = *$2*	G =
H =	I =	J =	K =	L =	M =	N =
O =	P =	Q =	R =	S =	T =	U =
V =	W =	X =	Y =	Z =		

What is your name worth now? _____

What is the math sentence above worth now? _____

What Is Your Name Worth?

To find the **AVERAGE**, or the **MEAN**, is to find the equal distribution of something.

Take some common words, for example, and let's find the average number of letters in these words.

1	2	3	4	5	6	7	8	9
D	E	S	K	*R*	*P*			
P	E	N	C	I	L			
T	E	A	C	H	E	R		
P	R	I	N	C	I	P	A	L
M	A	T	H	*A*	*L*			

Some words are obviously longer and others shorter. However, we need to find out where the most of them are located, so we need to move some of the letters around.

You can see that the average number of letters in these words is 6.
Using the grid paper below, list 10 names of family members or friends.

1	2	3	4	5	6	7	8	9	10

Cut out each letter and line up the names. Move the letters at the right edge that are too long and add them to a shorter name, as we did above.

What is the average length of your family members' and friends' names? _____

Try another one on your own. You could use your favourite sports teams or the names of some TV shows. Your choice!

Eenie, MEANIE, Miney, Mo!

Another way to calculate the average, or mean, is to take the total number that you are working with and divide it by the number of items.

Jennifer babysat for her cousins for five days. On average, how many hours did she babysit each day?

	1	2	3	4	5	6	7	8	9	10
Monday										
Tuesday										
Wednesday										
Thursday										
Friday										

Monday	5
Tuesday	6
Wednesday	7
Thursday	9
Friday	8
TOTAL	35

Now take the total number and divide it by the number of days:

$$5)\overline{3\,5}\quad 7$$

The average, or mean, is 7.

Jennifer babysat 7 hours a day on average.

Lauren also babysat for five days. Use the chart to determine the average number of hours she babysat each day?

	1	2	3	4	5	6	7	8	9	10
Monday										
Tuesday										
Wednesday										
Thursday										
Friday										

First, write out the number of hours for each day. Then add the total, like this:

Monday	_____
Tuesday	_____
Wednesday	_____
Thursday	_____
Friday	+_____
TOTAL	_____

Now take the total number and divide it by the number of days:

Lauren's average, or mean, is _____.

Expand Your Horizons

Here's a review of our place value columns.

10 000s	1 000s	100s	10s	1s
Ten Thousands	Thousands	Hundreds	Tens	Ones
2	4	7	9	3

In this number the 2 is worth 20 000 because it is in the ten thousands column.

What is the 4 worth? _____   What is the 7 worth? _____

What is the 9 worth? _____   What is the 3 worth? _____

Write the worth (or value) of each circled number below.

1. 7⑧ 542   **2.** 6⑨ 214   **3.** 24 3⑤0   **4.** 45 16⑦   **5.** 73 ②41

_____   _____   _____   _____   _____

6. 90 ③72   **7.** 53 29⑥   **8.** 3② 407   **9.** 21 5①7   **10.** ⑥8 012

_____   _____   _____   _____   _____

The number we started with above was 24 793 or twenty-four thousand seven hundred ninety-three. We can expand the number by simply separating each place value, like this: 20 000 + 4 000 + 700 + 90 + 3. This is called expanded notation.

Write the following numbers in expanded and written form.

1. 53 708 = _____
       = _____

2. 91 245 = _____
       = _____

3. 46 320 = _____
       = _____

4. 74 836 = _____
       = _____

Mental Math for Multiplication

By using expanded notation, you can improve your mental math and impress everyone around.

Here's how.
- First look at your question (6 × 48).
- Then split up the two-digit number into place values (40 + 8).
- Then do the multiplication and add (6 × 40) + (6 × 8).

Try these questions and then find your answer in the number find.

1. 6 × 48 = (_6_ × _40_) + (_6_ × _8_) = _240_ + _48_ = _288_

2. 8 × 25 = (___ × ___) + (___ × ___) = _____ + _____ = _____

3. 7 × 53 = (___ × ___) + (___ × ___) = _____ + _____ = _____

4. 4 × 38 = (___ × ___) + (___ × ___) = _____ + _____ = _____

5. 6 × 82 = (___ × ___) + (___ × ___) = _____ + _____ = _____

6. 5 × 49 = (___ × ___) + (___ × ___) = _____ + _____ = _____

7. 9 × 27 = (___ × ___) + (___ × ___) = _____ + _____ = _____

8. 3 × 47 = (___ × ___) + (___ × ___) = _____ + _____ = _____

4	9	2	4	3
2	2	8	8	7
4	0	1	4	1
5	0	1	5	2

Here's another way that might help you with your mental math.
Round the 2-digit number to make it an easier computation, like this:

4 × 59 = (4 × 60) − (4 × 1) = 240 − 4 = 236

Try these ones.

1. 7 × 32 = (___ × ___) + (___ × ___) = _____ + _____ = _____

2. 3 × 91 = (___ × ___) + (___ × ___) = _____ + _____ = _____

3. 5 × 48 = (___ × ___) − (___ × ___) = _____ − _____ = _____

4. 6 × 91 = (___ × ___) + (___ × ___) = _____ + _____ = _____

5. 8 × 27 = (___ × ___) − (___ × ___) = _____ − _____ = _____

Remain a Crossword Expert

After completing the division questions, use the remainders as words for your crossword. Good luck, crossword expert!

ACROSS

1. 8)332
$$\begin{array}{r} 41 \\ 8\overline{)332} \\ \underline{32}\downarrow \\ 12 \\ \underline{8} \\ R4 \end{array}$$

2. 5)348   3. 5)361   4. 11)427   5. 8)774   6. 11)87

DOWN

1. 7)222   2. 3)215   5. 9)592   7. 10)428   8. 12)155

I never get cross doing a crossword.

FOUR

All Primed Up!

Find the prime factors for each number. If you look at these number problems, you'll notice the shape of a tree. These are actually called number trees. Use the trees to help you out by filling in the multiplication sentence for each layer of branches.

1. 100

10 × ___

2 × ___ × 2 × ___

The prime factors
are ___ & ___.

2. 99

33 × ___

3 × ___ × ___

The prime factors
are ___ & ___.

3. 60

10 × ___

2 × ___ × 2 × ___

The prime factors
are ___, ___ & ___.

4. 32

8 × ___

2 × 2 × ___ × 2 × ___

The prime factor
is ___.

5. 90

10 × ___

2 × ___ × 3 × ___

The prime factors
are ___, ___ & ___.

6. 84

12 × ___

2 × 2 × ___ × ___

The prime factors
are ___, ___ & ___.

7. 104

26 × ___

2 × ___ × 2 × ___

The prime factors
are ___, ___ & ___.

8. 136

34 × ___

2 × ___ × ___ × ___

The prime factors
are ___, ___ & ___.

9. 54

27 × ___

3 × ___ × ___ × ___

The prime factors
are ___, ___ & ___.

Prime numbers are numbers that can't be further divided by a number larger than 1. At the bottom of each branch layer, you should find only prime numbers.

List them below in order from smallest to largest, and then challenge yourself to figure out what will be the next prime numbers in the list.

___ ___ ___ ___ ___ ___ ___

___ ___ ___ ___ ___

Equal Bits

EQUIVALENT FRACTIONS show equal amounts.

For example:

$$\frac{1}{2} \quad = \quad \frac{2}{4} \quad = \quad \frac{4}{8} \quad = \quad \frac{8}{16}$$

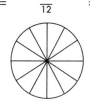

Colour in these equivalent fractions and fill in the numeric fraction above.

$$\frac{1}{4} \quad = \quad \frac{}{8} \quad = \quad \frac{}{12} \quad = \quad \frac{}{16}$$

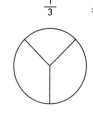  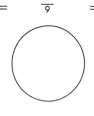 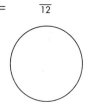

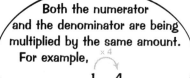

Both the numerator and the denominator are being multiplied by the same amount. For example,

$$\frac{1}{3} = \frac{4}{12}$$
×4 ... ×4

$$\frac{1}{3} \quad = \quad \frac{2}{6} \quad = \quad \frac{}{9} \quad = \quad \frac{}{12}$$

Find the equivalent fractions for the following.

(a) $\dfrac{3}{4} = \dfrac{6}{8} = \dfrac{9}{12} = \dfrac{12}{16} = \dfrac{15}{20}$

(b) $\dfrac{2}{5} = \dfrac{}{10} = \dfrac{}{15} = \dfrac{}{20} = \dfrac{}{50}$

(c) $\dfrac{2}{3} = \dfrac{}{6} = \dfrac{}{9} = \dfrac{}{12} = \dfrac{}{30}$

(d) $\dfrac{5}{8} = \dfrac{}{16} = \dfrac{}{64} = \dfrac{}{80} = \dfrac{}{96}$

(e) $\dfrac{2}{7} = \dfrac{}{14} = \dfrac{}{21} = \dfrac{}{49} = \dfrac{}{70}$

(f) $\dfrac{4}{9} = \dfrac{}{18} = \dfrac{}{36} = \dfrac{}{72} = \dfrac{}{81}$

(g) $\dfrac{3}{11} = \dfrac{}{22} = \dfrac{}{33} = \dfrac{}{66} = \dfrac{}{88}$

(h) $\dfrac{7}{10} = \dfrac{}{20} = \dfrac{}{30} = \dfrac{}{50} = \dfrac{}{80}$

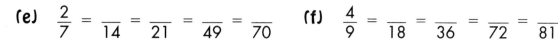

Greater? Smaller?

Cut out all of the fractions and keep in an envelope.

1

| $\frac{1}{2}$ | $\frac{1}{2}$ |

| $\frac{1}{3}$ | $\frac{1}{3}$ | $\frac{1}{3}$ |

| $\frac{1}{4}$ | $\frac{1}{4}$ | $\frac{1}{4}$ | $\frac{1}{4}$ |

| $\frac{1}{5}$ | $\frac{1}{5}$ | $\frac{1}{5}$ | $\frac{1}{5}$ | $\frac{1}{5}$ |

| $\frac{1}{6}$ | $\frac{1}{6}$ | $\frac{1}{6}$ | $\frac{1}{6}$ | $\frac{1}{6}$ | $\frac{1}{6}$ |

| $\frac{1}{7}$ | $\frac{1}{7}$ | $\frac{1}{7}$ | $\frac{1}{7}$ | $\frac{1}{7}$ | $\frac{1}{7}$ | $\frac{1}{7}$ |

| $\frac{1}{8}$ | $\frac{1}{8}$ | $\frac{1}{8}$ | $\frac{1}{8}$ | $\frac{1}{8}$ | $\frac{1}{8}$ | $\frac{1}{8}$ | $\frac{1}{8}$ |

| $\frac{1}{9}$ | $\frac{1}{9}$ | $\frac{1}{9}$ | $\frac{1}{9}$ | $\frac{1}{9}$ | $\frac{1}{9}$ | $\frac{1}{9}$ | $\frac{1}{9}$ | $\frac{1}{9}$ |

| $\frac{1}{10}$ | $\frac{1}{10}$ | $\frac{1}{10}$ | $\frac{1}{10}$ | $\frac{1}{10}$ | $\frac{1}{10}$ | $\frac{1}{10}$ | $\frac{1}{10}$ | $\frac{1}{10}$ | $\frac{1}{10}$ |

| $\frac{1}{11}$ | $\frac{1}{11}$ | $\frac{1}{11}$ | $\frac{1}{11}$ | $\frac{1}{11}$ | $\frac{1}{11}$ | $\frac{1}{11}$ | $\frac{1}{11}$ | $\frac{1}{11}$ | $\frac{1}{11}$ | $\frac{1}{11}$ |

| $\frac{1}{12}$ | $\frac{1}{12}$ | $\frac{1}{12}$ | $\frac{1}{12}$ | $\frac{1}{12}$ | $\frac{1}{12}$ | $\frac{1}{12}$ | $\frac{1}{12}$ | $\frac{1}{12}$ | $\frac{1}{12}$ | $\frac{1}{12}$ | $\frac{1}{12}$ |

Using your fraction pieces, compare the following. Fill in the circle with greater than, equal to, or smaller than. For example, for the first question find and line up 3 of the $\frac{1}{5}$. Then find and line up 7 of the $\frac{1}{11}$. Compare.

(a) $\frac{3}{5}$ ◯ $\frac{7}{11}$ (b) $\frac{4}{5}$ ◯ $\frac{6}{8}$ (c) $\frac{5}{9}$ ◯ $\frac{2}{4}$ (d) $\frac{3}{6}$ ◯ $\frac{5}{10}$ (e) $\frac{1}{3}$ ◯ $\frac{4}{9}$

(f) $\frac{6}{7}$ ◯ $\frac{3}{4}$ (g) $\frac{2}{8}$ ◯ $\frac{1}{4}$ (h) $\frac{8}{11}$ ◯ $\frac{2}{3}$ (i) $\frac{1}{5}$ ◯ $\frac{3}{11}$ (j) $\frac{5}{6}$ ◯ $\frac{3}{4}$

How Do You Score?

PERCENTAGE actually means the 'part per hundred,' that is to say, how much out of 100.

Let's say you get back a test and you score 38/50.
For the percentage, we need to make it out of 100.

Your percentage looks like this $\dfrac{38}{50} = \dfrac{76}{100}$

or it could be written like this   0.76

Colour in the percentage for each of the following fractions and write down the percentage in decimals.

Remember that $\dfrac{1}{100} = 0.01$

1.

$\dfrac{42}{100} = 0.\underline{\quad}$

2.

$\dfrac{7}{100} = 0.\underline{\quad}$

3.

$\dfrac{84}{100} = 0.\underline{\quad}$

Change these fractions to a fraction out of 100.

4. $\dfrac{40}{50} = \dfrac{80}{100}$ **5.** $\dfrac{31}{50} = \dfrac{\quad}{100}$ **6.** $\dfrac{12}{20} = \dfrac{\quad}{100}$ **7.** $\dfrac{4}{25} = \dfrac{\quad}{100}$

8. $\dfrac{3}{50} = \dfrac{\quad}{100}$ **9.** $\dfrac{6}{10} = \dfrac{\quad}{100}$ **10.** $\dfrac{24}{25} = \dfrac{\quad}{100}$ **11.** $\dfrac{17}{20} = \dfrac{\quad}{100}$

Now write each of the fractions above into decimals.

4. 0._____   **5.** 0._____   **6.** 0._____   **7.** 0._____

8. 0._____   **9.** 0._____   **10.** 0._____   **11.** 0._____

Angie received her math test back and she got 22/25. What was her percentage?
Write the fraction and the decimal.

$\dfrac{22}{25} = \dfrac{\quad}{100} = 0.\underline{\quad}$

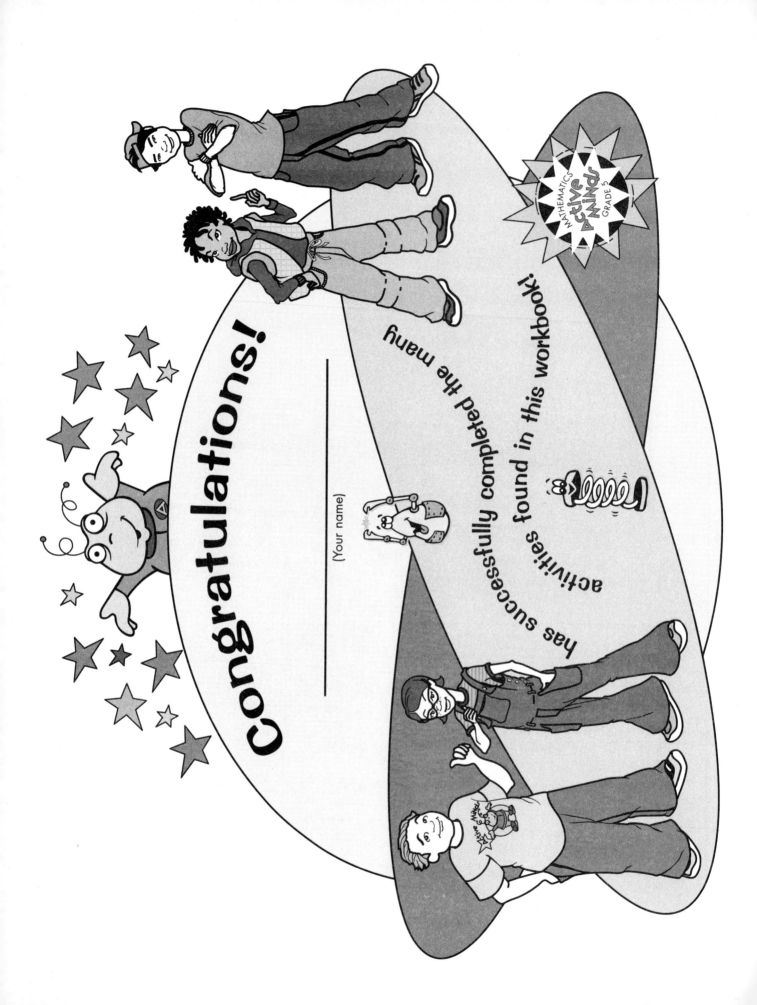

Spelling Booster
Grades 5 & 6

This workbook belongs to:

_____

Table of Contents

Starting off ~~Propperly~~ Properly

Spelling correctly isn't hard. Just use these five ideas when you have a problem spelling a word. You can use the rest of this book to practice and improve your skills.

1. **Use what you know.** If one word sounds like another, often you spell it the same way. For example: *might — right — sight*

2. **Break it up.** Long words are easy to spell when you split them up into smaller parts. For example: *tomorrow = to - mor - row autograph = auto - graph*

3. **Use the rules.** You know that "i" comes before "e" in words like *piece* because of the "i"-before-"e" rule. You know that a final "y" changes to an "i" before endings are put on. For example: penny — pennies.

4. **Use your memory.** Good spellers make up their own memory clues for tough words. You can look for the shape of a word, or use an exaggerated pronunciation (lan-gu-age, choc-o-late), or make up a silly rhyme (the principal is your pal).

5. **Try it out.** When you misspell a word on a computer, the program will often give you three or four suggestions of ways to spell it right. You can do this yourself. Just take a word you're not sure of and write it out two or three ways. You'll usually be able to see the right one.

guverment   *government*   *governmint*

Even good writers make mistakes in spelling, so don't feel bad if you make a few. Better to use ~~wunderfull~~ wonderful words when you write than to get scared off by spelling. The trick is to get better each week, making fewer and fewer mistakes... until you're ~~perfekt~~ perfect!

I used to have a hard time spelling "environment."

It's easy if you break it into syllables: en – vi – ron – ment.

See if you can find **10** spelling mistakes. Circle and correct them.

Freddie's Math Triumph

Freddie looked trubbled. There was a math test in school the next day and he didn't feel ready at all. Luckily, his three best freinds were there to help him do some last minnit studying.

Freddie's mother provided the four companions with plenty of snacks and drinks with which to takle the math. Though Hiro and Suzy were better at it than he, they all knew that Francine was the sertified genius of the group.

Hours passed and they manajed to cover all the material that would be on the test. Freddie felt confadent.

The next day in class, Freddie completed his test. It was more difficult than he had thought it would be. Fortunately, because of his preperation, he was ready for it.

A few days later, they recieved their graded tests back from the teacher. Freddie was ecstatic.

"Guys!" he shouted. "I passed the test. I got a B!"

As it turned out, everyone had learned from thier studying. Hiro and Suzy each received an A, and Francine, of course, scored perfectly.

If you can't find the mistakes, it helps to read slowly.

Or try reading backwards from the end of a sentence.

Use What You Know

You already know how to spell many small words.
Use what you know to spell words you're not sure of.

1. You know the word bore. Now spell:

— — — — — — — — a way to swing the racket in tennis

— — — — — — — — where the ocean meets the land

— — — — — — — — a place to buy medicine

2. You know the word last. Now spell:

— — — — — — — someone skilled at acrobatics

— — — — — — — when the weather looks bad

— — — — — — — — a control on your television

3. You know the word treat. Now spell:

— — — — — — doing something over and over again

— — — — — — a grain grown in Saskatchewan

— — — — — — the loss of a battle or a game

4. You know the word end. Now spell:

— — — — — — — — — — to understand

— — — — — — — to protect something or someone

— — — — — — — — — — to give in to an opponent

5. You know the word right. Now spell:

— — — — — — shining, like the sun

— — — — — — — — — — to be very afraid.

— — — — — — strong as a bull

6. You know the word ice. Now spell:

___ ___ ___ ___ ___ ___ ___ ___ ___ to give up something you value

___ ___ ___ ___ ___ ___ something easier to give than to receive

___ ___ ___ ___ ___ ___ ___ ___ this makes perfect

7. You know the word other. Now spell:

___ ___ ___ ___ ___ ___ ___ the male version of a sister

___ ___ ___ ___ ___ ___ ___ ___ covered completely

___ ___ ___ ___ ___ ___ ___ ___ a word that means "in addition to"

8. You know the word chess. Now spell:

___ ___ ___ ___ ___ ___ something you feel when there is too much work

___ ___ ___ ___ ___ ___ ___ to admit to something

___ ___ ___ ___ ___ ___ ___ ___ to move forward

Now let's try some larger words. Which of the eight words above could help you spell these big words:

_____ ignore _____	_____ bore _____
_____ breakfast _____	_____
_____ defeat _____	_____
_____ tightening _____	_____
_____ cowardice _____	_____
_____ bothered _____	_____
_____ digress _____	_____

Word Building

Spelling follows patterns—sometimes more than one.
Try these...

1. Use these letter tiles to build as many words as you can in 10 minutes.

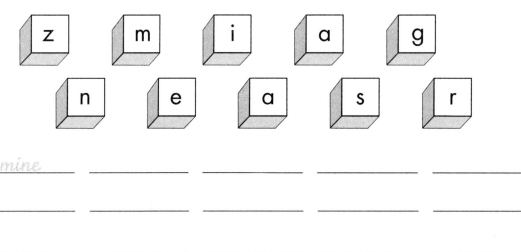

mine

2. Now sort your words into families.

words with two "a"s	plurals	your own category
words ending in silent "e"	words ending in "ing"	your own category

three-letter words	four-letter words	five-letter words

six-letter words	seven-letter words	eight- or more letter words

Hint: One eight-letter word is something you can read.

Hinkie Pinkies

Rhyming words can give you patterns that can help with spelling.

Try each of these riddles. The answer is a pair of rhyming words.

1. What's an angry father?

m _ad_ d _ad_

2. When a sorcerer scratches, she has a

w _____ i _____

3. What's a tune that goes on and on?

_____ _____

4. What's a diary made of corn?

_____ _____

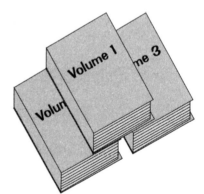

5. What's a thief that steals encyclopedias?

_____ _____

6. What's a diver who has lost weight?

_____ _____

7. What do you call a short-lived sorrow?

_____ _____

7. What's another phrase for a tired question?

_____ _____

8. What do you call an author who has lost weight?

_____ _____

9. What do you call a runaway bird?

_____ _____

10. What's a sleepy flower?

_____ _____

Here are some answers. You make up the riddle.

11. mice dice _____

_____

12. goat boat _____

_____

13. boring snoring _____

_____

What do you call a frozen screwdriver?

Easy! It's a cool tool!

Syllable Stunts

Sometimes to spell a word right, you have to hear it right.
By breaking a word up into syllables, you can hear the parts.

1. Break these 10 words into syllables.

(a) interesting   *in   ter   est   ing*

(b) forgetful   _____

(c) attentive   _____

(d) drastically   _____

(e) refrigerator   _____

(f) carefully   _____

(g) marshmallow   _____

My full name is
Fred-er-ick.

(h) tangerine   _____

(i) monopoly   _____

(j) ambulance   _____

2. Now let's make some big three-syllable words!

<u>bas</u> + <u>ket</u> + <u>ball</u> = _basketball_

<u>gas</u> + <u>o</u> + <u>line</u> = _____

<u>kan</u> + <u>ga</u> + <u>roo</u> = _____

<u>par</u> + <u>a</u> + <u>chute</u> = _____

 3. These words have their syllables all mixed up.
See if you can put them back together.

knuck	ver	time	_knuckleball_
o	e	ters	_____
ho	plet	ball	_____
sum	quar	ing	_____
a	le	sive	_____
com	ney	do	_____
con	bra	moon	_____
tux	mer	ed	_____
head	fus	head	_____

Can you make five more imaginary words using the syllables above, then
make up a meaning (e.g, hoverball = the sport of the future) You'll need your
own piece of paper for this one.

Game Time

Use these syllables to create as many three-syllable words as you can. Some of the syllables may be combined different ways, but there is only one way to use all of them. If you give up, check the answer key for that one.

fi	im	dence	mag	og
a	net	naut	tion	ges
as	ful	late	care	nize
o	ic	ly	ti	di
gine	con	tro	si	mul
rec	choc	tive	ply	po

Some starting syllables and examples:

im _agine_   choc _____   mag _____

_____   _____   _____

_____   _____   _____

_____   _____   _____

_____   _____   _____

_____   _____   _____

Man Hunt

The syllable "man" can be found in many words. Find the "man" sound that solves the riddles below.

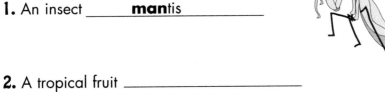

1. An insect _____**man**tis_____

2. A tropical fruit _____

3. The shelf above a fireplace _____

4. A trough for feeding cattle _____

5. A province in Canada _____

6. To make by hand or machine _____

7. Numerous _____

8. Person in charge _____

9. A large house _____

10. Treatment for fingernails _____

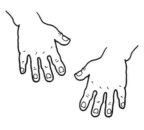

Active Minds

Compound Your Fun

 Write a word in the blank between each of the given words that creates a compound with both the word before it and the word after it.

1. dug ____out____ side

2. girl _____ ship

3. basket _____ room

4. hill _____ walk

5. touch _____ stairs

6. quarter _____ bone

7. some _____ ever

8. arrow _____ line

9. foot _____ ladder

10. tea _____ belly

11. camp _____ place

12. drug _____ keeper

13. flash _____ house

14. look _____ doors

Have you ever danced at a ballroom?

No, just at the school gym. It was intense.

In tents? I thought it was at the gym.

Check Your Skills

 Proofreading:
Can you find and correct the 10 errors in this passage?

Barbie's Bio

In March 1959 the first Barbie doll was dissplayed at a toy fair in New York City. She had been created by Ruth Handler in 1945 and named after her daughter, Barbara. While raising her dawter and her son, Kenneth, Handler noticed how much the young girl liked to play pretend with paper dolls and decided to invent a three-dimensionle model for her to play with.

In 1961 Handler's son had his name made immortal in plastic when the Ken doll, Barbie's male companyun, was introdused. Barbie quickly became the world's most populer doll. The Barbie group now includes four younger siblings, a number of friends, and a welth of accessories—each sold separately.

Barbie may have begun life as a teenage fashion model but, over the years, she took on other jobs. Barbie has been a ballerina, a registered nurse, an airline stewerdess, a surgeon and a U.S. Air Force pilot. In 1992 she ran for President, but unfortunately, lost.

More than 800 million dolls in the Barbie line have been sold over the last fourty years. Adult collectors have spent thousands of dollars on specially made Barbie dolls. Recently, the life of Barbie was recorded in a book titled *Forever Barbie: The Unauthorized Bigraphy of a Real Doll.*

Opposites Attract

Prefixes are syllables we add to the beginning of a root word. Prefixes are easy because they never change the spelling of the root word.

1. Add "un," "im," "in" or "dis" to make each of these root words mean the opposite.

_____ possible   _____ competent

_____ connect   _____ happy

_____ justice   _____ approve

_____ used   _____ interest

_____ able   _____ known

_____ like   _____ fair

2. Use any five of your new words to make sentences:

_____

_____

_____

_____

_____

_____

_____

Prefix Party

Some other common prefixes are:

sub – under or lower   **ex** – outside

trans – across   **re** – again

mis – not, incorrect   **dis** – not or negative

in – not or negative

Add two endings to each prefix to make two different words.

trans _____transportation_____   _____

mis _____   _____

ex _____   _____

dis _____   _____

in _____   _____

re _____   _____

What if "fred" were a prefix?

Then your car would be "fredportation!"

Word Addition

When you add a suffix to the end of a word, you sometimes have to change the root word.

1. For many one-syllable words with a short vowel, double the final letter.

slug + ed = *slugged*

swim + ing = _____

plan + er = _____

slim + er = _____

clip + ing = _____

skip + ing = _____

2. Words that end with silent "e" lose the "e" before the suffix is added.

slice + ing = *slicing*

slime + y = _____

intrude + ing = _____

wire + ed = _____

confuse + ing = _____

enforce + ing = _____

3. When a word ends in a consonant and a "y," change the "y" to an "i" then add the suffix.

happy + er = *happier*

holy + est = _____

dry + est = _____

party + ed = _____

skinny + er = _____

silly + est = _____

4. Fix it up. Five of the words with suffixes in this story are misspelled. Circle the word and write the correct spelling above it.

Francine and Freddy were waitting for their friends at the mall. The four friends hopped to see a movie.

"So what movie should we see?" asked Francine.

"I'd like to see Night of Terror 2," said Freddie. "I heard that was one of the scaryest movies ever made!"

"I heard it's a little disgustting in some parts," Francine replied.

Just then, Hiro and Suzy arrived. The four friends moved to the ticket window to buy their movie passes. Hiro and Freddie, to no one's surprise, got tickets to see Night of Terror 2. Francine and Suzy sensibley chose to avoid it.

"I'll see any movie with Brad Pitt acting in it," Suzy declared.

Confusable Suffixes

 It's hard to know exactly which spelling of some suffixes will be correct with certain root words. We'll give you a general rule, but you'll need a dictionary or spell-checker to be sure you're right.

Suffixes: -er, -or, -ar

The most common is "-er," but there are many common words that use "-or" or "-ar."

teach**er**	robb**er**	swimm**er**	wait**er**
act**or**	sail**or**	accelerat**or**	direct**or**
begg**ar**	li**ar**	schol**ar**	burgl**ar**

 Now fill in the blanks with the correct suffix.

My teach___ went to the beauty parl___ shop to get a haircut. On her way, she realized she'd be late for her appointment so she put her foot down hard___ on the accelerat___.

Only a minute later, she saw flashing lights in her mirr___. It was the police. She immediately pulled ov___ to the curb. The offic___ approached the car.

"Where are you going in such a hurry?" asked the policeman.

"I'm sorry. I am late for an appointment, and I didn't want to be any lat___ than I already am."

"Well, you should obey the speed limit. I'll let you off with a warning this time."

As the officer left and my teacher drove away, she realized she couldn't be any lucki___!

> When in doubt, use -er.

Suffixes: -ible, -able

You'll need to use memory tricks on page 55 or your own ideas to remember these suffixes.

So my teacher arrived at the hairdresser's just in time for the appointment. Her stylist was so depend_____ and reli_____ that it was hard to get time booked with him. She sat on the chair and had her hair washed.

"What kind of style would you like this time?" asked the stylist.

"How about something not_____, but not regret_____."

"I know just the thing!" he said.

Minutes went by and hair fell to the floor. When the stylist was finished, my teacher examined her new hairstyle.

"Oh, it's ador_____. When it comes to cutting hair, you're unbeat_____!"

Suffixes: -ery, -ary, -ory

The suffix **-ery** is used for places where jobs are carried out.
-ory is a place or geographical location.
-ary is for adjectives.

And now we approach the end of my st_____. My teacher, with her new hairstyle had only two more errands to run. First to the bak_____, and then to the groc_____ store.

You may be wondering what the point of all of this is. Well, on her way home she spotted some falcons on a nearby cliff_____ and they gave her an idea: a field trip to an avi_____.

Well, my class was happy to be going to an observat_____ just for birds. After the trip was cleared by the secret_____, everything was ready. The trip is next week.

Explode-a-Word

How many words can you make by adding prefixes and suffixes to the word in the cloud?

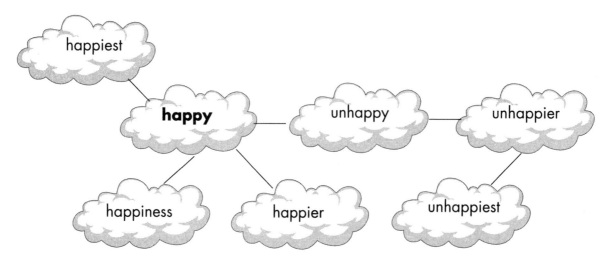

happiest

happy — unhappy — unhappier

happiness   happier   unhappiest

astro

hope

friend

metre

cover

Spelling Charades

Here's a fun game that can be played with as many people as you like.

1. Cut out the cards on the next pages.

2. Put the cards in a large envelope and mix them all up.

3. The first player draws a card from the envelope. The player becomes the actor and must read the card, then try and act out what the word is. He or she isn't allowed to talk, but can use gestures to indicate when a guess is close.

4. The remaining players must not only guess what word the actor is playing, but must also spell it correctly. The player who guesses and spells correctly earns a point and becomes the next actor.

5. The game is over when one player reaches ten points.

I love charades!

Yeah, but it wouldn't make a very good videogame.

Now how would you act out the word "videogame"?

sailor	bird	tackle
astronaut	defeat	navigate
celebrate	collecting	reaching
burglar	parachute	investigate
drummer	accelerating	carpenter
teaching	volcano	gymnastics

swooping	temper	electricity
disassemble	handkerchief	precipitation
paralyzed	butchering	touching
break	beggar	mining
bribing	scholar	flatter
disgusting	surprise	submarine

Multiplicity

You remember that to make most words plural you just add "s." When the word ends in "s," "ch" or "ss," you have to add "es" to make it plural.

1. Make each of these words plural by adding "s" or "es."

fox	*foxes*	lass	_____
rock	_____	crunch	_____
bus	_____	forget	_____
exercise	_____	lock	_____
tomato	_____	house	_____
church	_____	king	_____

2. When you have a word that ends in "f," it changes to a "v" before adding "es." Try these.

calf	*calves*	thief	_____
shelf	_____	half	_____
elf	_____	leaf	_____

A Pack of Plurals

1. Circle the correct plural spelling.

scarf	scarfs	scarves
goose	geese	gooses
moose	mooses	moose
child	childs	children
tax	taxes	taxies
crisis	crisises	crises
deer	deers	deer
cargo	cargos	cargoes
zero	zeros	zeroes

2. Not all words get an "s" to become plural. Sometimes the word doesn't even change. Try these.

man → *men* woman → _____

foot → _____ sheep → _____

ox → _____ fish → _____

die → _____ leaf → _____

3. Find all the plurals hidden in the word find.

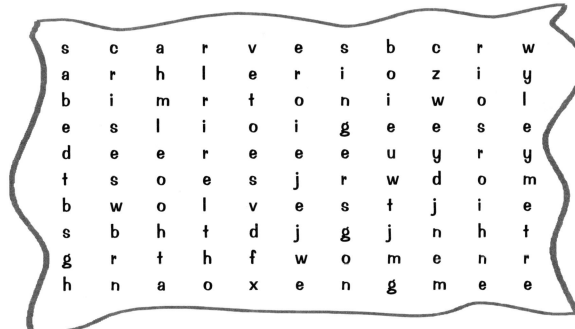

s	c	a	r	v	e	s	b	c	r	w
a	r	h	l	e	r	i	o	z	i	y
b	i	m	r	t	o	n	i	w	o	l
e	s	l	i	o	i	g	e	e	s	e
d	e	e	r	e	e	e	u	y	r	y
t	s	o	e	s	j	r	w	d	o	m
b	w	o	l	v	e	s	t	j	i	e
s	b	h	t	d	j	g	j	n	h	t
g	r	t	h	f	w	o	m	e	n	r
h	n	a	o	x	e	n	g	m	e	e

crises   **deer**   **geese**
oxen   **scarves**   **singers**
vetoes   **wolves**   **women**

Speller's Toolbox

A tool box?

A good speller uses different tools to spell difficult words.

Our first tool is how a word looks. Use the little words you find contained in the big words to remember how to spell them.

1. Draw a box around the little words in each big word.

homecoming	housewarming
extraordinary	hyperactive
supernatural	neighbourhood
illegal	technically
deliverance	antagonize
tarpaulin	wadding
plumage	maintenance

2. Now use the little word in the toolbox to make three more words.

backrest

backyard

backspace

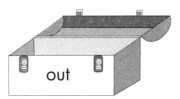

_____

_____

_____

_____

_____

_____

3. This is a word puzzle. The letters above each column fit in the squares directly below them. When placed correctly, the letters will spell out a message!

s c	o p o	b l n	g z e v	r i z	s l n a	t e g n	u e	t l e l	l a h x	i y c t e	i r s o	u o l	l t n	s r m e	n u i	c o s t	t n	y
					a													
																	k	
		u				.												
										e								
					p							!						

Ham It Up!

Sometimes you can exaggerate or change the sounds in a word to remember the spelling.

 1. First, pronounce the word properly.
Then circle the correct spelling.

Febuary	(February)
library	libary
goverment	government
comfortable	comffterable
temperature	temprature
environment	enviroment
Wensday	Wednesday
langwage	language
often	offen
diamond	diemond

Now write a sentence using three of these words:

_____

_____

_____

Here's a story done phonetically, in the kind of voice a computer might use.

Goldilocks and the Three Bears

Wun dae, ah litul gerrul bi thuh naym uv Gowldeelox wuz wahnderring thru thuh forrest. She fownd a howse in a smal kleering.

Gowldeelox enterrd the howse and fownd thrie bolls uv porraj. Sihns she wuz hongri, Gowldeelox deesided to eet sum uv it. She trid thuh furst boll but it wuz too hot! She trid the sekund boll but it wuz too cowld. She trid thuh last boll ahnd it wuz just rite! She aet thuh holl boll.

Geting sleapi, Gowldeelox deesided to taek a nap. She fownd thrie bedz inseyed thuh howse. She trid thuh furst bed but it wuz too hard. She trid the sekund bed but it wuz too sawft. She trid the thurd bed ahnd it wuz just rite! She kwiklie fel assleap.

Just thehn, the onerz uv the howse got howm. It wuz thuh thrie barez!

✏️ Now rewrite the story with proper English spellings:

_____

_____

_____

_____

_____

_____

_____

_____

_____

_____

Shhh! Silent Letters

One of the hardest things about spelling is the silent letters.

1. Add the correct silent letters in the blanks in the sentences below.

(a) I can _w_rite perfectly!

(b) It's polite to __nock on someone's door before entering the house.

(c) You can sometimes see a __recking ball at a construction site.

(d) You should always be careful when using a sharp __nife.

(e) When playing the piano, you should always raise your __rists.

(f) Thanks to school, I __now lots of different things.

(g) When in-line skating, always wear __nee pads.

(h) Those small, annoying bugs in the summer are called __nats.

2. Sometimes, the silent letter appears in the middle of a word.

(a) Ta__king during a movie will get popcorn thrown at you.

(b) W__at could be better than spelling?

(c) You need t__o tickets to get on the rollercoaster.

(d) In Europe, many people visit the cas__les.

(e) He dou__ted that she was right.

(f) He took the threats as a si__n to keep moving.

(g) Tenderizing a piece of meat will sof__en it.

(h) W__is__ling is a very tricky skill when you first start.

Sometimes a silent letter will be at the end of a word.

(a) There wasn't even a crum___ on the floor when he cleaned up.

(b) Use a com___ to fix your hair.

(c) Try to keep your math homework in a neat colum___.

(d) You might use lam___ meat in a stir-fry.

(e) Some people like to clim___ the highest mountains.

(f) Since it was interfering with the power lines, they had to remove a lim___ from the tree.

(g) My favourite season is autum___.

(h) Each hand has four fingers and one thum___.

Proofreading:

 There are five misspelled words that contain, or should contain silent letters. Find, circle and correct them.

It was a cold and rainy autum when I left the hall. I glanced at my watch. It was far too late for anyone still outside to be up to anything good. Hastily, I wissled for a taxi and climed inside.

"Where to, Mac?" came the gruff voice of the driver. He sounded just like the cabbies you see in movies.

"Just take me to the corner of Portage and Main," I said, not really caring where I headed, so long as it was away from here.

Nervously, I looked around as we drove through the dark nite. Perhaps I shouldn't have been surprised, but there was a car following behind us. I felt my pulse quicken in my rists.

How could I get myself out of this one?

World of Words

Many words in our language come from languages of countries all over the world. Take a look:

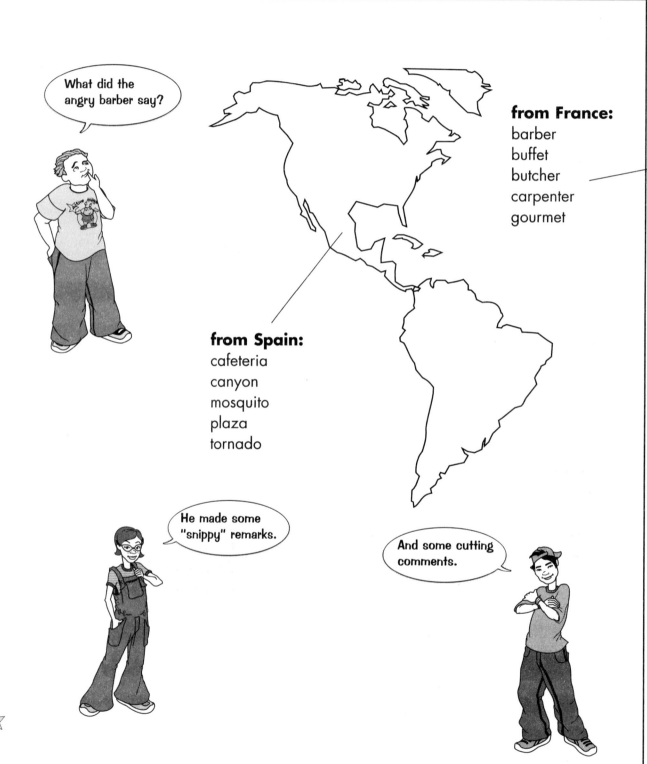

What did the angry barber say?

from France:
barber
buffet
butcher
carpenter
gourmet

from Spain:
cafeteria
canyon
mosquito
plaza
tornado

He made some "snippy" remarks.

And some cutting comments.

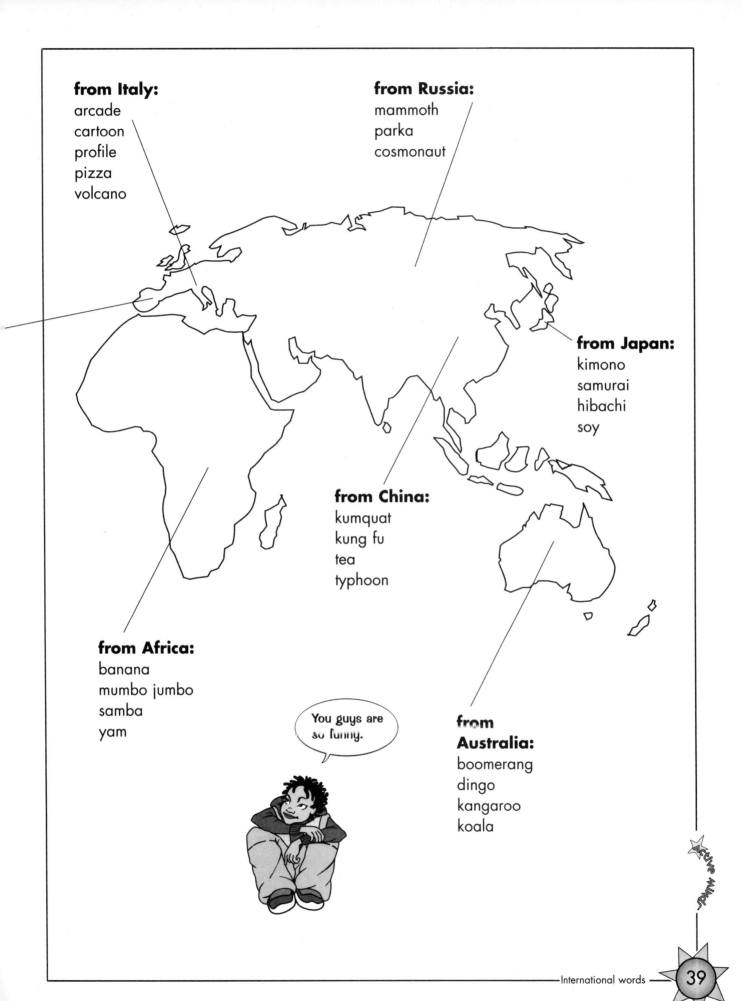

from Italy:
arcade
cartoon
profile
pizza
volcano

from Russia:
mammoth
parka
cosmonaut

from Japan:
kimono
samurai
hibachi
soy

from China:
kumquat
kung fu
tea
typhoon

from Africa:
banana
mumbo jumbo
samba
yam

You guys are so funny.

from Australia:
boomerang
dingo
kangaroo
koala

Now let's try spelling a wide world of words.

1. Circle the correct word from the two choices offered:

(a) You probably wouldn't drink tee/tea while eating a kumkwat/kumquat.

(b) I like to keep a low profyel/profile in the arcade/arkade.

(c) You go to the barbre/barber to cut your hair, not the bucher/butcher!

(d) I wish I could ride a woolly mamoth/mammoth to cosmonaut/cosmanaut school!

(e) Soy/soi burgers can taste just fine so long as you cook them on a hibichi/hibachi.

2. Now go back to all the words on pages 38 and 39 and fill in the blanks so these make sense.

(a) While travelling in the Australian outback, I spotted many _____ and _____ at least one_____.

(b) My _____ training in China was interrupted by an enormous _____!

(c) The teacher tried to explain the _____ dance, but it was all just _____to me.

(d) I was bitten by too many _____in the_____.

(e) I found a _____ restaurant in Italy last summer. Alas, my meal was interrupted by a_____.

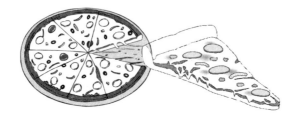

Around the World

1. A drink made from leaves

2. An explosive mountain

3. A Russian astronaut

4. A sweet potato

5. A storm of wind

6. An Australian hunting weapon

7. An extinct relative of the elephant

8. Speaking nonsense

9. An annoying bug

10. One who cuts meat

11. A huge storm

12. A sideways view of a person

13. (across) Animated drawings

14. (down) A crevice in the Earth

15. A place to play video games

16. A wild Australian dog

What's in a Name?

Many words originated from the names of famous people or inventors. See how you can do with these questions.

1. What country was named after the sailor Amerigo Vespucci?

_____

2. What food was named after the Earl of Sandwich?

_____

3. What flower was named for Anders Dahl?

_____

4. What part of a man's hair was named after General Ambrose Burnside?

_____

5. What electrical term was named for Count Alessandro Volta?

_____

6. What instrument gets its name from inventor Antoine Sax?

_____

7. What slang term for a man is named after Guy Fawkes?

_____

Crazy Combos

Portmanteau words are created by combining two words together. For example, smog was created by combining smoke and fog.

Can you guess what portmanteau words are created by combining each of these pairs?

1. breakfast   +   lunch   =   _____brunch_____

2. gleam   +   shimmer   =   _____

3. motor   +   pedal   =   _____

4. smack   +   mash   =   _____

5. splash   +   spatter   =   _____

6. television   +   marathon   =   _____

7. twist   +   whirl   =   _____

Weird Words

1. Some words began as a set of initials and then dropped the periods. See if you can figure out what each of these terms were shortened to.

    (a) self contained underwater breathing apparatus _____*scuba*_____

    (b) light amplification by stimulated emission of radiation _____

    (c) radio detecting and ranging _____

    (d) sound navigation ranging _____

    (e) special weapons action team _____

2. Computer words can be tricky. Almost all of them are short forms of large terms, or are acronyms like those in question 1. See if you can guess the correct terms.

    (a) random access memory _____

    (b) digital video device _____

    (c) Megabytes _____

    (d) compact disc – read only memory _____

    (e) central processing unit _____

3. Some words are chopped down versions of longer words.
Try to figure out the short word from each long word.

(a) influenza

_____

(b) advertisement

_____

(c) spectacles

_____

(d) cafeteria

_____

(e) laboratory

_____

(f) veterinarian

_____

(g) penitentiary

_____

(h) taxicab

_____

(i) gymnasium

_____

(j) typographical error

_____

Crossword

Here are **20** frequently misspelled words.
Write the words correctly, then put them in the crossword.

1. clothse

2. wnated

3. (across) before

4. (down) beleive

5. thrugh

6. thear

7. intirest

8. sckool

9. startad

10. thouhgt

11. diffirent

12. freind

13. treid

14. untill

15. whith

16. haerd

17. poeple

18. recieved

19. suprise

20. verry

Answer Key

Many of the pages in this workbook contain creative activities and spaces for open-ended responses. Only those that require a correct answer are included in this answer key.

Page 3
troubled, friends, minute, tackle, certified, managed, confident, preparation, received, their

Page 4 & 5
1. forehand, seashore, drugstore
2. gymnast, overcast, contrast
3. repeat, wheat, defeat
4. comprehend, defend, surrender
5. bright, frightened, mighty
6. sacrifice, advice, practice
7. brother, smothered, another
8. stress, confess, progress

Page 6 & 7
Possible answers. You may find more.
3 letters – nag, sag, sin, ear, rim, age
4 letters – game, grin, near, gear
5 letters – games, grime, image
6 letters – grease, meagre, images
7 letters – searing
8+ letters – magazine, magazines

Page 8 & 9
1. mad dad   2. witch itch
3. long song
4. kernel journal
5. book crook
6. slimmer swimmer
7. brief grief   8. weary query
9. lighter writer
10. loose goose
11. lazy daisy

Page 10 & 11
1. in(ter)est(ing)
for)get)ful
at)ten)tive
dras)tic)al)ly
re)frig)er)a)tor
care)ful)ly
marsh)mal)low
tan)ger)ine
mon)op)o)ly
am)bu)lance

2. gasoline   kangaroo
parachute
3. overhead   honeymoon
summertime   abrasive
completed   confusing
tuxedo   headquarters

Page 12
imagine   chocolate
magnetic   confidence
multiply   position
recognize   carefully
astronaut   digestive

Page 13
1. mantis   2. mango
3. mantle   4. manger
5. Manitoba   6. manufacture
7. many   8. manager
9. mansion   10. manicure

Page 14
1. out   2. friend
3. ball   4. side
5. down/up   6. back
7. where/how   8. head
9. step   10. pot
11. fire   12. store
13. light   14. out

Page 15
displayed, daughter, dimensional, companion, introduced, popular, wealth, stewardess, forty, Biography

Page 16
1. impossible, incompetent, disconnect, unhappy, injustice, disapprove, unused, disinterest, unable, or disable unknown, dislike, unlike, unfair

Page 17
You may find more.
transportation, transcontinental
misuse, mistake, misunderstand
exercise, exhale, exterior, extreme
disability, discomfort, disgrace
intrude, inspect, inhabit, inherit
redesign, reiterate, respect

Page 18 & 19
1. slugged, swimming, planner, slimmer, clipping, skipping
2. slicing, slimy, intruding, wired, confusing, enforcing
3. happier, holiest, driest, partied, skinnier, silliest
4. waiting, hoped, scariest, disgusting, sensibly

Page 20 & 21
teacher, parlor, harder, accelerator, mirror, over, officer, later, luckier
dependable, reliable, notable, regrettable, adorable, unbeatable
story, bakery, grocery, aviary, observatory, secretary

Page 22 & 23
astronaut, astrological, astrology, etc.
hopeful, hopeless, hoping, etc.
friendship, boyfriend, friendly, etc.
kilometre, centimetre, decametre, etc.
undercover, covered, covering, etc.

Page 29

1. foxes, lasses, rocks, crunches, buses, forgets, exercises, locks, tomatoes, houses, churches, kings

2. calves, shelves, elves, thieves, halves, leaves

Page 30 & 31

1. scarves, geese, moose, children, taxes, crises, deer, cargos, zeros or zeroes

2. men, feet, oxen, dice, women, sheep, fish,leaves

```
s c a r v e s b c r w
a r h l e r i o z i y
b i m r t o n i w o l
e s l i o i g e e s e
d e e r e e e u y r y
t s o e s j r w d o m
b w o l v e s t j i e
s b h t d j g i n h t
g r t h f w o m e n r
h n a o x e n g m e e
```
(scarves, geese, deer, wolves, women, oxen circled)

Page 32 & 33

1. home coming
house warming
extra ordinary
hyper active
super natural
neighbour hood
ill egal
technical ly
deliver ance
ant agonize
tar paul in
w ad ding
plum age
main ten ance

2. backrest, backspace, backyard, etc
outhouse, outside, outing, etc.
knowing, unknown, knowledge, etc.

3. Congratulations on solving this tricky puzzle. You must be an excellent speller!

Page 34

February, library, government, comfortable, temperature, environment, Wednesday, language, often, diamond

Page 35

One day, a little girl by the name of Goldilocks was wandering through the forest. She found a house in a small clearing.

Goldilocks entered the house and found three bowls of porridge. Since she was hungry, Goldilocks decided to eat some of it. She tried the first bowl, but it was too hot. She tired the second bowl, but it was too cold. She tried the last bowl, and it was just right. She ate the whole bowl.

Getting sleepy, Goldilock decided to take a nap. She found three beds inside the house. She tried the first bed, but it was too hard. She tired the second bed, but it was too soft. She tried the third bed, and it was just right. She quickly fell asleep.

Just then, the owners of the house got home. It was the three bears!

Pages 36 & 37

1.(a) write   **(b)** knock
  (c) wrecking **(d)** knife
  (e) wrists   **(f)** know
  (g) knee   **(h)** gnats

2.(a) talking   **(b)** what
  (c) two   **(d)** castles
  (e) doubted **(f)** sign
  (g) soften   **(h)** whistling

3.(a) crumb   **(b)** comb
  (c) column   **(d)** lamb
  (e) climb   **(f)** limb
  (g) autumn   **(h)** thumb

Proofreading: autumn, whistled, climbed, night, wrists

Page 40 & 41

1.(a) tea, kumquat
  (b) profile, arcade
  (c) barber, butcher
  (d) mammoth, cosmonaut
  (e) soy, hibachi

2.(a) kangaroos, dingo, koala
  (b) kung fu, typhoon
  (c) samba, mumbo jumbo
  (d) mosquitoes, canyon
  (e) pizza, volcano

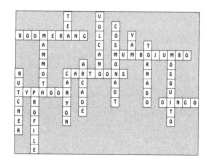

Page 42

1. America   **2.** sandwich
3. dahlias   **4.** sideburns
5. voltage   **6.** saxophone
7. guy

Page 43

1. brunch   **2.** glimmer
3. moped   **4.** smash
5. splatter   **6.** telethon
7. twirl

Page 44 & 45

1.(a) scuba   **(b)** laser
  (c) radar   **(d)** sonar
  (e) SWAT

2.(a) RAM   **(b)** DVD
  (c) Mb   **(d)** CD-ROM
  (e) CPU

3.(a) flu   **(b)** ad
   (c) specs   **(d)** caf
   (e) lab   **(f)** vet
   (g) pen   **(h)** taxi or cab
   (i) gym   **(j)** typo

Page **46**

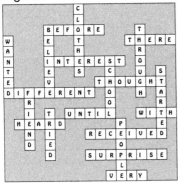

Page **51**
   1. chew   **2.** ewe
   3. weed   **4.** edible
   5. letter   **6.** erase
   7. season   **8.** once
   9. celebrate   **10.** terrible
   11. lesson   **12.** Ontario

Page **52 & 53**
   1. two   **2.** too
   3. to   **4.** too
   5. two, to   **6.** too, to, two
   7. two, to, too   **8.** there
   9. they're   **10.** there
   11. their   **12.** they're, their
   13. there, there   **14.** they're, their
   15. there, their

Page **54**
   1. whole   **2.** knew
   3. whether   **4.** who's
   5. seems   **6.** hair
   7. wrote   **8.** pried
   9. sow   **10.** vain
   11. we've   **12.** waste
   13. principle   **14.** rapped
   15. taught   **16.** cite
   17. week   **18.** plain
   19. we   **20.** which

Answer for cover: 12 plus us!

Page **57**
   1. hoarse horse   **2.** rose rows
   3. plain plane   **4.** whole hole
   5. weak week   **6.** sail sale
   7. fur fir   **8.** towed toed

Page **58 & 59**
Proofreading: wouldn't, else's, projects, desks, couldn't
   1.(a) books'   **(b)** baby's
   (c) cats'   **(d)** losers'
   (e) students', teacher's
   2.(a) its   **(b)** there's
   (c) yours   **(d)** theirs

Pages **60 – 63**
budget, box, butter
finger, feather, finicky
   1. especially   **2.** dirigible
   3. sedated   **4.** complexity
   5. reformation   **6.** distinct
Colours: chartreuse, azure, vermilion, crimson, mauve
Body parts: tibia, abdomen, coccyx, tendon
Plants: chrysanthemum, ibis, snapdragon, foxglove, hemlock, loosestrife

Page **69**
stiff, cycle, cake, mouse, race, know
Message: Now make yours!

Page **70**
   1. (a) neighbours
      (b) valour   **(c)** honour
      (d) flavour
      (e) favourite, colour
   2. (a) metres, kilometre
      (b) centre   **(c)** theatre
      (d) litre
      (e) centimetres, metre

Page **71**
   1. British Columbia (2),
Alberta (3), Saskatchewan (4), Manitoba (5), Ontario (6), Quebec (7), New Brunswick (11), Nova Scotia (10), Prince Edward Island (9), Newfoundland (8), Nunavut(13)
   2. Ottawa, Toronto, Winnipeg, Regina, Edmonton, Victoria, Quebec City, Halifax, Fredericton, Charlottetown, St. John's, Iqaluit

Page **72**
   1. Ottawa
   2. Saskatchewan
   3. Vancouver
   4. Regina, Saskatoon
   5. Montreal, Toronto

Page **73**
   1. encyclopedia
   2. blonde   **3.** kilogram
   4. sympathize   **5.** surprise
   6. analyze   **7.** quarrelling
   8. jail   **9.** curb
   10. tire   **11.** gas
   12. demon

Page **75**
   1. forgot   **2.** arcade
   3. class   **4.** detained
   5. money   **6.** vacation
   7. nasty

Page **77**
I have a spelling checker / It came with my PC / It plainly marks for my review / Mistakes I cannot see. / I strike a key and type a word / And wait for it to say / Whether I am wrong or right, / It shows me straight away. / As soon as a mistake is made / It knows before too long, / And I can put the error right —/ It's rarely ever wrong. / I have run this poem through it, / I'm sure you're pleased to know / It's letter perfect all the way, / My checker told me so.

Pages 78
1. biology
2. biochemistry
3. biorhythm
4. biography
5. biophysics
6. hydroelectric
7. cyclone
8. hydroponics
9. dehydrated
10. hydrants

Page 79
1. general
2. generated
3. genetics
4. generation
5. genuine
6. diagram
7. grammar
8. hologram
9. parallelogram
10. telegram

Page 80
1. decapitated
2. cap
3. capital
4. capture
5. captain
6. contradict
7. predictable
8. benediction
9. diction
10. dictators

Page 81
1. intercept
2. translated
3. signature
4. gratitude
5. reception
6. elaborate
7. exception
8. transportation
9. ordinary
10. motivated
11. emigrate
Message: It's Greek to me!

Page 83
1. composer, musician
2. independent
3. expensive
4. hopeless
5. beautiful
6. transportation
7. discovery
8. expensive
9. independence
10. musician
11. independence, transportation, expensive
12. beautiful, transportation
13. musician
14. beautiful

Page 85
Passage: conversation, dishonest, valuable, irresponsible, misunderstood
1. valuable, invaluable, likeable
2. conversation, invitation
3. misunderstood, understood, mistaken
4. continuous, tin, continual
5. different, dependent

Page 87
1. employee
2. underweight
3. forecast
4. prehistoric
5. semifinal
6. performance
7. international, competition
8. underweight, overweight, understand
9. international, nationality, interdependent
10. prehistoric, forecast

Page 88

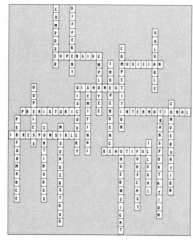

Page 89
cone – cane – lane – late – date – dare – dark – bark – park – part – cart – care – case – vase – vast – cast – fast – fist – list – last

Page 90 – 93
1. foretell, bookstore, seashore
2. gymnast, overcast, contrast
3. mantis
4. mango
5. mantle
6. manger
7. Manitoba
8. manufacture
9. light
10. out
11. impossible, incompetent, disconnect, unhappy
12. foxes, glasses, rocks, crunches, buses, forgets
13.(a) kangaroos, dingo or koala
(b) kung fu, typhoon
(c) samba, mumbo jumbo
(d) mosquitoes, canyon
(e) pizza, volcano
(answers may vary, just make sure the spelling is correct)
14. snore, reliable, letter, error, orange
15. whole, knew, whether, who's, seems
16. furiously, winning, grimaced, frustrated, whispered, controller, accepted, quickly, panic, confident

Page 94

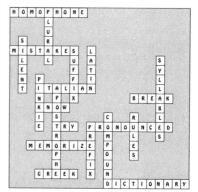

Read each clue and fill in the blank in the word next to it. The trick is to answer each clue using a word that starts with the last two letters of the word before it.

1. You do it while eating.   ch__ew__

2. A female sheep.   __ewe__

3. A garden problem.   _____ ed

4. If you can eat something, it's   _____ ible

5. You put this in the mailbox.   _____

6. You can do it to pencil, but not to pen.   _____

7. Winter is my favourite   _____

8. A single occurrence.   _____

9. You do it on birthdays.   _____

10. When something is really awful.   _____

11. What you take to learn to play tennis.   _____

12. A province in Canada.   _____

Confusables

Homophones are always confusing because they sound the same but are spelled differently and have different meanings.

To, Two, Too

to is easy to remember

two – think of connections to "twin" and "twice."

too – too has too many Os.

> Two pages are too much work to do.

 Now write the correct form of to/two/too in each blank.

1. There are _____ sets of twins in my family.

2. Can I come along _____?

3. Did you remember _____ brush your teeth?

4. There are far _____ many students goofing around.

5. For the last _____ years, we've travelled _____ three different national parks.

6. It's _____ late _____ watch _____ movies.

7. My _____ brothers go _____ the mall far _____ often.

The way to remember homophones is to think about the meaning in the sentence.

They're, Their, There

If the word means "they are," use **they're**.
The apostrophe takes the place of the "a" in *are*.

If the word means "belonging to them," use **their**.
Here's a sentence to help you: He and I are their cousins.

If the word means "in that place," use **there**. Can you think of a tip to remember the proper use of *there*?
(Hint: What little word do you see?)

Complete the sentences with the right there/they're/their:

8. Could you stand over _____?

9. _____ travelling across Canada on bicycles.

10. _____ is the jacket I lost last week!

11. My cousins returned to _____ cabin in the woods.

12. _____ looking forward to swimming in _____ new pool.

13. _____ used to be more newspapers than _____ are today.

14. _____ going with _____ mother to buy shoes.

15. _____ seems to be some confusion about _____ plan for a trip to British Columbia.

There are hundreds of other homophones in the English language.

 Choose the right word in each pair:

1. We ate a (whole, hole) pizza for lunch.

2. He (new, knew) all the answers on the test.

3. You're going to eat that broccoli (whether, weather) you like it or not!

4. (Whose, Who's) responsible for this mess?

5. This exercise may be harder than it (seams, seems).

6. He used too much gel in his (hair, hare).

7. I (rote, wrote) an essay for school yesterday.

8. Carefully, she (pried, pride) the boards away.

9. My grandmother always tells me, "You reap what you (sew, so, sow)."

10. I don't like Suzy because she's so (vane, vain, vein).

11. (Weave, we've) finally arrived at our destination.

12. Like they say: (waist, waste) not, want not.

13. In (principal, principle), you may be right.

14. I (rapped, wrapped) lightly on the door.

15. I've been (taut, taught) by many teachers over the years.

16. I have to (sight, cite, site) at least three sources in my report.

17. It's been a whole (weak, week) since I ran out of money.

18. The meaning of all of this is (plane, plain).

19. (We, Wee) need to stop doing this soon.

20. (Witch, Which) path will you choose next?

Let's hope Suzy doesn't see this page!

Memory Tricks

You only need to remember how to spell one of the words in a homophone pair and the other will come naturally.

Here are some memory tricks to help you:

break

brake

For safety's <u>sake</u>, use a br<u>ake</u>.

horse

hoarse

I r<u>oar</u>ed until I was h<u>oar</u>se

its

it's

The dog f<u>its</u> in <u>its</u> house.

Choose eight words from page 54 and think of a trick to remember the correct spelling.

_____

_____

_____

_____

_____

_____

_____

_____

Fun with Homophones

I blew up balloons until my face turned blue.

While playing golf, I had tea at the tee.

Use each pair of words in a sentence. Feel free to be silly!

(rowed, road) _____

_____

(threw, through) _____

_____

(meet, meat) _____

_____

(thrown, throne) _____

_____

(rose, rows) _____

_____

(foul, fowl) _____

_____

(main, mane) _____

_____

Homophone Riddles

Answer each of these riddles with a homophone pair.

1. What do you call a pony with a sore throat?

A hoarse horse!

2. What do you call flowers all in a line?

3. What do you call a boring aircraft?

4. What do you call the entire gap?

5. What do you call seven days without any strength?

6. What do you call a bargain on ships?

7. What do you call a shaggy tree?

Challenge!

8. What do you call an amphibian on water skis?

Now make up one of your own:

Apostrophe Agony!

Why are apostrophes so confusing?

There are really only four main rules for apostrophes.

1. Use an apostrophe to replace missing letters in a contraction.
For example: in *don't*, the apostrophe replaces the "o" in *do not*.

2. Use an apostrophe with "s" to indicate that something owns something else.
For example: Sally's bait.

3. Don't use an apostrophe to show possession with personal pronouns: his, hers, theirs, ours and its (belonging to it) are complete, just as they are

4. Never use an apostrophe to make a word plural.

 Find the five apostrophe mistakes in the passage below.
Circle and correct them.

Ashley had just finished her science project for tomorrow. She would'nt even let her parents see the finished product. Everyone was dying to know what lay beneath the sheet she had covered it with.

The next day, she brought her project with her to school still carefully concealed. On arriving in class, she could see everyone elses project's on their desk's. She already knew that hers was better.

One by one, the class presented their science projects until at last it was time for Ashley to present. She could'nt wait to see the looks on their faces.

With a flourish, she removed the sheet from her project and the class gasped at what they saw...

Now for the tricky part.

For words that are plurals ending in "s," just add an apostrophe after the "s" to make them possessive. For example: the cats' meows.

 1. Choose the correct word for each sentence below.

   (a) All the (book's, books') covers were torn off.

   (b) The (baby's, babies') mother rocked him to sleep.

   (c) The (cat's, cats') food wouldn't last between all four of them.

   (d) The (losers', loser's) fate looked grim after the battle.

   (e) The (student's, students') papers were all locked in the (teacher's, teachers') desk.

For a little more practice, remember that our possessive pronouns do not use apostrophes.

   The cat licked <u>its</u> paws.
   Those games are <u>theirs</u>, not ours.
   The towels were labelled <u>his</u> and <u>hers</u>.

 2. Choose the correct word for each sentence below.

   (a) You can't judge a book by (it's, its) cover.

   (b) (There's, Theirs) my favourite restaurant.

   (c) Is this pen (yours, your's) or mine?

   (d) That's not his soccer ball, it's (there's, theirs).

Dictionary Digging

A print dictionary can be a good tool for helping you spell words correctly.

At the top of each page in the dictionary are two words. They're called guide words. These are the first and last words on the page they appear on. You can use them to help you find a word on that page.

If the guide words on a page were **road** and **runt**, what words might you find on that page? Words like *robin*, *ruler*, and *roar* would be on the page because they fall between the guide words when sorted alphabetically.

Put a check beside each of the words that would belong on each of these pages.

___ budget

___ boring

___ box

___ bat

___ butter

___ bitter

___ fist

___ farther

___ finger

___ feather

___ forgetful

___ finicky

 **But how can you use a dictionary for spelling if you can't spell the word?**
Easy! Use the beginning sound, then let your fingers do the walking.

Suppose you wanted to look up the word *knowledge*.

When you want to look up a word, write down all the ways you can possibly think to spell it. You can use your dictionary to help find the right one.

Use your dictionary to help you choose the correct spelling of these words. Circle them.

1. especially   exspecially   espeshally

2. diragible   dirigible   dirigable

3. sidated   sedeted   sedated

4. complecsity   complexity   complexiti

5. reformation   refomation   reformasion

6. distinkt   dustinct   distinct

Now get a dictionary and see how fast you can find these words.

 Start your timer!

(a) foghorn   Dictionary page: _____

(b) gimmick   Dictionary page: _____

(c) frenetic   Dictionary page: _____

(d) zeppelin   Dictionary page: _____

(e) expendable   Dictionary page: _____

(f) searchlight   Dictionary page: _____

(g) abysmal   Dictionary page: _____

(h) wherewithal   Dictionary page: _____

Stop your timer!

How did you do?

5 minutes
As fast as

10 minutes
As speedy as

15 minutes
As hasty as

Francine

Suzy

Hiro

You can also use your dictionary to help boost your vocabulary.

 Which of these words are names of colours? Circle them.

chartreuse   plethora

azure   chard

vermillion   crimson

mauve   trellis

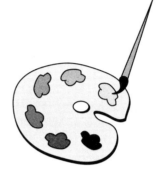

 Which of these words are parts of the body? Circle them.

tibia   abdomen

fluoride   coccyx

humus   creatine

odious   tendon

 Which of these words are the names of plants? Circle them.

chrysanthemum   ibis

sapphire   snapdragon

foxglove   fuchsia

hemlock   divinity

pachelbel   loosestrife

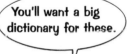
You'll want a big dictionary for these.

Dictionary Delight

Here's a sample page from a dictionary. Use it for the questions on pages 65.

sad **sail**

sad *adjective* (**sadder, saddest**) unhappy; showing sorrow or unhappiness, **sadly** *adverb* in a sad way, **sadness** *noun* being sad, the state of unhappiness

sadden *verb* (**saddens, saddening, saddened**) to make someone sad or unhappy

saddle *noun* (*plural* **saddles**) 1. a seat for riding a horse or other animal 2. the seat of a bicycle

safari *noun* (*plural* **safaris**) (pronounced sa – **far** – i) an expedition to see or hunt wild animals

safari park *noun* (*plural* **safari parks**) a park where wild animals are kept in large enclosures

safe *adjective* (**safer, safes**t) 1. free from danger; protected 2. not causing danger, as in Drive at a safe speed. **safe** *noun* (*plural* **safes**) a secure enclosure in which valuable things can be locked safely. **safely** *adverb* in a safe way, as in Drive safely.

safeguard *noun* (*plural* **safeguards**) a protection **safeguard** *verb* to provide protection, as in The soldier safeguarded the castle.

safety *noun* being safe; protection

safety belt *noun* (*plural* **safety belts**) a belt to hold a person securely in a seat, a seat belt

safety pin *noun* (*plural* **safety pins**) a curved pin made with a clip to protect the point, often used for cloth diapers or in clothing

sag *verb* (**sags, sagging, sagged**) to sink slightly in the middle due to pressure or gravity.

saga *noun* (*plural* **sagas**) a long story with many heroic adventures, especially Icelandic sagas

sail *noun* (*plural* **sails**) 1. a piece of strong cloth attached to a mast to make a boat move, 2. a short sea voyage **sail** *verb* 1. to travel in a ship, 2. to control or steer a boat or ship, 3. to be moved along by means of a sail or sail. The boat sails smoothly.

Now answer these questions using the words from the preceding page.

1. What two words on this page can be both a noun and a verb?

_____

2. Give an example of the kind of animal on which you might use a saddle.

_____

3. Create a sentence that contains the word *safeguard*.

_____

4. Can you think of another words for *saga*?

_____

5. Draw a picture of a safety pin.

6. Where would you be likely to go on a safari?

_____

7. Use *sail* as a noun and as a verb in one sentence.

_____

8. What's one rule of safety that you know?

_____

9. What's an activity that you would do sadly?

_____

10. What valuables would you put in a safe?

_____

Have a Try

Sometimes making a guess is a good way to start spelling a word. If you can get down to two or three possible spellings, often you'll see which one looks right.

Suppose I wanted to spell comfortable. I know there's a trick to the word, so I write down all the ways I can think of to spell it.

cumfterball   **comfterble**

cumfertible   **comfortable**

Aha! Comfortable just looks right. It's like a bell rings in your head!

Now try it yourself.

1. Think of a kind of food. Spell it all the different ways you can. Circle the one that looks right.

_____   _____

_____   _____

2. Think of the name of a dog breed. Spell it all the different ways you can. Circle the one that looks right.

_____   _____

_____   _____

_____   _____

3. Think of the name of a car. Spell it all the different ways you can. Circle the one that looks right.

_____   _____

_____   _____

 4. Think of the name of a piece of clothing. Spell it all the different ways you can. Circle the one that looks right.

_____   _____

_____   _____

 5. Think of the name of a place. Spell it all the different ways you can. Circle the one that looks right

_____   _____

_____   _____

 6. Think of the name of a game. Spell it all the different ways you can. Circle the one that looks right.

_____   _____

_____   _____

Scrambled Message

This is a game can be tough to solve but is easy to make! First, select a message that you want to tell someone. Then, choose a list of smaller words that contain all of the letters in your message. Scramble the smaller words, and put the scrambled letters beside boxes that mark the key letters. When all of the small words have been unscrambled, the key letters will also unscramble to make your secret message. Don't forget to leave blanks for the message so the descrambler will know how many words there are.

Take a look this one to get the hang of it.

GEFROT

(F)	O	R	(G)	E	T

NEDCAL

C	A	(N)	D	(L)	E

RETGTA

T	A	R	G	(E)	T

BULROA

(L)	A	B	O	(U)	R

SACHRT

(S)	T	A	R	C	H

KEES

(S)	E	E	K

NPINIGS

S	(P)	(I)	(N)	N	(I)	N	G

The circled key letters in this puzzle are: **FGNLELUSSPINI**

S _ _ _ _ _ _ _ _   _ _   _ _ _ _

Now, try this one for yourself, or make your own and spread the message!

TISFF

◯				

CECLY

	◯			◯

KECA

		◯	◯

MUESO

◯	◯	◯		

CREA

◯	◯	C	

NWKO

	◯	◯	◯

This is way cool!

Answer: __ __ __   __ __ __ __   __ __ __ __ __!

Canadian, Eh?

Some words that Americans spell with "or" at the end, we spell with "our" – like honour, colour, neighbour and favour.

The differences on this page aren't the only ones.

Check out an American book or magazine and see if you notice any other differences.

1. Try to fill in the blank with the correct Canadian "our" spelling.

(a) I went to the show with some of my _neighbours_ .

(b) As a soldier, my grandfather won a medal of _____.

(c) On Remembrance Day, we _____ our veterans.

(d) I dislike this_____of ice cream.

(e) I think purple is definitely my _____ _____.

2. Words that Americans end with "er" we sometimes end with "re."
Examples include *metre*, *centimetre* and *litre*. Fill in the blanks with the Canadian "re" spelling.

How come we say zed instead of zee, but not ged instead of gee?

(a) There are 1000 metres in every _____.

(b) City hall is usually near the _____ of a city.

(c) I'd rather see a movie at the _____.

(d) I was so thirsty I drank a _____ of water!

(e) There are 100 _____ in every _____.

Good question Suzed!

1. Fix the spellings and write the number that corresponds to the location on the map.

Britesh Culumbiya _____   Albreta _____

Sascachewan _____   Mantoba _____

Onatario _____   Quebek _____

Nu Brunswic _____   Noonavut _____

Price Edard Isand _____

Nufunland _____   Nova Scosha _____

2. Now fix the spellings of each capital city.

Otawa _____   Torono _____

Sharlottown _____   Rigina _____

Edmuntun _____   Viktoriya _____

Kwebec City _____   Halifacks _____

Fredriktun _____   Winapeg _____

St. Jons _____   Ikaluit _____

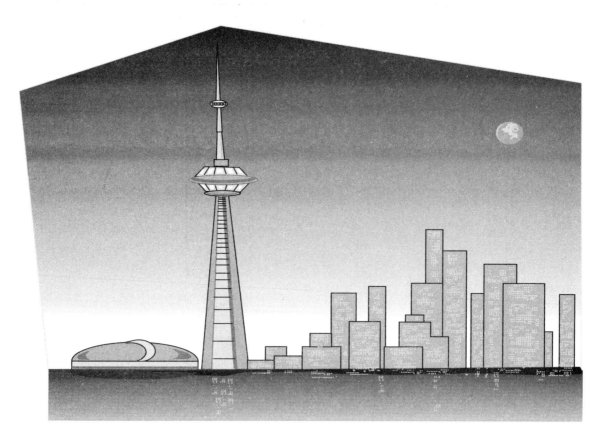

Pick the correct spelling for these Canadian locations:

1. The capital of Canada is in (Ottawa, Otawa).

2. You'll find a place called Elbow in the province of (Saskachewin, Saskatchewan).

3. (Vancouver, Vancoover) is a great place to start touring the Canadian Rockies.

4. (Rejina, Regina) is a city about 300 kilometres south of (Saskatune, Sakatoon.)

5. The biggest hockey rivalry is between the (Montrael, Montreal) Canadiens and the (Toronto, Tronto) Maple Leafs.

Remember from page 70 the Canadian spelling methods? Well, sometimes Canadians spell things like Americans do instead of the way the British do.

See if you can circle the traditional Canadian spelling of each of these words. One will be Canadian, and the other will be its British or American equivalent.

1. encyclopedia   encyclopaedia

2. blond   blonde

3. kilogramme   kilogram

4. sympathise   sympathize

5. surprise   surprize

6. analyse   analyze

7. quarrelling   quarreling

8. gaol   jail

9. curb   kerb

10. tire   tyre

11. petrol   gas

12. daemon   demon

Spelling on Screen

Your computer will show you when you make many spelling mistakes, but it often can't fix mistakes without your help.

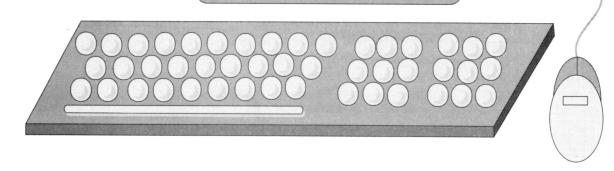

My Science Project

For my experiment I choze to do tests on my sister to prove …

SPELLING ⊠

Your spell-checker suggests:
choose, chose, choke, chore, chaos

The computer offered these choices for some misspelled words.
Circle the best choice so the sentences make sense.

1. I  my pencils today.

2. We could head to the  after school.

3. I couldn't pay attention during music 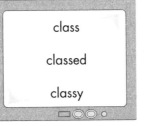 today.

4. Jordan was  by the principal for being late.

5. Make sure you save some of your 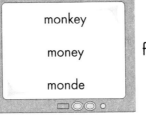 for later.

6. We're going on  this summer.

7. Jason and Joseph were going to pull a  trick on them.

A Real Challenge

There are over 40 mistakes in this funny poem.
Rewrite it correctly on Page 77.

Eye halve a spelling chequer,

It came with my pea sea;

It plainly marques four my revue

Miss steaks eye kin knot sea.

Eye strike a key and type a word

And weight four it two say

Weather eye am wrong oar write,

It shows me strait a weigh.

As soon as a mist ache is maid

It nose bee fore two long,

And eye can put the error rite —

Its rare lea ever wrong.

Eye have run this poem threw it,

I'm shore your pleased two no

Its letter perfect awl the weigh,

My chequer tolled me sew.

-Web Author Unknown

I wish I wrote this.

Computer spelling anomalies

I have a spelling checker

It came _____

_____

_____

_____

_____

_____

_____

_____

_____

_____

_____

_____

_____

_____

My computer caught the word "cheque."

"Cheque" is a Canadian spelling. Americans use "check."

So "cheque" is right in Winnipeg but wrong in Washington!

Ancient Roots

Many of our words in English — especially the long, polysyllabic ones — come to us from Greek and Latin root words. The good part of this is that these "derivatives" are pretty easy to spell. You just have to put the various parts together.

The Ancient Greek word **bio** means life. From this, we get words such as biology, biorhythm, biography, biophysics and biochemistry. See if you can fit the right "bio-" word into the blanks.

1. The study of plant and animal life is called _____.

2. Doctors have to study _____ to understand how chemicals work in the body.

3. The daily cycle of our body is referred to as a _____.

4. I read a _____ of Wayne Gretzky the other day.

5. Some astronauts need to know _____ to know how muscles work in space.

The Greek word **cycle** means circle or ring, and bicycle is the most obvious example (the "bi-" prefix means two, for the two wheels). The Greek monster Hydra — the sea monster with many heads — gives us the prefix "hydro" or "hydra" for water. See if you can choose the best word with these roots for the following sentences, then write it in the blank.

6. A dam produces _____ power. (hydrofoil/cyclotron/hydroelectric)

7. A _____ is a serious tropical storm. (hydrometer/cyclone/hydraulic)

8. _____ is the science of growing plants in water.
(Hydroponics /Hydrolysis/Hydrant)

9. When you're thirsty, you're _____. (dehydrated/hydraulic/cyclical)

10. Firefighters rely on water from_____. (hydrocarbons/hydrants/citizens)

78 ——Greek derivatives——

An interesting Greek root is "**gen-**," meaning birth or race. We get all sorts of words from this, from *gene* to *gentile*. See if you can choose the best word with these roots for the following sentences, then write it in the blank.

1. In _____, you should always brush your teeth. (generate/general/genetics)

2. Hydroelectric power is _____ by water.
   (telegrammed/generic/generated)

3. I would like to study _____ in university.
   (genealogy/biosphere/genetics)

4. My father doesn't understand since he's from a different _____.
   (archetype/generation/genesis)

5. This artifact is definitely _____. (genus/genuine/gentry)

Yet another Greek root that we see often is words using "**-gram**." This root indicates something that is written, or a letter of the alphabet. See if you can choose the best word with this root for the following sentences, then write it in the blank.

A telegram is like ancient email.

6. She drew a _____ to illustrate her idea.
   (anagram/diagram/ideogram)

7. Spelling and _____ are essential writing skills.
   (grammar/hologram/monogram)

8. In the future, we won't watch flat TVs. It will be a 3D _____ .
   (ideogram/telegram/hologram)

9. A _____ is a shape with two sets of parallel sides.
   (grammatical/diagram/parallelogram)

10. In the old days people would send a _____ , but now we have email. (monogram/telegram/epigram)

Much of English comes from Latin, the other classical language. Some very common words may surprise you with their very ancient roots.

From the Latin word **caput** meaning "head," we get the root "–cap." See if you can choose the best word with this root for the following sentences, then write it in the blank.

1. The prisoner was to be _____ that afternoon.
   (captor/decapitated/capitalized)

2. I like to wear my Toronto Maple Leafs _____. (cap/captain/capital)

3. The_____ of Canada is Ottawa. (capitalism/capitalize/capital)

4. Everyone I know loves the game _____ -the-flag.
   (captor/capture/captivate)

5. I wish I could be the _____ of the football team.
   (captain/captor/capital)

From the Latin word **dic**, many languages get words for speaking (French: *dire*, Italian: *dice*). We have English words too. Choose the best word with this root for the following sentences, then write it in the blank.

6. I don't want to _____ what you say, but that's not true.
   (predict/verdict/contradict)

7. The future is not very_____. (dictum/predictable/valedictory)

8. A _____ is a blessing, sometimes for a meal.
   (dictionary/valedictory/ benediction)

9. When you speak, use proper _____. (diction/dictionary/contradiction)

10. It's no coincidence that _____ are often great public speakers.
    (dictators/verdicts/predictions)

Let's try a puzzle with these words from Latin roots. Fill each sentence with the right word and the first letters of the words you use will spell out a secret message.

transportation	elaborate	gratitude	
exception	translated	ordinary	motivated
signature	emigrate	intercept	reception

1. The spy managed to _____ the message en route from headquarters.

2. This book is _____ from the original Latin.

3. Put your _____ down here on the dotted line.

4. He showed much _____ after receiving the gift.

5. Please check in at _____ when you arrive at your hotel.

6. Would you please _____ on your ideas.

7. There is always at least one _____ to every rule.

8. Plane, train and ship are three means of _____ .

9. He may look _____ , but deep down that guy is fantastic.

10. I just don't feel _____ to do my homework.

11. Peter wants to _____ to another country.

The secret message is a phrase from Shakespeare:

__ __ ' __   __ __ __ __ __ k __   __ __   __ __ !

Latin roots — 81

Two Dozen Words Make It Easy

If you can master the spelling of just 24 words, you can spell thousands of others. We'll just do eight every other page with a little exercise in between to help you practice.

discovery The prefix "dis-" changes a word to the opposite. The suffix "-y" makes it into a process. So *discovery* is *cover* with "dis" and "y" added.

hopeless The root word is *hope* and the suffix is "-less." *Hope* keeps its final "e," otherwise the word would be *hopless*, the fate of an overweight kangaroo.

composer A composer composes music, so the root word is *compose*. The "-er" suffix gives you the person who does all this, as in *teacher* or *writer*.

musician Since we're on music, a *musician* is a person who makes it. In the same way, a *magician* makes magic and a *physician* makes "physique," which is an old word for medicine.

independence We start with *depend*, then add the prefix "-in" (meaning not) to get the opposite. A person who doesn't depend on anyone else is independent, so the only thing to remember is the ending "-ent" or "-ence," depending on whether you want the adjective or the noun.

transportation The root word *port* comes from the French *porter*, meaning to carry. The prefix "trans-" takes us to carry across and the rest gives you a noun rather than a verb. If you can spell this, you can also spell *transmit*, *transfusion* and *transitive* verbs.

expensive With an "ex-" at the front and an "-sive" at the back, we have a very basic word *pen* in the middle. Spell this and you can tackle *inexpensive* (which sounds better than cheap) and *offensive* (which sounds nicer than nasty).

beautiful That "beau-" prefix comes to us from French where it means *beauty*, but not the beast. The ending is useful for many words: *painful*, *merciful* and *plentiful* (just remember to change the "y" to an "i" before adding a suffix).

Use the words on page 82 to complete each of these sentences.

1. A _____ is a type of _____ who writes music.

2. When you're no longer dependent on your parents, you're _____ .

3. If something costs a lot, we say it's _____ .

4. When the score was 50 – 0, the team felt that winning was _____ .

5. The opposite of ugly is _____ .

6. Subways, airplanes and cars are forms of _____ .

7. The _____ of North America was made by the Vikings long before

Columbus.

Now think about the structure of the words and use them to answer the following
questions.

8. Which word requires you to change the "y" to an "i" before adding the ending?

_____

9. Which word has four syllables and four "e"s? _____

10. Which word is made from the root word *music*? _____

11. Which three words have both a prefix and a suffix?

_____ _____ _____

12. Which two words come from French root words?

_____ _____

13. In which word does "ci" make a "sh" sound? _____

14. Which word has more vowels than consonants? _____

Eight more words...

conversation   There are many words with the "-ation" suffix. Consider *reservation* and *conservation*...both spelled with the same pattern.

continuous   We start with *continue* and add the suffix "-ous" after dropping the final "e." The same pattern works for danger/dangerous and nerve/nervous.

valuable   Again, start with a root word like *value* and drop the "e" before putting on that "-able" suffix. This is a valuable spelling pattern, for sure.

irresponsible   Here we have the "ir-" prefix (to give us the opposite of responsible), with the "r" doubled.

dishonest   The "dis-" prefix meant opposite or negative long before kids would ever "dis" each other.

illegal   The "il-" prefix is another negative. The pattern is found in many words like *illegible* and *illegitimate*.

misunderstood   Our last negative prefix. "Mis-" also leads us to *mistake*, *mislead* and *misinterpret*.

different   A word we use a lot. Just remember that the suffix is "-ent." Here's a simple memory trick: "There's no ant in different!"

Use the words from page 84 to complete each of the sentences and the questions below.

Suzy and Francine were in a heated _____ about Freddie. They thought that Freddie had done something_____ on a math test.

Freddie had brought in some notes on a small sheet of paper. Afterwards, he said that the notes and formulas had been very _____ to him on the test. Suzy was angry.

"Freddie, you're _____ !" she said.

Freddie just blushed. "The teacher said I could bring in something to help me," he replied.

"The teacher meant a calculator, not a cheat sheet!" Francine told him.

Freddie blushed even more. "I guess I just _____ ."

1. Which word has the ending "able"? _____
   What word would you have if you added the prefix "in"? _____
   Use the same idea to add "able" to *like*. _____

2. Which word is spelled from the root word *converse*, to talk? _____
   Add the "ation" suffix to *invite*. _____

3. Which word has the small word *under* in it? _____
   What word do you get if you take off the prefix? _____
   What word do you get if you add "mis" to *taken*? _____

4. Which word has the small word *tin* in it? _____
   What is the root word? _____
   What word do you get when you add "al" to the root word?

   _____

5. What three-syllable word is formed from the root word *differ*?

   _____

   What word do you get when you add the suffix "ent" to *depend*?

   _____

Eight more words...

prehistoric Take the root word *history*, add "-ic" to make it an adjective, then put a "pre-" before it to take us further back in time. The result: *prehistoric*. The spelling works the same with *prefix*, *preview* and *predict*.

employee The suffix "-ee" means "a person who." In this case, it's the person who is employed. *Nominee* and *referee* follow this pattern.

international The suffix "inter-" means "between." Add that to the root word *nation* and you have the basis for everything that goes on between countries. The same idea works for *intersection* and *intervention*.

semifinal Semi- means "half," so the *semifinal* takes you halfway to victory. A *semicolon* (;) is halfway to a colon (:). And many other words such as *semiannual* and *semisweet* follow the pattern.

competition Speaking of sports, you always *compete* in a *competition*. The suffix "tion" turns the verb into a noun.

underweight *Under* means "below," both as a prefix and as a word. This also shows you who to spell *underground*, *undertow* and *underprivileged*.

performance The root word here is from the Latin *forma*, to do. Add the prefix "per-" to make it an action for other people and the suffix "-ance" to turn it into a noun.

forecast A *forecast* is a prediction. We spell it with the prefix "fore-," meaning "before" and the root word *cast*, for seeing. The words *foresight*, *foreshadow* and *forewarn* follow the same pattern.

I forecast showers.

But I took one this morning.

Use the words from page 86 to complete the sentences and answer
the questions below.

1. The manager gave the _____ a raise.

2. People who don't eat enough may be sickly and_____ .

3. The weather _____ predicted a storm.

4. Woolly mammoths and sabre-toothed tigers roamed the earth in
_____ times.

5. If our team wins the _____ game, we'll go on to the finals.

6. The dancers gave a wonderful_____ of *Sleeping Beauty*.

7. Sandra Schmirler won a medal at the _____ curling

_____ .

8. Which word has the root word *weigh*? _____
What word do you get when you change this word to mean the opposite?

_____

What word do you get when you add the prefix "under" to *stand*?

_____

9. What word has five syllables? _____
What word do you get when you add the suffix "ity" to *national*? _____
What word do you get when you add the prefix "inter" to *dependent*?

_____

10. Which two words have prefixes that mean "before"?

_____ _____
What word is formed by adding the prefix "over" to the root word *cast*?

_____

Puzzle Pizzazz

This puzzle uses the **24** key words on the previous pages. See how you do.

1. A writer of music

2. Not the same

3. Has worth

4. A struggle

5. Costly

6. A worker

7. Freedom

8. A player of music

9. Desperate

10. Found.

11. (down) Untruthful

12. (across) Halfway to final

13. Before history

14. Involves many countries

15. Use it to go from A to B

16. Talking

17. What actors do for a living

18. Not ending

19. Got the wrong impression

20. Reckless

21. Looks better

22. Very light

23. A prediction

24. Against the law

Pattern review puzzle

Change-a-Letter

Use the clues to help you fill in the blanks. The only letter that will change between one word and the next is the letter that is circled.

1. An ice cream accessory   c   o   n   e

2. A walking aid

3. Where you go bowling

4. Took too long

5. A dried plum

6. Risk

7. A lack of light

8. The dog's noise

9. Where one can play

10. A piece

11. You can push it

12. To be concerned

13. Detective's work

14. Put some flowers in it

15. Very wide

16. For healing broken bones

17. Speedy

18. A clenched hand

19. Words in a column

20. This word

The Final Quiz

This final quiz checks everything you've learned from this book in five short pages. Each correct answer is worth 2 points for a total of 100 points for the whole test. Good luck!

1. You know the word more. Now spell:

— — — — — — — — a fortuneteller's job

— — — — — — — — — a place to buy novels

— — — — — — — — where the ocean meets the land

2. You know the word fast. Now spell:

— — — — — — — someone skilled at acrobatics

— — — — — — — — when the weather looks bad

— — — — — — — — a control on your television

Find the "man" syllable in each answer.

3. An insect. _____

4. A tropical fruit. _____

5. The shelf above a fireplace. _____

6. A trough for feeding cattle. _____

7. A province in Canada. _____

8. To make by hand or machine. _____

Fill in the blanks to create compound words on each side.

Ah, the great outdoors!

9. flash _____ house

10. look _____ doors

11. Add "un," "im," "in" or "dis" to make each of these root words mean the opposite.

___possible

___competent

___connect

___happy

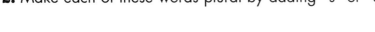

12. Make each of these words plural by adding "s" or "es."

fox _____

glass _____

rock _____

crunch _____

bus _____

forget _____

13. Fill in the blanks with the international words you've learned.

    (a) While travelling in the Australian outback, I spotted many _____ and at least one _____ .

    (b) My _____ training in China was interrupted by an enormous _____!

    (c) The teacher tried to explain the _____ dance, but it was all just _____ to me.

    (d) I was bitten by too many _____ in the _____ .

    (e) I found a _____ restaurant in Italy last summer. Alas, my meal was interrupted by a _____ .

14. Read each clue and fill in the word in the blank next to it. The trick is to answer each clue using a word that starts with the last two letters of the word before it.

You do it while sleeping.	snore
Someone who is dependable is …	re_____
You put this in a mailbox.	_____
A mistake on a test.	_____
A kind of fruit.	_____

15. Choose the right word from each pair:

(a) We ate a (whole, hole) pizza for lunch.

(b) He (new, knew) all the answers on the test.

(c) You're going to eat that broccoli (whether, weather) you like it or not!

(d) (Whose, Who's) responsible for this mess?

(e) This quiz may be harder than it (seams, seems).

16. There are 10 errors in this passage. Find and correct them. You get two points for finding the error and two points for correcting it properly.

Freddie and Hiro were battling furiusly. Not in real life of course, but playing a game on Freddie's brand new Vega Steamblast videogame. The two were playing a game of hockey.

Hiro gloated. "Well, Freddie, it looks like I'm wining!"

Freddie grimased as one of his players was body-checked hard into the boards.

Of course, Suzy and Francine appeared as the game was just finishing. Hiro had stomped Freddie with a score of 5 to 0. Freddie looked very fustrated, and Hiro looked very smug.

Suzy wispered for a second into Freddie's ear. He smiled widely and handed over his controler to her. Hiro gladly acsepted the challenge.

Unfortunately for Hiro, Suzy had owned this game for quite some time. His smugness qwickly turned to panik as Suzy mopped the floor with him.

"Sorry, Hiro," she said when their game was finally over. "I guess that's just what you get for being too confidant!"

Hiro sighed, and the friends laughed together.

How'd you do? (Check the correct answers on page 50)

____ / 100

Strategy Puzzle

Across

1. A _____ is two words that sound the same, like rowed and road.
4. Even good writers make _____ in spelling, but you should get better each time you write.
9. The words pizza and volcano come to us from the _____ language.
11. One way to handle a long word is to _____ it up.
12. In spelling, you always start by using the words you already _____ .
15. A good way to test a spelling is to _____ it out by writing it down.
16. Some words must be _____ carefully before you can spell them.
17. Some tough words you just have to _____ .
18. Many words have come to us from Ancient _____ .
19. If you're really having trouble spelling a word, use a _____ .

Down

2. You can make a word _____ by using "s" or "es" … or sometimes nothing at all.
3. Some words have _____ letters like "w", "l" or "g."
5. A _____ comes after a root word.
6. Many words in our language come from _____ roots.
7. Breaking a word into _____ will sometimes help you spell it.
8. A hinkie _____ is a pair of rhyming words, like "mad dad."
10. Remember, never use an _____ to make a word plural.
13. Words that have two or more parts stuck together are called _____ words.
14. There are many spelling _____ . Some of them work most of the time.
16. A _____ comes before a root word.

My Words

Everybody has trouble with some special words.

I can never spell "ukulele" right. I always miss the second "u."

And I mess up "refrigerator" every time because "fridge" has a "d" in it!

The trick is to make a list of words that are difficult for you. Then figure out what part of the word gives you trouble. Then make up your own personal spelling dictionary.

This list is mine.

Word	Tough Part	My Memory Trick
difficult	double f	Think dif-ficult.
let's	apostrophe	Think let us.
chocolate	second o	I'm late for choco!
harbour	our	It's our harbour!
muscle	silent c	Say, "mus-kle,"
swimming	mm	Mmm...I like swimming.

Use the last page of this workbook for your own word list.

My Spelling Dictionary

Now make up a spelling dictionary of your own. Put in any words that you have trouble with. Add words that you find in places like books, school magazines or wherever a tough word is to be found.

Word	Tough Part	Memory Trick
Dictionary	-ary	Not stationery, dictionary!

Math Booster
Grades 5 & 6

This workbook belongs to: _____

Table of Contents

Walk Through Memory Lane

Stroll down Memory Lane, and let's see if you remember your math stuff!

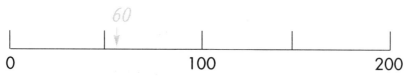

1. Place these numbers on the number line.

(a) 60   **(b)** 170   **(c)** 19   **(d)** 125

60

```
|----+----|----+----|----+----|----+----|
0             100            200
```

2. Place these numbers on the number line.

(a) 400   **(b)** 753   **(c)** 200   **(d)** 995

```
|----+----+----+----+----|----+----+----+----+----|
0                                            1000
```

Don't forget your place value columns!

Ones · Decimal · Tenths · Hundredths · Thousandths
1 · 3 · 5 · 7

3. Count by tenths.

  (a) 1.3, 1.4, _1.5_, _____, _____, _____

  (b) 0.6, 0.7, _____, _____, _____, _____

  (c) 14.8, 14.9, _____, _____, _____, _____

4. Count by hundredths.

  (a) 0.31, 0.32, _0.33_, _____, _____, _____

  (b) 1.19, _____, _____, _____, _____

  (c) 3.96, _____, _____, _____, _____

5. Count by thousandths.

  (a) 0.752, _0.753_, _____, _____, _____, _____

  (b) 5.998, _____, _____, _____, _____, _____

  (c) 0.044, _____, _____, _____, _____, _____

6. Multiplying madness

(a) $8 \times 9 =$ ___72___   (b) $6 \times 7 =$ _____   (c) $11 \times 11 =$ _____

(d) $5 \times 12 =$ _____   (e) $7 \times 9 =$ _____   (f) $12 \times 8 =$ _____

7. Dizzy from dividing

(a) $132 \div 11 =$ __12__   (b) $56 \div 7 =$ _____   (c) $64 \div 8 =$ _____

(d) $81 \div 9 =$ _____   (e) $96 \div 12 =$ _____   (f) $48 \div 8 =$ _____

8. What fractions are shown on each grid?

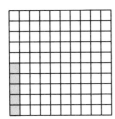 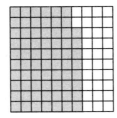 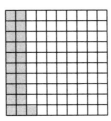 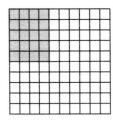

(a) $\dfrac{5}{100}$ (b) _____   (c) _____   (d) _____

9. Write each of the following amounts as a fraction and then as a percentage.

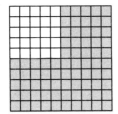 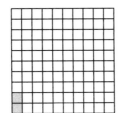 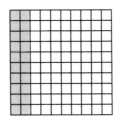 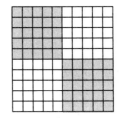

(a) $\dfrac{75}{100}$ (b) _____   (c) _____   (d) _____

   75% _____   _____   _____

If $\dfrac{1}{3}$ is a third …

How come $\dfrac{1}{2}$ isn't a tooth?

10. Complete these questions and notice the patterns.

    (a) 0.782 × 1000 = _____

         0.782 × 100 = _____

         0.782 × 10 = _____

    (b) 623 × 1000 = _____

         623 × 100 = _____

         623 × 10 = _____

    (c) 0.045 × 1000 = _____

         0.045 × 100 = _____

         0.045 × 10 = _____

    (d) 3.8 × 1000 = _____

         3.8 × 100 = _____

         3.8 × 10 = _____

11. Fill in the boxes by continuing the pattern.

    (a)

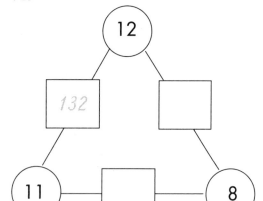

    (b)

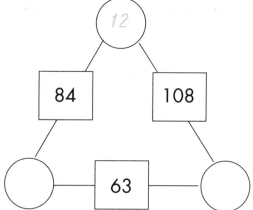

12. Write an improper fraction and a mixed number to describe the shaded parts.

    (a)   **(b)**   **(c)**

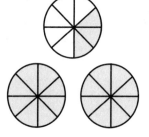 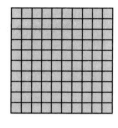 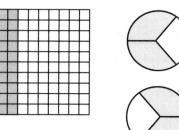

$$\frac{19}{8} = 2\frac{3}{8}$$

_____ = _____   _____ = _____   _____ = _____

13. Find the perimeter and area of the following shapes.

(a)   **(b)**

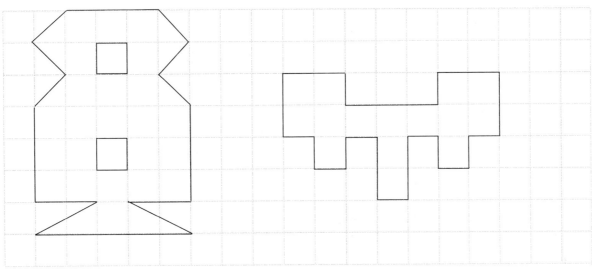

(a) perimeter _____   area _____

(b) perimeter_____   area _____

14. Estimate the length of the following lines in centimetres.

(a)    **(b)**

The end of your finger is often very close to a centimetre. Use it for estimations.

(c)   **(d)**

15. Make a line graph using the following data.

Movie Rentals in Each Month of the Year	
January	14
February	16
March	12
April	10
May	6
June	5
July	12
August	8
September	2
October	8
November	10
December	11

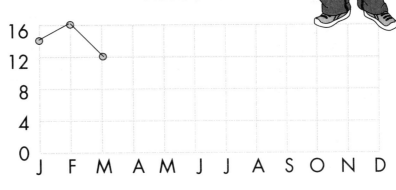

Movie Rentals

Words of Wisdom

Clues are always helpful for solving mysteries. In all math word problems there are lots of clue words to help you out. Be sure to use them.

When you do a problem, you must choose an operation like adding, subtraction, dividing or multiplying to get the solution. There are many different operation words for you to use and understand in your problems. Look for them in the word find below and place in them under the appropriate operation.

Clue Words for **Addition**

amount to

_____

_____

_____

_____

_____

Clue Words for **Division**

_____

_____

_____

_____

_____

Clue Words to **Subtraction**

_____

_____

_____

_____

_____

Clue Words for **Multiplication**

_____

_____

_____

_____

Here are the words:			
altogether	amount to	both	by
difference	divide	fewer	fraction
groups of	left	less than	multiply
part	plus	product	separated
split	subtract	sum	cut
take away	times	add	total

```
h  a  p  g  r  o  u  p  s  o  f  y  l  p  i  t  l  u  m
b  e  a  m  o  u  n  t  t  o  q  b  w  d  n  r  u  k  o
t  n  d  s  r  v  a  e  d  i  v  i  d  m  a  e  v  c  t
f  y  d  f  p  k  p  l  u  s  x  d  e  r  h  h  p  n  c
e  j  e  h  e  l  s  a  j  u  k  a  n  t  t  t  a  o  u
l  n  g  a  k  w  i  r  s  m  t  e  i  n  s  e  j  i  d
o  d  w  h  i  g  e  t  c  a  r  t  b  u  s  g  n  t  o
i  a  t  c  o  l  i  r  d  a  f  i  m  g  e  o  y  c  r
y  o  s  a  s  m  k  i  a  l  a  t  o  t  l  t  r  a  p
b  e  c  n  e  r  e  f  f  i  d  p  c  a  u  l  r  r  d
f  o  r  s  d  a  s  e  p  a  r  a  t  e  d  a  v  f  e
```

Here are some problems. Simply write what operation you would need to solve the problem and add it to the crossword. Then calculate the answers.

1. Jehan has 7 juggling balls. Rahul has 4 fewer juggling balls than Jehan. How many does Rahul have?

subtraction $7 - 4 = 3$

2. Six tee-ball clubs each had 43 members. How many members did they have in total? _____   _____

3. While shopping on the weekend, a family spent $34 at the pharmacy, $120 at the grocery store, and $45 at Chapters. What was the total cost of the shopping trip?

_____   _____

4. A bookstore sold 1200 copies of a math workbook in three months. If the amount was split evenly each month, how many copies did they sell in 1 month?

_____   _____

5. Marla's classroom is 10 m long by 14 m wide. What is the area of her classroom?

_____   _____

6. A CD store sold 521 CDs in November and 890 in December. How many did the store sell in the 2 months combined?

_____   _____

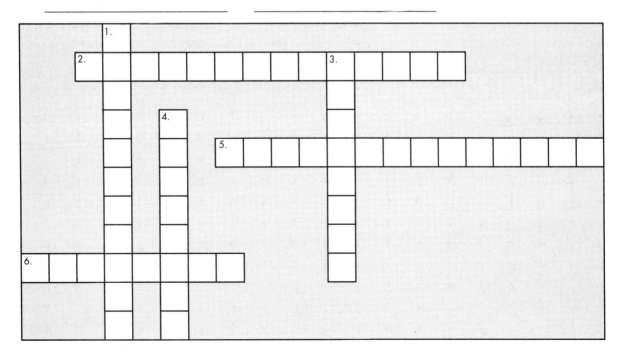

Sign Here, Please!

Join the signs with their meanings.

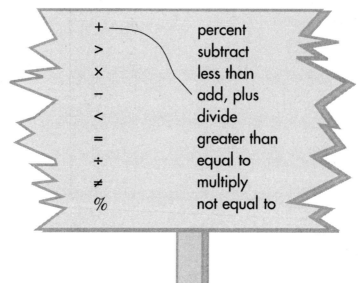

+	percent
>	subtract
×	less than
–	add, plus
<	divide
=	greater than
÷	equal to
≠	multiply
%	not equal to

1. Put the appropriate signs in the boxes.

(a) 5 + 4 [≠] 10   (b) 0.95 [ ] 0.5

(c) 9 [ ] 8 [ ] 72   (d) 25 [ ] 5 [ ] 1 = 4

(e) 72/100 = 72 [ ]

2. Complete the following questions using each integer in the cloud only once.

(a) ___–8___   <   – 6

(b) 9   >   _____   >   – 2

(c) – 6   <   _____   <   – 4

(d) 0   <   _____   >   2

(e) – 7   <   _____   >   – 3

(f) 3   >   _____   >   – 1

(g) 2   >   _____   <   – 1

–5   7   3
–4   2   0
–8

3. Answer the following questions using the math clue words to help.

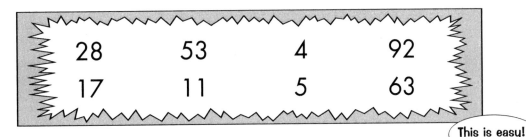

| 28 | 53 | 4 | 92 |
| 17 | 11 | 5 | 63 |

This is easy!

From the box above, pick a pair of numbers ...

(a) ... with a sum of less than 18. _____ _____

(b) ... with a difference of 64. _____ _____

(c) ... with a total of more than 150. _____ _____

(d) ... with a product of more than 250. _____ _____

4. Answer the following questions using the math symbols to help.

Numbers	Signs	Words

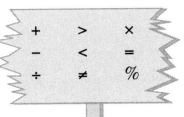

Numbers:
100   0.75
0   7   2
0.25   − 21
$\frac{5}{10}$ $\frac{1}{4}$

Signs:
+   >   ×
−   <   =
÷   ≠   %

Words:
percent   sum
difference   compare
factor   decimal
product   fraction

Choose two numbers and one sign to form a math sentence. Then choose at least one corresponding word.

(a) $\frac{5}{10}$ < 2   *compare*

(b) _____

(c) _____

(d) _____

(e) _____

(f) _____

Common Knowledge

Among the many words that we need to know for math, these ones should be common knowledge.

Factor	**Multiple**	**Prime**	**Composite**
• any of the numbers that are multiplied to form a product	• a number that has been multiplied	• a number that can not be divided by anything other than 1 and itself	• a number that can be divided by a number other than 1 and itself

2 and 6 are factors of 12. 3 and 4 are factors of 12.

Some multiples of 3 are 6, 9,12 and 15.

3,5, and 11 are prime numbers because they can only be divided by 1 and themselves.

24 is a composite number because it can be divided by 3, 4, 6, 8, or 12.

1. List all of the factors for these numbers.

(a) 8 _1,_   _2,_   _4,_   _8_

(b) 15 ____ ____ ____ ____

(c) 24 ____ ____ ____ ____ ____ ____ ____ ____

2. List all the factors for each number.
Then circle the greatest common factor.

(a) 4 _1, 2, 4_ _____

    6 _1, 2, 3, 6_ _____

(b) 9 _____

   30 _____

(c) 16 _____

   20 _____

Greatest common factor means the largest of the common factors.

3. Write two different numbers with a common factor of...

(a) ... 4 _16_   _12_

(b) ... 6 _____   _____

(c) ... 9 _____   _____

(d) ... 15 _____   _____

3. List the next four multiples of the following numbers.

(a) 4   _8_   _12_   _16_   _20_

Just multiply to get these multiples.

(b) 7   _____ _____ _____ _____

(c) 9   _____ _____ _____ _____

(d) 11 _____ _____ _____ _____

(e) 12 _____ _____ _____ _____

(f) 13 _____ _____ _____ _____

4. Circle the composite numbers.

8	5	12	22	11
3	17	24	16	7
33	9	13	42	39

5. Continue this list of prime numbers.

1   2   3   5   _____ _____

_____ _____ _____ _____ _____

6. Give examples of the following.

(a) odd composite numbers   _____ _____

(b) even prime number   _____

(c) prime numbers between 32 and 42   _____ _____

(d) largest prime number less than 100   _____ _____

(e) largest prime number between 50 and 75   _____ _____

Who Am I?

Using the clues, calculate the answer for each of the following puzzles.

1. I am a prime number.
I have 2 digits.
My 2 digits add up to 10.
I am a number between 30 and 40.
What number am I?

37

Is a prime number like a prime minister?

2. I am a composite number.
I am divisible by 2.
My second greatest factor is 7.
I have a multiple of 126.
What number am I?

3. I am a prime number.
My 2 digits add up to 4.
I am a factor of 39.
What number am I?

4. I am a composite number.
I am divisible by 5.
I am a factor of 150.
I am number between 15 and 29.
What number am I?

Sure. They both think they're important.

5. I am a prime number.
I am a factor of 45.
I have only 2 multiples between 22 and 28.
I have only 1 digit.
What number am I?

**TO SEE WHETHER YOUR NUMBERS ARE CORRECT,
CHECK TO SEE WHETHER ALL FIVE ANSWERS HAVE A SUM OF 92!**

1. What symbol and number is missing from the following patterns?

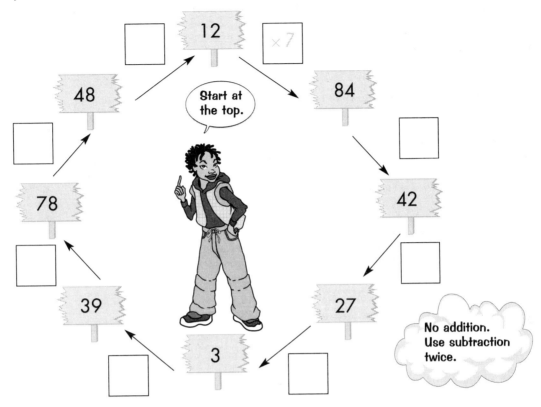

Start at the top.

12   × 7

84

48

42

78

27   No addition. Use subtraction twice.

39

3

 2. You may use a calculator if you need to.

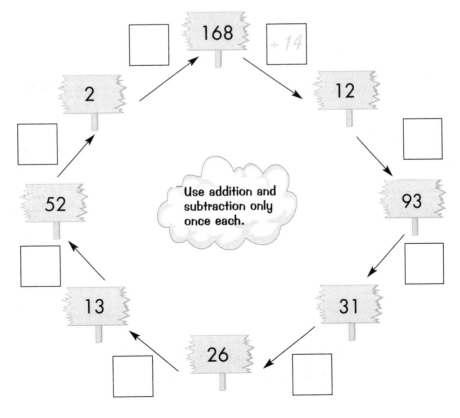

168   ÷ 14

2

12

52   Use addition and subtraction only once each.

93

13

31

26

Strategize While You Exercise!

Problem solving is much easier when you have a bag of tools to use when fixing the problems. Here are some of the tools that you need to use to become a better problem solver. We'll practise each of them on the pages to follow.

Read and reread

Some problems aren't always clear when you read them for the first time. It is important to read and reread the problem until you understand it.

Work backwards

Problems can often require you to work through them in various orders. Working through them backwards can sometimes be the best method.

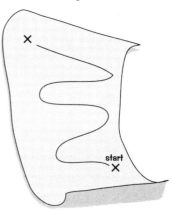

Eliminate information you don't need, then circle the information that is important

Many problems have too much information that isn't useful to you. Stroke out the information that you don't need. This way you have less information to confuse you. Then underline or circle the information that is important.

~~STACY~~ drives
(10 kilometres)
~~every day to go to~~
~~work at her new~~
~~marketing job.~~

Eliminate the possibilities

If you are working through a problem that offers a variety of answers, eliminate the answers that are impossible. Then start working through the others.

I am a multiple of 5.
I have 2 digits and add up to 8.

(a) ~~13~~
(b) 35
(c) ~~25~~
(d) ~~8~~

Draw a picture or use manipulatives

Pictures don't just make something more interesting to look at, they let you look at problems in a different way. Another way to visualize problems is to use manipulatives or objects, like counters and solids.

Make a chart, graph or list

Many problems need a plan before they can be solved. Charts, graphs, and lists help you to organize the information before looking at the solutions.

Estimate

An estimate is made by using your knowledge to make a good guess that will be close to the answer. When you do math, your estimate will tell you whether your answer is close or even possible.

$$28 \times 3 = ?$$

Guess and Check

Sometimes it's OK just to guess and see whether it works. This strategy is always helpful when you don't know where to start. Just try an answer and then see whether it is the right answer. Don't forget that you must always check to see whether your solution actually works.

Look for the patterns

Sometimes solving a problem requires you to find the pattern. Look carefully for the patterns!

In the farm yard, Zachary saw 8 heads and 22 feet. How many pigs & chickens are there?

3 pigs and 5 chickens.

laces	no laces
5	10

laces
‖‖‖

no laces
‖‖‖ ‖‖‖

28 is close to 30, and 30 x 3 is 90, so 28 x 3 must be close to 90!

?

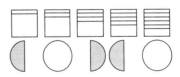

Over and Over Again!

Read & Reread

For each of the following problems, use your reread strategy to help you out. Problems are sometimes not what they appear to be at first. Others may simply be complex and confusing. It is helpful simply to reread if you do not understand the first time. It might even take **2** or **3** extra readings to get your head around the problem. It's OK if you need to do this. It's a great strategy to use.

(a) Betty has three sisters and two brothers. How many siblings are there altogether in the family?

Answer: **6**

The question did not ask how many siblings does Betty have, so the answer cannot be 5. Be careful to read not only the numbers but also the question. It asks how many siblings are there *altogether* so we must include Betty in the answer.

(b) Archie, Joey, and Jake left the movie theatre after seeing *Jaws V*. It was dark when they left, and each was wearing the jacket and the shoes of someone else! Archie was wearing Joey's jacket and Jake's shoes. Whose jacket and whose shoes was each one wearing?

_____

_____

(c) Mina and Marcela love playing games. They play a game of checkers every Tuesday afternoon. For the last four weeks, both Mina and Nina have won all of their checker games. How many games have they won each?

_____

(d) A glug is more than an bleep.
A glug is not the greatest of the whole group.
A sshh is not the least.
Only one thing is less than the bloop.
A yikes is more than a sshh.
More than one thing is greater than the sshh.
Put the glug, bleep, sshh, bloop, and yikes in order from largest to smallest.

Yikes! This is tricky.

_____

_____

Backwards Billy!

Work Backwards

Working backwards is what some kids do best. You may find it to be a very useful tool when solving math problems. Take a look. (You might also have to start practising your elimination skills if there is too much information!)

1. Sasha and Dave live in Ottawa and went shopping to buy a house last month. The first house they saw was very nice but was a little small. Although it was $50 000 less than their favourite, they decided they needed a bigger place. The second house they saw was certainly large enough, but was too far away from any schools for their children. It was also $20 000 more than their favourite. The next house that they saw was in Toronto and though they loved the idea of moving to Toronto, this house was $400 000! Way too much! Finally, they found their dream home. It had a basement with a pool table, a big yard for parties, and much more. And it was a whopping $180 000 less than the Toronto home. It was definitely their favourite.

Place the homes in order from least expensive to most expensive.

Too Small	Favourite Home	Far away from Schools	Toronto Home
$170 000	$220 000	$240 000	$400 000

Start here since we know the price of this home. Then work backwards through the problem.

2. When they moved into their home they worked on the music room first. They bought a new piano for the room, and also a table for $100, paint for $50, and a music stand for $40. Altogether they spent $1 390. How much was the piano?

Start at the end with the total and work backwards subtracting the other amounts. You should be able to work this one out in your head. Give it a try!

3. Getting to Sasha and Dave's house from the bus station is quite complicated because of one-way streets. Use the clues by working backwards with the information. Then draw the path.

   - If you see the church you've gone too far.
   - The last thing you should pass is the corner store.
   - Before the corner store, you will go by a school and a gas station.
   - The first thing you'll see outside the station is a grocery store. Do not go the direction of the mall.

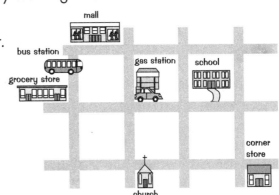

The Eliminator!

Eliminate Information

Eliminating what you don't need is a very useful skill. Then you will only see what is important. These problems have way too much information! Stroke out the information you don't need before solving.

1. ~~Leslie and Rob go grocery shopping every Sunday afternoon. They keep a list throughout the week so that they will know what they need when they arrive at the store. The closest market, which is on Dupont Avenue,~~ takes 12 minutes to walk to. ~~They usually~~ take about 50 minutes to do the shopping. How many minutes does it take Leslie and Rob from the time they leave their home, to the time they arrive back again?

   $$12 + 50 + 12 = 74 \text{ minutes}$$

2. When making their list, Leslie and Rob make 5 different categories – fruits and vegetables, meats, breads and cereals, drinks and snacks, and other household items. They do this to make it easier when they are going down each aisle in their market that since it is categorized in the same manner. They spend about 25% on fruits and vegetables, 25% on meats, 10% on breads and cereals, 10% on drinks and snacks, and 30% on other household items. At the end of each trip, they like to calculate how much money they spent on each category. This week they spent a total of $300 because they are planning a big party at the end of the week. How much did they spend on each category?

3. The party that Leslie and Rob are preparing for is for Leslie's birthday on July 29. She is turning 30, and they want to celebrate it with a lot of other people. They sat down one evening to decide on their guest list and the following week invited 30 guests. They always include games and prizes as a part of the day. For one of the party games, everyone will be divided into 8 teams. How many people will be on each team?

4. Leslie receives a lot of presents at her birthday party. Her favourite gift is the new stereo from her parents. After the party, she made piles of her cards and presents so that she could start writing thank you cards to her friends. She had a total of 15 cards to write for her 20 presents. She was able to find a packet of 15 cards at the book store for only $10.00. How many presents were given by 2 people?

Eliminate the possibilities as you proceed through each clue in these puzzles.

5. I am a number between 10 and 20.
I am divisible by 4.
My digits add up to 7.

    (a) 13
    (b) 21
    (c) 16
    (d) 12
    (e) 18

6. I am a multiple of 6.
I have 2 digits whose sum is 3.
I am a number between 20 and 35.

    (a) 14
    (b) 21
    (c) 3
    (d) 24
    (e) 30

7. Ken, Laurie, Sarah, and Peter are seated at a table. Their jobs are drummer, artist, teacher, and actor. Use the following clues to decide which seating arrangement below is the correct one. Eliminate an answer that you know is incorrect, and then work with the answers left over.

    (a) The actor sat on Sarah's left.
    (b) The artist sat across from Peter.
    (c) Ken and Peter sat next to each other.
    (d) A woman sat on the teacher's right.

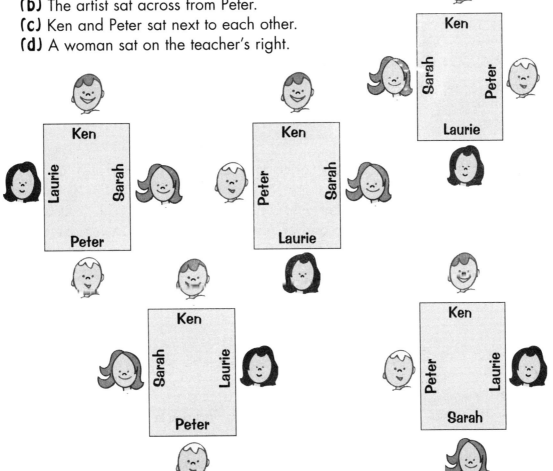

Buildarama!

Now you have the opportunity to be an artist! Draw away to solve these problems. Try not to use many other strategies so that you get practise with your art work!

You have been contracted for a number of very different building jobs.
Your first is to build bridges.

A bridge 1 storey high takes 6 rods.

A bridge 2 storeys high takes 8 rods.

What if I can't draw?

How many rods will you need to build a bridge of...

.... 3 storeys _____

.... 4 storeys _____

.... 8 storeys _____

.... 10 storeys _____

Then use your imagination!

Another style of bridge is needed to cross larger rivers and valleys.

A bridge 1 storey high takes 10 rods.

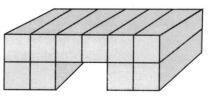

A bridge 2 storeys high takes 14 rods.

How many rods will you need to build...

... one bridge 3 storeys high and two bridges 4 storeys high? _____

... two bridges 5 storeys high and three bridges 10 storeys high? _____

I've Lost My Legs!

You are now a carpenter building tables and stools.
Your shop makes 3-legged round stools and 4-legged square tables.

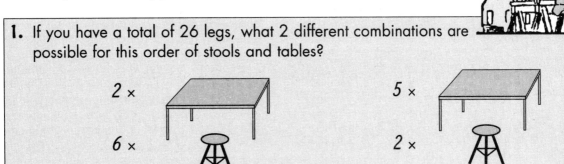

1. If you have a total of 26 legs, what 2 different combinations are possible for this order of stools and tables?

2 ×   [table]   5 ×   [table]

6 ×   [stool]   2 ×   [stool]

2. For another order you need a total of 52 legs, as well as 15 tops for the tables and stools. How many of each will you be making?

3. Four customers have identical orders. They have each asked for 4 stools and 2 tables. How many legs and tops will you need for all four orders?

4. What are four different orders that can be made with 31 legs?

Line Up!

Draw a Picture

Number lines can almost be like a picture or drawing to help you out with problems. Take a look at this question.

Mrs. Riley has 13 students in her swimming class. They have 3 lanes to swim in at the pool. How many people will be in each lane?

Question: **13 ÷ 3**

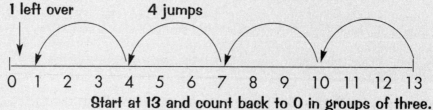

1 left over   4 jumps

0 1 2 3 4 5 6 7 8 9 10 11 12 13

Start at 13 and count back to 0 in groups of three.

Answer: **4 Remainder 1 (or 4 R1)**

0 1 2 3 4 5 6 7 8 9 10 11 12 13 14 15 16 17 18 19 20 21 22 23 24 25

As you can see, you can even do division with pictures.
Using the number line above, try these.

1. 14 ÷ 3 = _____   **2.** 16 ÷ 5 = _____

3. 15 ÷ 4 = _____   **4.** 13 ÷ 5 = _____

Complete the question and then write the remainder for each in the crossword below.

Across

1. 20 ÷ 7 = _____ R _____

2. 22 ÷ 4 = _____ R _____

4. 19 ÷10 = _____ R _____

5. 17 ÷ 6 = _____ R _____

6. 18 ÷ 5 = _____ R _____

Down

1. 23 ÷ 8 = _____ R _____

3. 19 ÷ 6 = _____ R _____

5. 16 ÷ 6 = _____ R _____

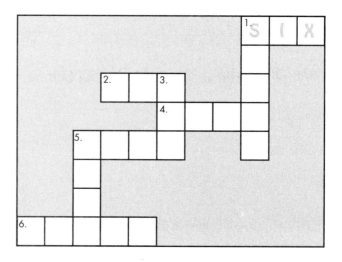

Don't Pick Your Teeth!

Use Manipulatives

Manipulatives like buttons, counters, and other objects are very handy to visualize a problem. Use toothpicks, straws, or drawings to help you out with these questions.

1. Use 7 toothpicks to make 3 triangles.

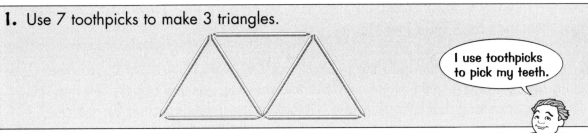

I use toothpicks to pick my teeth.

2. Use 11 toothpicks to make 5 triangles. Draw them below.

3. Use 12 toothpicks to make 6 triangles.

4. Use 9 toothpicks to make 5 triangles.

That's gross!

5. Use 30 toothpicks to make 26 triangles.

Walk Like an Egyptian!

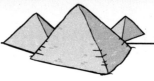

Make a Chart

Charts can be very helpful to see your information in an organized manner.

Here's an example. Miss Norman's class is working on an Egyptian theme this month. Help them plan their unit using charts.

1. The class first takes a trip to the public library to research Ancient Egypt. The librarian explains to the students about the fines for overdue books. The fine is $0.25 each day that a book is late. Complete the following chart for the class.

Number of Books Overdue

	1	2	3	4	5	6
Day 1	$0.25	$0.50	$0.75			
Day 2	$0.50	$1.00	$1.50			
Day 3	$0.75	$1.50				
Day 4						
Day 5						
Day 6						
Day 7						

Number of Days Overdue

2. For their trip to the Egyptian display at the museum, the class needs to plan their bus tickets to the museum. Fill in the chart to help them calculate the cost of their tickets.

Ticket Cost	$4.00					
# of Students	5	10				

If there are 30 students in the class, how much will it cost? _____

3. Miss Norman has suggested they celebrate the end of their theme with an Egyptian Day. The other classes will be visiting to see their work. The classes will be arriving every 40 minutes, except for the lunch period. Fill in this schedule for their Egyptian Day Celebration.

Time	9:00						12:20					Yeah!
Class	Rm 10	Rm 13	Rm 14	Rm 27	Rm 28	Lunch	Rm 22	Rm 23	Rm 24	Rm 21		End of Day

Unit 2 – Strategies in problem solving

Colourful Math

Make a List

Lists are helpful for organizing your information. Make lists to solve these problems.

1. Vivian has three tiles to make mosaics with – blue, yellow, and red. How many different patterns can she make with her three colours?

- _____blue_____   _____yellow_____   _____red_____
- _____blue_____   _____red_____   _____yellow_____
- _____   _____   _____
- _____   _____   _____
- _____   _____   _____
- _____   _____   _____

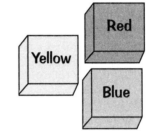

2. The tiles cost Vivian $7.50. If she had a $5.00 bill, 3 toonies, 4 loonies, 2 quarters, and 5 dimes, list some of the different ways that Vivian could have paid for her tiles.

- _$5, $2, $0.25, $0.25_____
- _____
- _____
- _____
- _____
- _____

3. Sometimes, Vivian works with her mosaics in an interesting way. Instead of using a pattern, she throws 5 darts at her dartboard to see what the colour order will be for each piece of art. List the different orders she may use through her chance method of art.

- _purple, yellow, blue, red, purple_____
- _____
- _____

Yellow	Blue
Red	Purple

What's Your Best Estimate?

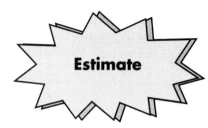

Estimate

Learning to make an estimate will make your life a lot easier. Here's why:
- You often need to make estimates in daily life.
- Sometimes you don't need an exact answer.
- Making an estimate before computing an exact answer allows you to see whether your answer is close.

Practise your estimations with the following questions.

1. Round one of the numbers to make your computations easier.

(a) 9 × 48   = ___*10 × 48*___ = ___*480*___

(b) 5 × 29   = _____ = _____

(c) 11 × 64   = _____ = _____

(d) 28 × 4   = _____ = _____

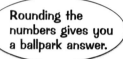

Rounding the numbers gives you a ballpark answer.

2. Round both numbers for the following questions.

(a) 59 × 9   = _____ = _____

(b) 12 × 29   = _____ = _____

(c) 98 × 49   = _____ = _____

(d) 31 × 48   = _____ = _____

3. Round these numbers to the nearest hundreds and tens to estimate the product.

(a) 412   is about   ___*400*___

    × 58   is about   _×   *60*_

                24 000

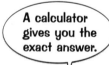

A calculator gives you the exact answer.

(b) 289   is about   _____

    × 31   is about   _____

                _____

(c) 892   is about   _____

    × 23   is about   _____

                _____

Phone Number Math

Using the columns and rows of the phone keypad below, answer the following questions. Use estimation first, then calculate to see whether your estimation is accurate.

- The order of numbers on the keypad may be up, down, forwards, or backwards!

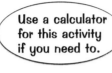

Use a calculator for this activity if you need to.

(a) _123_ + _258_ + _654_ = 1 0 3 5

(b) _____ + _____ + _____ = 2 0 1 0

(c) _____ + _____ + _____ = 7 7 4

(d) _____ + _____ + _____ = 1 2 3 3

(e) _____ + _____ + _____ = 1 7 6 4

(f) _____ + _____ + _____ = 8 3 7

(g) _____ + _____ + _____ = 1 3 6 8

(h) _____ + _____ + _____ = 1 5 6 6

What is the largest number you can make from the keypad?

(i) _____ + _____ + _____ = _____

What is the smallest number you can make from the keypad?

(j) _____ + _____ + _____ = _____

Create 2 more problems of your own and answer them.

(k) _____ + _____ + _____ = _____

(l) _____ + _____ + _____ = _____

Guess and Check

Guess and Check

If you ever find yourself in a tricky math situation, and you don't know where to start, just try something and check to see whether it is the right answer. If your first guess doesn't work, try again!

Which way will I go?

From the starting point, each person takes a path with different math instructions as they go. They all end up with very different totals!

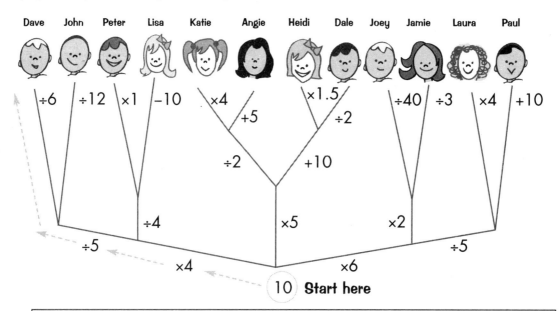

Dave John Peter Lisa Katie Angie Heidi Dale Joey Jamie Laura Paul

÷6 ÷12 ×1 −10 ×4 ×1.5 ÷40 ÷3 ×4 +10

+5 ÷2

÷2 +10

÷4 ×5 ×2

÷5

×4 ×6 ÷5

(10) **Start here**

Example:

Which path will give me the answer of 20?

Let's try Dave's path. $10 \times 12 = 120 \div 5 = 24 \div 6 = 4$
No, it's not Dave's path.
Let's try Peter's path. $10 \times 12 = 120 \div 4 = 30 \times 1 = 30$
No, it's not Peter's path.
Let's try Lisa's path. $10 \times 12 = 120 \div 4 = 30 - 10 = 20$
                               I am right! It's Lisa's!

Your turn.

Which path will give you ...

(a) ...the smallest answer? _____   **(b)** ...the answer of 7?   _____

(c) ...the largest answer? _____   **(d)** ...the answer of 15? _____

Fill in the shapes to make math sentences. The matching shapes in each question below must have the same numbers. Try a number and check to see whether it can make an accurate sentence. If not, just try again! Look at the example below:

1.

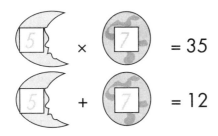

$5 \times 7 = 35$

$5 + 7 = 12$

2.

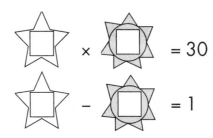

$\square \times \square = 30$

$\square - \square = 1$

3.

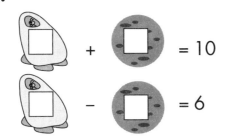

$\square + \square = 10$

$\square - \square = 6$

4.

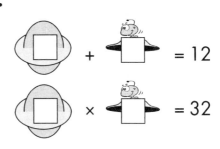

$\square + \square = 12$

$\square \times \square = 32$

5.

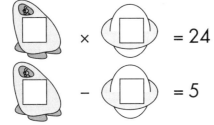

$\square \times \square = 24$

$\square - \square = 5$

6.

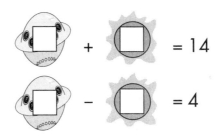

$\square + \square = 14$

$\square - \square = 4$

7.

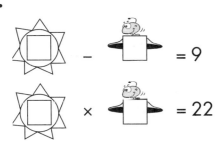

$\square - \square = 9$

$\square \times \square = 22$

8.

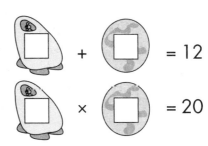

$\square + \square = 12$

$\square \times \square = 20$

9.

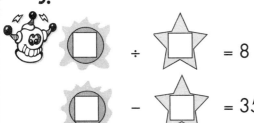

$\square \div \square = 8$

$\square - \square = 35$

10.

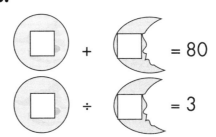

$\square + \square = 80$

$\square \div \square = 3$

Look Again!

Patterns

Patterns are everywhere, and they can be helpful friends for solving problems.

Look carefully at the numbers below. Then look again.
List all of the patterns that you see.

18	9	9	81
27	24	3	72
49	47	2	94
499	497	2	994

$81 = 9 \times 9$ $18 = 9 + 9$

_____

_____

_____

_____

_____

_____

_____

Continue these patterns.

1. 8, 16, 24, _____, _____, _____

2. a, d, g, _____, _____, _____

3. 120, 100, 80, _____, _____, _____

4. ab, ef, ij, _____, _____, _____

5. AC, ZX, DF, _____, _____, _____

6.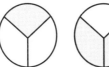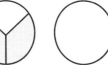

Patterns are everywhere!

7.

8. a, 2, c, 4, _____, _____, _____

9. 1, 2, 4, 7, _____, _____, _____

Now continue the pattern and write the rule.

10. 2, 4, 8, 16, *32*, *64*, *128*   *multiply by 2*

11. 1, 5, 3, 7, 5, _____, _____, _____   _____

12. 20, 10, 12, 6, 8, _____, _____, _____   _____

Is there a pattern to explain how you're treating me?

It's simple: I'm ignoring you.

Use Your Head!

Whenever you have a problem to solve, you need strategies to work through it. Now that you have the strategies, you need a plan.

Read this script showing how Hayley solves a problem in Ms. Walker's Grade 5 math class.

Miss Walker:	Hayley, what is the answer to 72 times 4?
Hayley:	I don't know. I'll need to get some paper.
Miss Walker:	Why not try to solve it in your head?
Hayley:	It's too difficult.
Miss Walker:	Then let's make it easier. What is 70 times 4?
Hayley:	280.
Miss Walker:	What is 2 times 4?
Hayley:	8.
Miss Walker:	Now just add them together for the answer.
Hayley:	Hey, that's easy. It's 288!

Hayley is smarter than she thinks.

As you can see, there are many steps to solving a problem. Try to remember it this way.

THINK

$72 \times 4 =$
How can I make this easier?

PLAN

$72 \times 4 =$
$(70 \times 4) + (2 \times 4)$

SOLVE

$280 + 8 =$
$= 288$

Take a look at the questions below.

1. 50 + 50 =   **2.** 19 + 3 =

3. 12 + 18 =   **4.** 25 + 37 =

5. 20 + 20 + 20 =   **6.** 28 + 54 =

7. 75 + 25 =   **8.** 56 + 27 =

Which of the questions above are easier to do in your head?

_____

_____

Why?

_____

_____

How can you plan the two questions below to make them easier to do in your head? Explain your plan in words.

(a) 79 + 24 = _____

I could add the 70 and 20 first (which is 90). Then I could add the 9 and 4 (which is 13). Then I would add them together. The answer is 103. OR I could change the 79 to 80 (which will be 1 extra, add on the 24 (to make 104), and then take away the 1 extra. The answer would be 103.

(b) 35 × 6 = _____

_____

_____

_____

_____

Planning Puppetry

Francine is building a puppet theatre for the Grade 6 class. The students are writing scripts that they will perform for their reading buddies.

100 centimetres

Curtains

Puppetry space

60 centimetres

3 cm

Table platform

120 centimetres

Think of the shape and the number of equal sides!

1. What is the shape of the puppetry space? _____

2. Explain everything you know about perimeter and about rectangles.

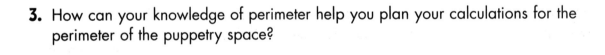

_____

_____

_____

3. How can your knowledge of perimeter help you plan your calculations for the perimeter of the puppetry space?

_____

_____

_____

4. What is the perimeter of that space?

_____

5. Francine takes a trip to buy more wood for the theatre. She has already completed the platform. Now she needs to buy wood for the 2 walls and the top of the theatre. The wood that she wants only comes in lengths of 100 centimetres and may not be cut to shorter lengths. How should Francine plan her purchase? Explain your reasoning.

_____

_____

_____

6. The wood costs $1.39 for every 100 centimetre length. Francine must then calculate 15% tax on top of the total wood cost. When calculating her purchase, why is it good to estimate?

_____

_____

_____

7. Have you ever seen someone in business do an estimate? What did they do and why did they do it?

_____

_____

_____

8. Francine buys 2 boxes of nails for her theatre project. Each costs $0.89. What 2 methods can you use to calculate the cost? Explain.

I estimate this job will take 20 hours.

_____

_____

_____

_____

_____

Francine's classes will be making their own hand puppets.
She plans what supplies she will need before going shopping.

# of Puppets	Material for Body	Buttons for Eyes	String for Hair	Paint
1	4dm²	2	15 pieces	10 mℓ
5	20 dm²	10		
10				
15				
20				

9. How does using a chart or diagram help to plan your problem solving?

_____

_____

_____

10. Explain how you would calculate the amounts for each column using the information already provided.

_____

_____

_____

11. What other strategies that you learned in Chapter 2 might be helpful to plan for the purchase of Francine's supplies?

_____

_____

_____

Fill in the chart at the top of the page.

12. Francine does not want to spend more than 10% of her $200 art budget for the school year. What does percent mean? Explain using words, pictures, and numbers.

_____

_____

_____

13. How would you calculate 10% of $200? Explain using words, pictures, and numbers.

_____

_____

_____

_____

My budget is pretty tight.

14. How can you change 10% into a decimal?

_____

_____

_____

15. Explain how decimals and percentages are related using Francine's budget as an example.

_____

_____

_____

Picture Perfect

Pictures are more than photos of favourite events, they help you out a lot with math. Pictures can be used as a strategy to solve a problem, but they can also be used to show your work. Instead of using words this time, simply write a number using the pictures.

Show your work with pictures!

Write an appropriate fraction for the following "pictures."

1. _1.57_

2. _____

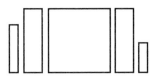

3. _____

4. _____

Instead of using numbers, now say "Cheese!" and draw the following fractions.

5.

6.

7.

8.

9.

10. 0.45

Greatest Ever

Which fraction is greater? Find the answers by colouring in these fractions.

1. $\frac{2}{3}$ or $\frac{3}{4}$

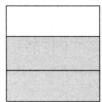 

$\frac{2}{3} < \frac{3}{4}$

2. $\frac{3}{8}$ or $\frac{1}{3}$

_____

3. $\frac{4}{5}$ or $\frac{5}{7}$

_____

4. Draw Suzy's grandmother's quilt by using the instructions below.

The quilt must be…

… $\frac{1}{8}$ dots in the top half

… $\frac{1}{4}$ smiley faces in the top half

… $\frac{1}{4}$ triangles anywhere

… $\frac{1}{8}$ stripes in the bottom half

… $\frac{1}{8}$ squares anywhere

… $\frac{1}{16}$ curvy lines on the left half

… $\frac{1}{16}$ rectangles on the right half

Silly Scooter

Many times we only need numbers to show our work. In this number problem, Scotty is saving his money to buy a scooter. Find out how he will get enough money to buy his scooter by writing the letter for your number answers in the appropriate spaces below.

Show your work with numbers!

(A) 7 × 8 = 56

(B) 121 ÷ 11 = ▢

(D) 58 + ▢ = 92

(E) 101 − 39 = ▢

(H)
```
    4  9
 +  6 ▢
 ───────
 1  1  6
```

(I)
```
   4  5  7
 − 3  9  8
 ─────────
   ▢     9
```

(N)
```
   1     3
 ×     ▢
 ───────
   5     2
```

(P)
```
   5  2
 + 3  9
 ──────
 ▢  ▢
```

(R)
```
 2  6  8
 − 1 ▢ 9
 ───────
    7  9
```

(S)
```
   1     1
 × ▢  ▢
 ─────────
   1  4  3
```

(T)
```
   1  2
 ×    9
 ──────
 ▢ ▢ 8
```

(Y)
```
   1  4
 ×    ▢
 ──────
   8  4
```

Scotty simply gets his scooter...

<u>A</u> ___ <u>A</u> ___ ___ ___ ___ ___ ___ <u>A</u> ___
56   13   56   11   5   8   10   7   34   56   6

___ ___ ___ ___ ___ ___ ___!
91   8   62   13   62   4   10

All in Order

When working with number problems, you must stay in order! In these math sentences there is a lot to do. You need to decide what to do first. Here are some things to remember.

ORDER TIP #1	Always do brackets first.	**(3 + 4) × 5** = 7 × 5 = 35
ORDER TIP #2	After brackets, do the multiplication and division in the order they occur.	**4 × (2 + 8)** = 4 × 10 = 40
ORDER TIP #3	Next do the addition and subtraction in the order they occur.	

 Complete the following questions.
Then write your answers in the crossword below.

Across

1. 9 + (10 ÷ 5) – 5

2. (24 + 11) ÷ 7 –3

3. (5 × 20) ÷ 10 + 1

4. (76 + 68) ÷ 12

5. 7 – (48 ÷ 8)

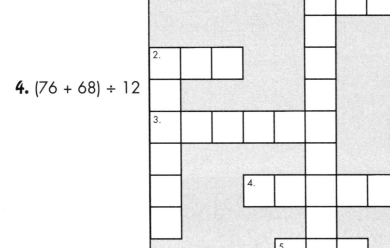

Down

1. 15 + (48 ÷ 12) – 2

2. 5 × (52 ÷ 13)

6. (32 + 12) ÷ 4 – 2

Ring-a-ling

Here is a magical ring. Write any number into the top circle and then follow the numeric instructions all of the way around the ring

Show your work with numbers and pictures!

That is amazing!

Try the ring again using a different number.

No, it's just cool math.

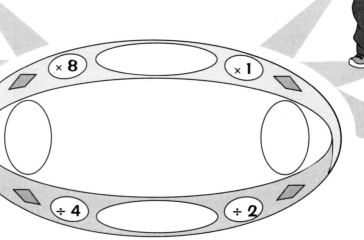

Wowzer Words!

No pictures, no numbers, just words. Here we go.

Show your work with words!

1. Using words instead of pictures or numbers, explain and describe your results from the number ring.

   _____

   _____

   _____

2. Do you think any number could work in the number ring? Why?

   _____

   _____

   _____

3. Tell whether it is possible to design another magical ring and explain how you would do it.

   _____

   _____

   _____

4. What must you do to see whether the ring is indeed magical?

   _____

5. What numbers would you use for your own magical ring?

   _____

Try it out.

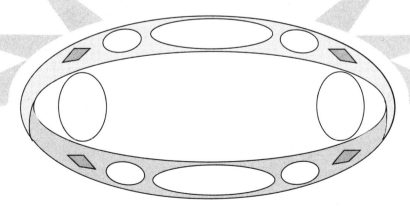

Phoning Frenzy!

Your friend Sam was away from school today and has called you about the day's school work. You had to describe the following diagram over the phone in order for him to draw it.

Write a list of directions for Sam to understand this pattern.

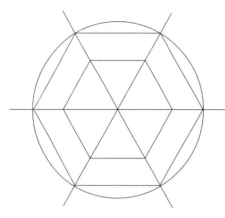

Draw a circle with a hexagon . . .

_____

_____

_____

_____

_____

Now try this one.

_____

_____

_____

_____

_____

Answer Key

Some of the pages in this workbook contain creative activities and spaces for open-ended responses. Only those that require a correct answer are included in this answer key.

Page 2

1.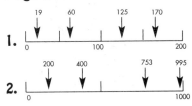

2.

3. (a) 1.5, 1.6, 1.7, 1.8
   (b) 0.8, 0.9, 1.0, 1.1
   (c) 15.0, 15.1, 15.2, 15.3
4. (a) 0.33, 0.34, 0.35, 0.36
   (b) 1.20, 1.21, 1.22, 1.23, 1.24
   (c) 3.97, 3.98, 3.99, 4.00, 4.01
5. (a) 0.753, 0.754, 0.755, 0.756, 0.757
   (b) 5.999, 6.000, 6.001, 6.002, 6.003
   (c) 0.045, 0.046, 0.047, 0.048, 0.049

Page 3

6. (a) 72   (b) 42   (c) 121
   (d) 60   (e) 63   (f) 96
7. (a) 12   (b) 8   (c) 8
   (d) 9   (e) 8   (f) 6

8. (a) $\frac{5}{100}$ (b) $\frac{68}{100}$

   (c) $\frac{21}{100}$ (d) $\frac{20}{100}$

9. (a) $\frac{75}{100}$, 75%   (b) $\frac{2}{100}$, 2%

   (c) $\frac{20}{100}$, 20%   (d) $\frac{50}{100}$, 50%

Page 4

10. (a) 782   (b) 623 000
        78.2   62 300
        7.82   6 230
    (c) 45   (d) 3 800
        4.5   380
        0.45   38

11. (a)   (b)
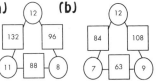

12. (a) $\frac{19}{8}$ = $2\frac{3}{8}$

(b) $\frac{130}{100}$ = $\frac{130}{100}$

(c) $\frac{4}{3}$ = $1\frac{1}{3}$

Page 5

13. (a) perimeter 26 cm, area 23 cm^2
    (b) perimeter 28 cm, area 15 cm^2
14. (a) 2.5 cm (b) 1 cm
    (c) 6 cm   (d) 4 cm
15.

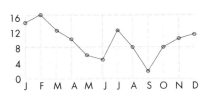

Page 6

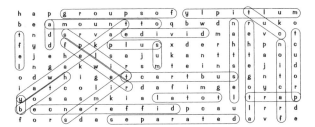

Page 7

1. subtraction   3
2. multiplication $258
3. addition $199
4. division   400
5. multiplication   140 m^2
6. addition   1411

Page 8-9

```
+                percent
>                subtract
×                less than
–                add, plus
<                divide
=                greater than
÷                equal to
≠                multiply
%                not equal to
```

1. (a) =   (b) >   (c) ×, =
   (d) ÷, –   (e) %
2. (a) – 8   (b) 7   (c) – 5
   (d) 3   (e) – 4   (f) 0
   (g) –2
3. (a) 4,5   (b) 92, 28   (c) 92, 63
   (d) many answers
4. Answers will vary.

Page 10
1. (a) 1, 2, 4, 8   (b) 1, 3, 5, 8
   (c) 1, 2, 3, 4, 6, 8, 24
2. (a) 4: 1, 2, 4,   6: 1, 2, 3, 6
   (b) 9: 1, 3, 9
         30: 1, 2, 3, 5, 6, 10, 15, 30
   (c) 16: 1, 2, 4, 8, 16
         20: 1, 2, 4 , 5, 10, 20
3. (a) 16, 12   (b) 12, 24   (c) 18, 90
   (d) 30, 45 (Answers may vary.)

Page 11
3. (a) 8, 12, 16, 20
   (b) 14, 21, 28, 35
   (c) 18, 27, 36, 45
   (d) 22, 33, 44, 55
   (e) 24, 36, 48, 60
   (f) 26, 39, 52, 65
4. 8, 12, 22, 24, 16, 33, 9, 42
5. 7, 11, 13, 17, 19, 23, 29, 31, 37
6. various answers

Page 12
2. 14   3. 13   4. 25
5. 3

Page 13

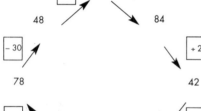

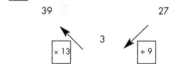

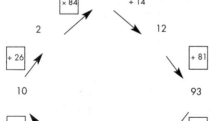

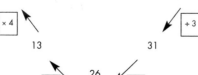

Page 16
(b) Jake has Joey's shoes, and Archie's jacket, and Joey has Jake's jacket and Archie's shoes
(c) Mina and Marcela did not play together, so they each won 4
(d) yikes, glug, sshh, bloop, bleep

Page 17
1. $170 000, $220 000, $240 000, $400 000
2. $1 200
3.

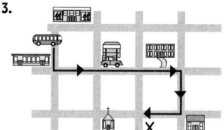

Page 18
2. $75 for fruits and vegetables, $75 for meats, $30 for breads and cereals, $30 for drinks and snacks, $90 for other
3. 30 + Leslie and Rob = 32 ÷ 8 = 4 members on each team
4. 10 presents from 2 people & 10 present from 1

Page 19
5. 16   6. 30

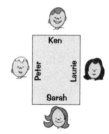

Page 20
... 3 storeys = 10 rods
... 4 storeys = 12 rods
... 8 storeys = 20 rods
... 10 storeys = 24 rods
    62 rods and 190 rods

Page 21
1. 2 tables & 6 stools, or 5 tables & 2 stools
2. 7 tables & 8 stools
3. 80 legs & 24 table tops
4. 4 tables & 5 stools, or 7 tables & 1 stools

Page 22
1. 4 R2   2. 3 R1
3. 3 R3   4. 2 R3

Page 22

(crossword)
- SIX
- SEVEN
- TWO
- NINE
- FIVE
- FOUR
- THREE

Page 23

2.

3.

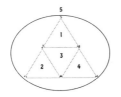

4.

5.

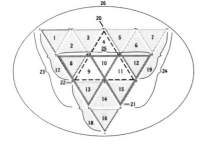

Page 24

Number of Books Overdue

	1	2	3	4	5	6
Day 1	$0.25	$0.50	$0.75	$1.00	$1.25	$1.50
Day 2	$0.50	$1.00	$1.50	$2.00	$2.50	$3.00
Day 3	$0.75	$1.50	$2.25	$3.00	$3.75	$4.50
Day 4	$1.00	$2.00	$3.00	$4.00	$5.00	$6.00
Day 5	$1.25	$2.50	$3.75	$5.00	$6.25	$7.50
Day 6	$1.50	$3.00	$4.50	$6.00	$7.50	$9.00
Day 7	$1.70	$3.25	$4.75	$6.25	$7.75	$9.25

Number of Days Overdue

2. $24.00

Ticket Cost	$4.00	$8.00	$12.00	$16.00	$20.00	$24.00
# of Students	5	10	15	20	25	30

3.

Time	9:00	9:40	10:20	11:00	11:40	12:20	1:00	1:40	2:20	3:00	3:40	Yeah!
Class	Rm 10	Rm 13	Rm 14	Rm 27	Rm 28	Lunch	Rm 22	Rm 23	Rm 24	Rm 21		End of Day

Page 25

1. - yellow, red, blue
- yellow, blue, red
- red, blue, yellow
- red, yellow, blue

2. & 3. Various answers

Page 26

1. (b) 150   **(c)** 640   **(d)** 120
2. (a) 600   **(b)** 300   **(c)** 5 000
   (d) 1 500
3. (b) 9 000   **(c)** 18 000

Page 27

(b) 369 + 654 + 987
(c) 147 + 258 + 369
(d) 123 + 654 + 456
(e) 321 + 654 + 456
(f) 123 + 456 + 258
(g) 258 + 654 + 456
(h) 789 + 123 + 654
(i) 963 + 987 + 852 = 2802
(j) 123 + 147 + 258 = 528

Page 28

(a) Jon   **(b)** Heidi
(c) Katie   **(d)** Peter, Angie, Dale

Page 29

2. 6, 5   **3.** 2, 8   **4.** 8, 4
5. 8, 3   **6.** 9, 5   **7.** 11, 2
8. 10, 2   **9.** 40, 5   **10.** 60, 20

Page 30

Answers will vary.

Page 31

1. 32, 40, 48   **2.** j, m, p
3. 60, 40, 20   **4.** mn, qr, uv
5. WU, GI, TR
6. ⊙ ⊙ ⊙   **7.** ⊕ ⊕
8. e, 6, g   **9.** 11, 16, 22
11. 9, 7   add 4, subtract 2
12. 4, 6   divide by 2, add 2

Page 33
Easier to answer:
1. 50 + 50, **3.** 12 + 18, **5.** 20 + 20 + 20,
7. 75 + 25 Because their sums have zeros in the ones column (i.e. 2 + 8 = 10 for 12 + 18 = 30), so they are easier to add
(b) I could multiply the 30 × 6 first (by taking away the 5), which is 180. Then I would do the 5 × 6 which is 30. Then I would add the 180 + 30 together to equal 210.

Page 34
1. rectangle
2. Perimeter = distance around a space, not the amount within the space.
Rectangle = 4-sided polygon with 4 90° angles. 2 sets of 2 equal sides
3. I could just multiply the length by 2 and the width by 2 and add them together.
4. 320 cm

Page 35
5. 3 full pieces
6. You can calculate an average which will take less time and can be done in your head.
7. Various answers.
8. 89 + 89 or 89 × 2

Page 36

# of Puppets	Material for Body	Buttons for Eyes	String for Hair	Paint
1	4dm²	2	15 pieces	10 ml
5	20 dm.	10	75 peices	50 ml
10	40 dm²	20	150 peices	100 ml
15	60 dm²	30	225 peices	150 ml
20	80 dm²	40	300 peices	200 ml

9. It helps you to visually organize your information. You don't have to sort through words as you would in a paragraph or in sentences.
10. Find the ratios (1 puppet to 4 dm² of material), then multiply for each column (5 × 4).
11. I could use pictures (like for the buttons), pictographs, bar graphs, etc.

Page 37
Word answers will vary. Full answers would include drawings or charts.
12. Percent means per 100. It represents a part of the 100.
13. I could multiply $200 by .10 or just divide $200 by 10 to get the answer. Answer: $20
14. I could change 10% into a decimal by

dropping the percent sign and putting a decimal point in front of the 10. Answer: .10
15. Decimals and percentages really show the same thing. Ten percent of Francine's art budget is the same as $\frac{1}{10}$ of that budget.

Page 38
2. 4.57   **3.** 1.51   **4.** 3.59

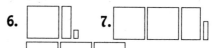

Page 39
2. $\frac{3}{8}$ **3.** $\frac{4}{5}$

Page 40
(A) 56   **(B)** 11   **(D)** 34   **(E)** 62
(H) 7   **(I)** 5   **(N)** 4   **(P)** 91
(R) 8   **(S)** 13   **(T)** 10   **(Y)** 6
Scotty simply gets his scooter…
… as a birthday present!

Page 41

```
        S I X
        E
T W O   V
W       E       N
E L E V E N     I
N       T       N
T   T W E L V E
Y       E
        O N E
```

Page 43
1. You always ended up at the same number that you started with.
2. Yes, because the pattern allows you to arrive back at the original number.
3. Yes.
4. Try various numbers to see if it works.

Page 44
Answers will vary; here's one approach: Draw a circle with a hexagon inside it. The points of the hexagon will touch the circles circumference. Draw three lines connecting the hexagon points and going outside the circle. Then draw a smaller hexagon inside the larger one. Its points are on the lines, about $\frac{2}{3}$ of the way from the centre to the circle.

Page 53

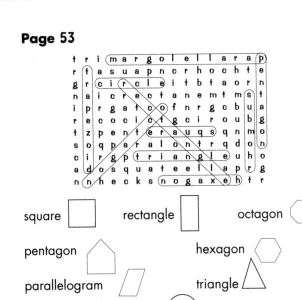

square ▢ rectangle ▯ octagon ⬡

pentagon ⬠ hexagon ⬡

parallelogram ▱ triangle △

trapezoid ◹ circle ◯ rhombus ▱

Page 54

1. It has been sorted into triangles, quadrilaterals, and other polydrons with different numbers of sides.
2. One triangle is an equilateral (all sides equal), another is a isosceles (with only 2 equal sides), and the last is a scalene (with no equal sides).
3. Prisms have 2 equal bases on either end with rectangles connecting the 2 bases. Pyramids have 1 base with triangles connecting the base to a vertex.

Page 55

1. Yes **2.** No **3.** No **4.** No
5. Yes **6.** No **7.** No **8.** No
Use these definitions to help you understand.
Parallelogram = quadrilateral with opposite sides parallel and equal in length
Rectangle = quadrilateral with opposite sides parallel and equal in length, and with 4 90° angles
Rhombus = quadrilateral with opposite sides parallel and all 4 sides equal
Square = quadrilateral with 4 equal sides and 4 right angles
Trapezoid = quadrilateral with exactly 2 parallel sides.

Page 56

1. No **2.** Yes, cube **3.** Yes, cube
4. Yes, Square-based pyramid **5.** No
6. Yes, Triangular-based pyramid

Page 57

1.  2.

3. 4.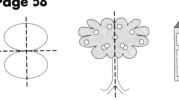

5.

Page 58

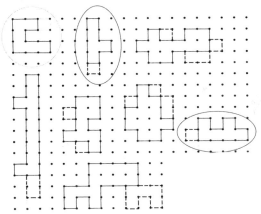

Isoceles triangle has 1 line of symmetry.
Equilateral triangle has 3 lines of symmetry.
Scalene triangle has no line of symmetry.

Page 59

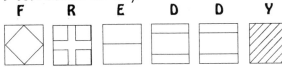

Page 60
Answers will vary.

Page 63
1–15. Answers will vary.
F R E D D Y

Page 64

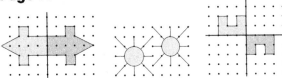

Answer key 49

Page 65

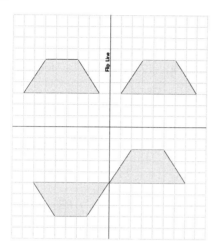

Page 67

C, E, A, B, D
(A) pictograph (B) line graph (C) bar graph
(D) Venn diagram (E) pie graph

Page 68

Most? O   Least? J, X, Q, Z

Page 69

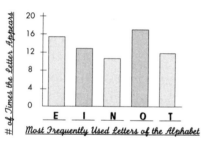

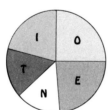

| 1. > | 2. < | 3. > |
| 4. < | 5. < | 6. > |

Pages 70 – 71

Number Rolled	Player A's Score (# x 2)	Player B's Score (# + 20)
13	26	33
25	50	45
19	38	39
11	22	31
7	14	27
34	68	54

Better chance: Player B
Which numbers: Smaller numbers for Player B, Larger numbers for Player A
Fair: almost (only 1 point away)

Page 72

Number of Octopi	1	2	3	4	5	6
Number of Legs	8	16	24	32	40	48

Number of Pigs	1	2	3	4	5	6
Number of Tails	1	2	3	4	5	6

Number of Puppies	1	2	3	4	5	6
Number of Paws	4	8	12	16	20	24

Number of Camels	1	2	3	4	5	6
Number of Humps	2	4	6	8	10	12

Page 73

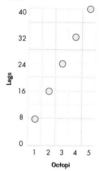
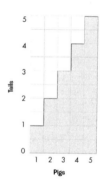

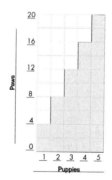

Page 75

Tip # 4
21 × 5 = 105   38 × 5 = 190
8 × 25 = 200   12 × 25 = 300

Page 76

Tip #1
32, 58, 76, 124, 22, 70, 882, 402, 30
Tip #2
21, 57, 42, 63, 84, 27, 112, 54, 243
Tip #3
232, 336, 724, 508, 3304, 212

Page 77
Tip #4
110, 575, 790, 645
Tip #5
230, 40, 320, 520
Tip #6
42, 84
Tip #7
81, 306, 45, 63, 27, 54, 522

Page 78
1. soccer = 115° = obtuse
basketball = 80° = acute
volleyball = 100° = obtuse
hockey = 65° = acute

2. soccer = $\frac{23}{72}$

basketball = $\frac{2}{9}$

volleyball = $\frac{5}{18}$

hockey = $\frac{13}{72}$

Page 79
3. Basketball   0.2222222   0.22
   Volleyball   0.2777777   0.28
   Hockey   0.1805555   0.18
4. 22%, 28%, 18%
5. (Answers will vary.) Fractions, decimals and percentages all show parts of a whole...

Page 80
1. 32   2. Hockey   3. 28
4. 56   5. 18   6. 9
7. 22   8. 66   9. about 12
10. about 16

Page 81

Soccer   Hockey

Basketball   Volleyball

Pie graphs and grids are useful because you can visually see you information and can read the amounts faster than sorting through many words and sentences.

You could also make a bar graph, pictograph, line graph, etc.

Page 82

Shapes/Angles	Definitions	Letters with shape/angle
triangle	three sided, closed shape	A, F, G
quadrilateral	four sided, closed shape	B, C, D, E
right angle	angle = 90°	A, B, C, F, G
acute angle	angle < 90°	A, D, E, F, G
obtuse angle	angle > 90°	D, E

Page 84
1. Week 1 $175
   Week 2 $695
   Week 3 $870
2. Total $1740

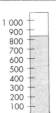

Page 85
3. Percentage raised: 85%
4. You can make an estimate by using the thermometer visually.
5. Week 1 < Week 3
   Week 2 > Week 1
   Week 3 > Week 2
   Week 1 & 2 = Week 3
6. 25% more: about $2 200

Page 86
1. 10:15   2. 11:00   3. 14:45
4. 1h 45 m   5. 3h 45m   6. 6 h 45 m
7. 14:15   8. 17:15

Page 87
2. North
3. West
4. West
5. North (or Northeast)
6. East (or Southeast)
7. Southeast
8. Northeast
9. Northwest
10. Southeast

Page 88
1. $72.50
2. Divide the amount in two.
3. about $35
4. $326.25

Page 89
It would take a total of 11 trips
(counting back and forth).

1st trip	2 children	(leave 1)
2nd trip (return)	1 child	
3rd trip	2 children	(leave 1)
4th trip (return)	1 child	
5th trip	1 adult	(leave 1 adult)
6th trip (return)	1 child	
7th trip	1 adult	(leave 1 adult)
8th trip (return)	1 child	
9th trip	2 children	(leave 1 child)
10th trip (return)	1 child	
11th trip	2 children	all

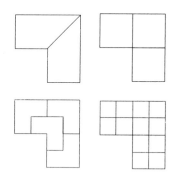

Page 90

Canoe	$120
Tentsites	$40
Food	$40

Page 91
1. 3-person tent
2. 3 of the 3-person tents
3. 3 of the 2-person tents & 1 of the 3-person tents
4. 6 of the 3-person tents & 1 of the 2-person tents

Page 93

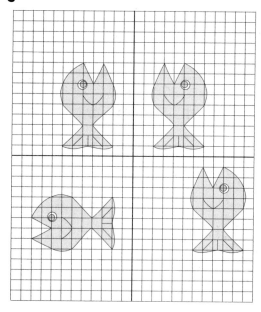

Page 94

There are 12 mammals on the cover, plus us!

Get in Shape!

Let's review shapes. Find as many words as you can in the word find.
List the words below. There are 10 in all.

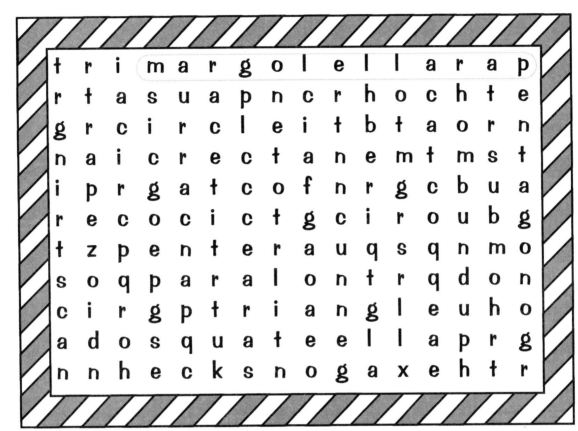

parallelogram

_____   _____

_____   _____

_____   _____

_____   _____

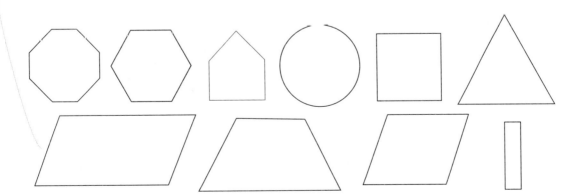

Now match the word to its shape above.

What's What?

Sort these shapes into the three different sets that have been started for you. Draw them below.

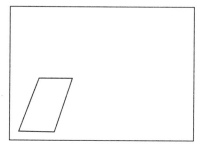
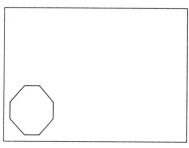
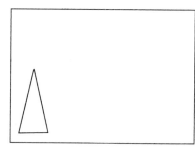

1. Explain how you sorted the shapes.

_____

_____

2. What is the difference between the three triangles?

_____

_____

Look at these prisms and pyramids.

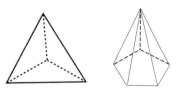

Pyramids

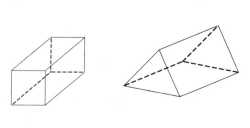

Prisms

3. Explain the difference between these shapes.

_____

_____

There are many things to think about when working with shapes. Think carefully before answering these questions. Once you have time to think about these, you will understand your shapes much better!

Take time to think!

1. Is a square a rectangle? Explain.

_____

_____

2. Is a rectangle a square? Explain.

_____

_____

3. Is a rectangle a rhombus? Explain.

_____

_____

4. Is a rhombus a rectangle? Explain.

_____

_____

5. Is a square a parallelogram? Explain.

_____

_____

6. Is a parallelogram a square? Explain.

_____

_____

7. Is a trapezoid a parallelogram? Explain.

_____

_____

Drawing the shapes might help!

8. Is a parallelogram a trapezoid? Explain.

_____

_____

A Net to Catch

A net is a 2-dimensional layout for a solid.

For example, here is a net for a cube.
Imagine folding it up into a cube.

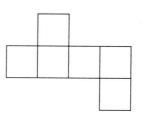

Look at these nets. Imagine folding them up to find out whether they can make a solid.
If they do, name the solid.

1. Does it make a solid?   **Yes or No**

   If yes, what solid?   _____

2. Does it make a solid?   **Yes or No**

   If yes, what solid?   _____

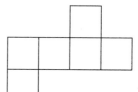

3. Does it make a solid?   **Yes or No**

   If yes, what solid?   _____

4. Does it make a solid?   **Yes or No**

   If yes, what solid?   _____

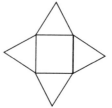

5. Does it make a solid?   **Yes or No**

   If yes, what solid?   _____

6. Does it make a solid?   **Yes or No**

   If yes, what solid?   _____

You can cut nets out
and fold them if it
helps you visualize!

Get Some Perspective!

Perspectives are different ways of looking at things. Here are different views of structures. Use some cubes to try to build each of these structures. Then try to sketch the structure below.

	Top	Front	Side	Sketch

1.

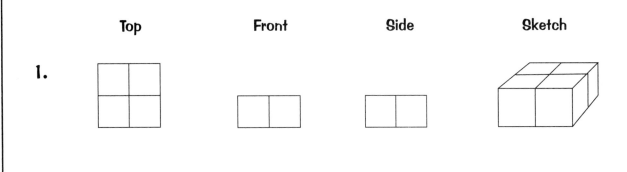

2.

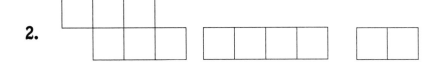

3.

4.

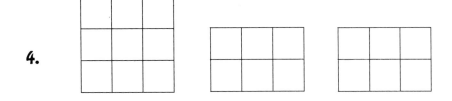

5.

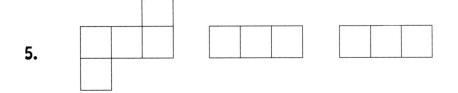

Mirror, Mirror on the Wall

A mirror reflects exactly the same image presented to it. Symmetry also shows an exact reflection. If you were to draw a line on a figure, hold on the line, and see 2 identical shapes, there is a line of symmetry. You can do this using a mirror.

Try finding the line of symmetry in the following figures. There may be more than one!

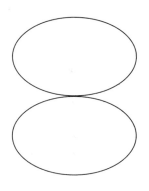  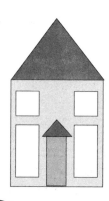

How many lines of symmetry does each triangle have?

Isosceles Triangle

It has _____ line(s) of symmetry.

I'm mostly symmetrical.

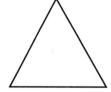

Equilateral Triangle

It has _____ line(s) of symmetry.

Most people are!

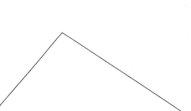

Scalene Triangle

It has _____ line(s) of symmetry.

Dot Calm

Is this shape symmetrical?

Can we make it symmetrical by only adding one square?

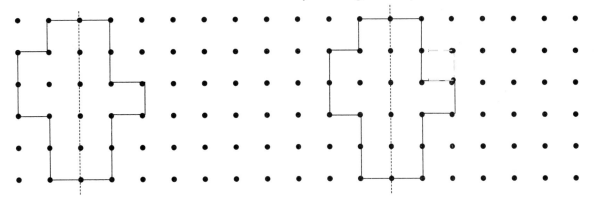

Circle the shapes that you can make symmetrical by adding only one square.
Add the square to be sure. Show how many squares are needed to make the other shapes symmetrical.

Don't go crazy with this one. Stay dot calm!

Go Logo!

You have been asked to design your very own T-shirt to win a trip to the tropical island Gologo! You must follow the instructions below.

Your design must have ...

... exactly 1 line of symmetry
... at least 7 sides
... at least 2 right angles
... at least 2 acute angles
... at least 1 obtuse angle
... a perimeter between 20 and 30 units
... an area greater than 22 units squared

Good Luck!

Angles
Use this guide to help you with your angles.

Right Angle = 90 °

Obtuse Angle = more than 90 °

Acute Angle = less than 90 °

Straight Angle = 180 °

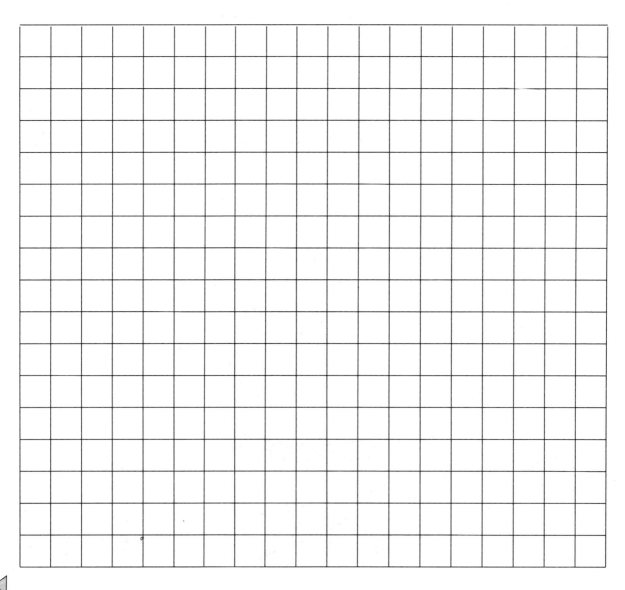

You're a Star!

Using the constellations below, label the following:

- at least 1 straight angle
- at least 6 acute angles
- at least 6 obtuse angles
- 1 straight angle

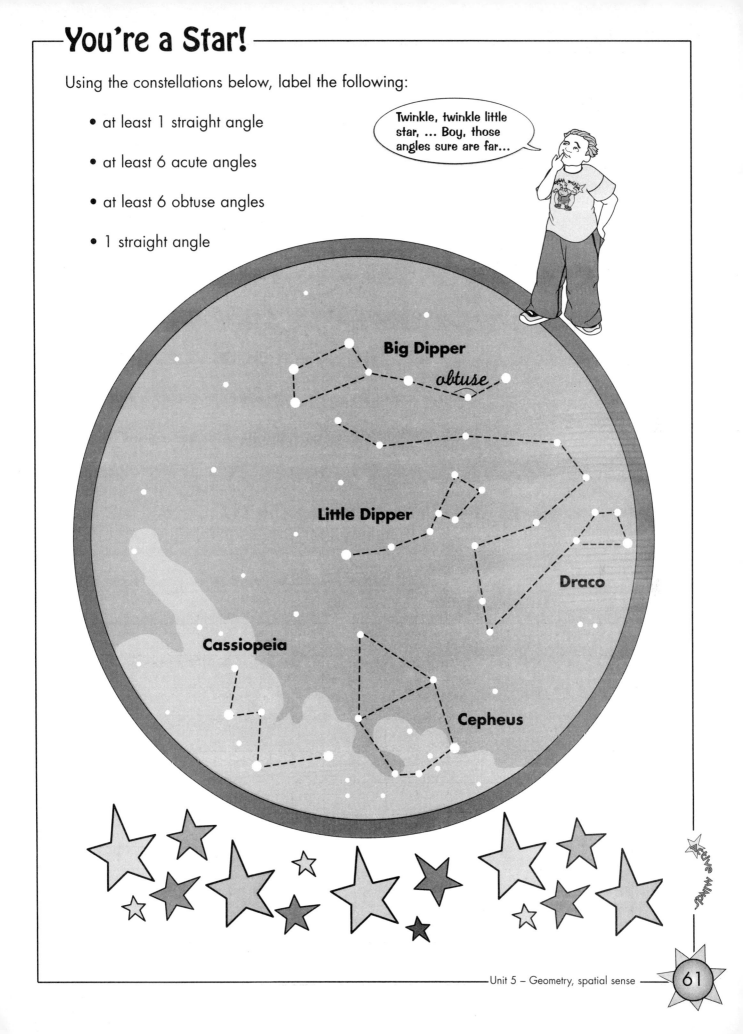

Fab Flags

International Alphabet Flags

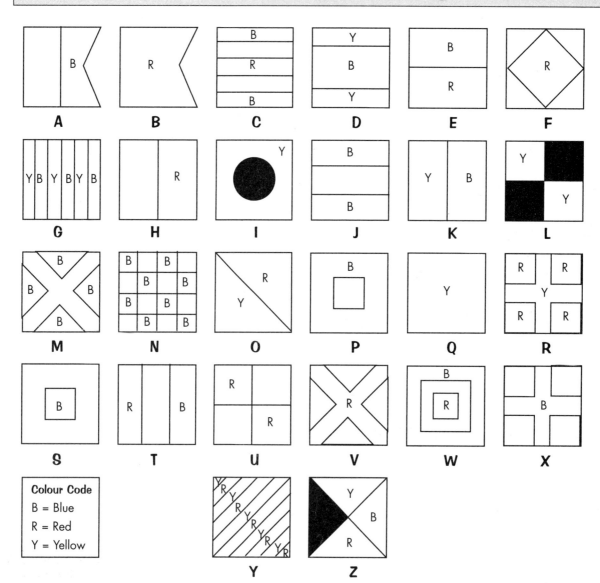

Colour Code
B = Blue
R = Red
Y = Yellow

International Numeral Pennants

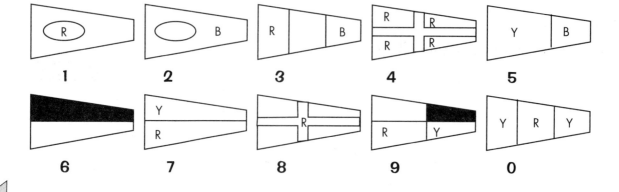

✎ List three letter flags that have a...

1. ... square   _____ _____ _____

2. ... isosceles triangle   _____ _____ _____

3. ... trapezoid   _____ _____ _____

4. ... rectangle   _____ _____ _____

5. ... 1 line of symmetry   _____ _____ _____

6. ... 2 lines of symmetry   _____ _____ _____

7. ... more than 2 lines of symmetry   _____ _____ _____

8. ... a right angle   _____ _____ _____

9. ... an obtuse angle   _____ _____ _____

10. ... an acute angle   _____ _____ _____

✎ List some letter flags that are

11. ... $\frac{1}{3}$ blue   _____ _____ _____

12. ... $\frac{1}{2}$ blue   _____ _____ _____

13. ... $\frac{1}{2}$ red   _____ _____ _____

14. ... 100% red   _____ _____ _____

15. ... 50% yellow   _____ _____ _____

> I wouldn't want to write my name like this all the time.

Try spelling Freddy's name in flags.

Flipping More Than Burgers!

A flip is simply an image that has been flipped. It's as simple as that! Take a look.

Here's a flip.   Now draw the flip for this image.

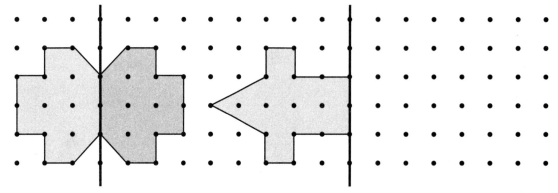

A slide is simply an image that has been slid. Boy, is this ever easy! Take a look.

Here's a slide. 4R, 3D   Now it's your turn. 1U, 5R

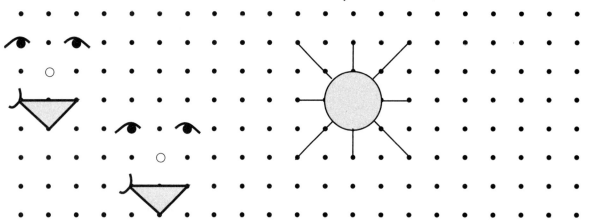

A turn takes a little more thinking than our funky flips and slides. A turn is a rotation of an image at a certain point. Find the rotation point for this example.

$\frac{1}{2}$ turn   Your turn to turn $\frac{1}{2}$ turn

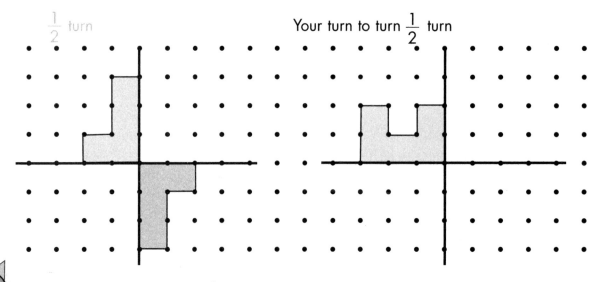

Tricky Trapezoid

 Using the shape provided on the grid below, follow the instructions in their order.

This is only for really smart kids.

1. Flip Tricky Trapezoid (TT1) over the flip line to make TT2.

2. Slide your new trapezoid (TT2) 8 down and 1 to the left to make TT3.

3. Turn (rotate) TT3 at 0,–5 a $\frac{1}{2}$ turn clockwise to make TT4.

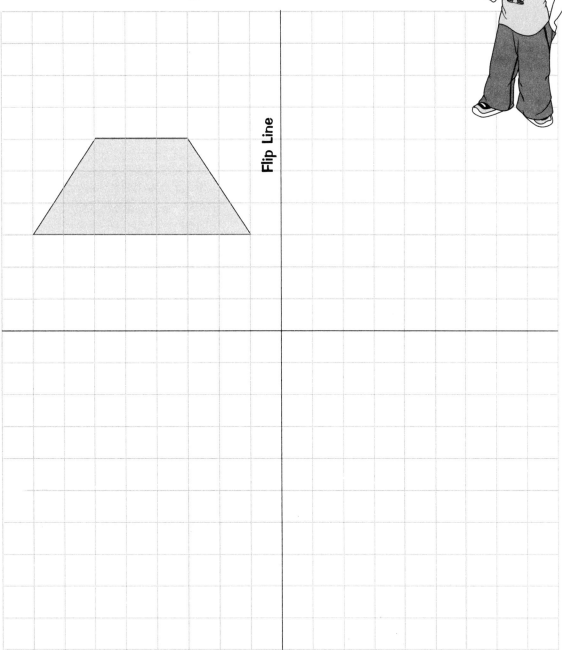

Flip Line

Baffled by Graphs!

Take a look at the graphs below. Each of these graphs tells us a lot.

A)

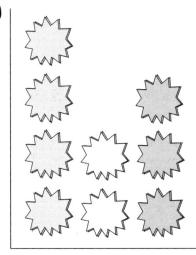

B)

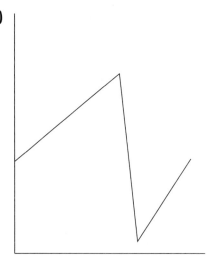

C)

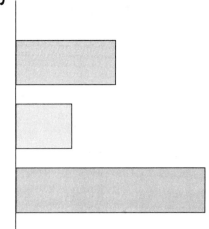

D)

My favourite graph is a pie graph!

It shows!

E)

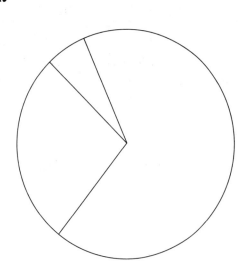

Match the graphs with their stories. Place the letter of the graph beside its story.

___C___ In Mina's class this year, there are many students with short hair, half as many with long hair, and a number between the short and long who have curly hair.

_____ Sports are very popular at school. On the soccer team 70% of the students are in Grade 6, 25% of the students are in Grade 5, and only 5% of the students are in Grade 4.

_____ The choir at Palmerston Public School has won many awards. They have collected nine ribbons already this year, most of them being a 1st place ribbon.

_____ Movie stores have noticed an increase in their movie rentals during the first three months of the year, a drop during the spring and summer months, and an increase in the last three months of the year.

_____ Five of Julie's friends are in the school band, 4 are in the school choir, and 3 of them are in both.

Graphs are excellent ways of organizing information.
There are many different kinds of graphs, as you can see.

Match the graphs with their proper names.

pie (circle) graph	pictograph	line graph	Venn diagram	bar graph
(A)	(B)	(C)	(D)	(E)

Letter of Letters

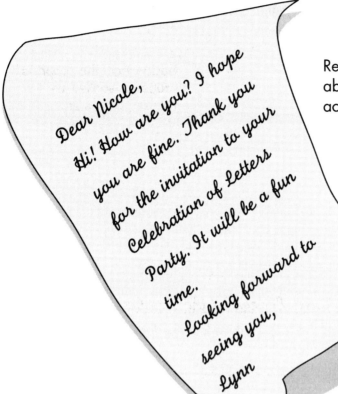

Dear Nicole,

Hi! How are you? I hope you are fine. Thank you for the invitation to your Celebration of Letters Party. It will be a fun time.

Looking forward to seeing you,

Lynn

Read this letter. Have you ever thought about the letters you read? That is, the actual letters of the alphabet?

Even a tally is a way of charting information.

What are the chances of having a *t* in a word, or how about an *x* in a sentence?

Well, let's find out. Tally the letters in this letter by counting every single letter and tallying them below.

For example, we've already done the tally for "dear." Continue for the rest of the letter.

A	B	C	D	E	F	G	H	I	J	K	L	M

N	O	P	Q	R	S	T	U	V	W	X	Y	Z

What letter appeared the most? _____

What letters appeared the least? _____

Make a bar graph showing the five most frequently used letters of the alphabet.

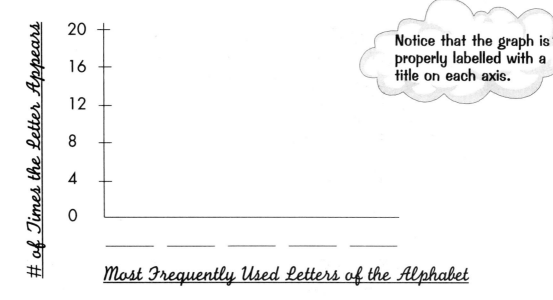

Notice that the graph is properly labelled with a title on each axis.

# of Times the Letter Appears

20
16
12
8
4
0

Most Frequently Used Letters of the Alphabet

Convert your bar graph into a pie graph by estimating their percentages.

Using your graphs, answer the following. Complete these questions using

<   >   =

1. t   >   s
2. l   r
3. e   a
4. i   o
5. f   p
6. z   a

Not Die Hard

This is not for die-hards, as you will see. Here is a net of the die for this game.

To play this game you will need 2 players. However, you will have an advantage if you plan your game first. Look at the rules of the game.

> • Player A always multiplies the number rolled by 2.
>
> • Player B always adds 20 to the number rolled.
>
> • The player with the greater score wins.

Which player would you choose to be? Explain why.

_____

_____

_____

_____

_____

Instead of guessing, let's chart it out.

Number Rolled	Player A's Score (# x 2)	Player B's Score (# + 20)
13		
25		
19		
11		
7		
34		

Now add the totals of the
two players' possible scores. _____ _____

Using the information from your chart, which player has a better chance of winning?

_____

Which numbers on the die made that player have a better chance of a higher score?
Explain your thoughts with words and numbers.

_____

_____

Do you think this game is fair? Make a suggestion to improve the game.

_____

_____

It's elementary,
my dear Francine.

How did you
calculate that
so quickly?

Top of the Charts

Use the following pictorial information to fill in the chart below.

1.

Number of Octopi	1	2	3	4	5	6
Number of Legs	8					

2.

Number of Pigs	1	2	3	4	5	6
Number of Tails						

3.

Number of Puppies	1	2	3	4	5	6
Number of Paws						

4.

Number of Camels	1	2	3	4	5	6
Number of Humps						

Draw a graph for each of the charts above.

From chart to graph!

1.

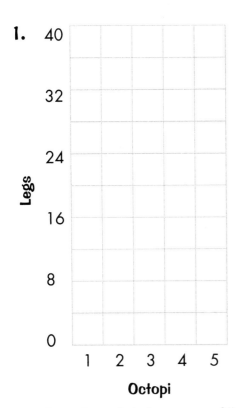

Legs

40
32
24
16
8
0

1 2 3 4 5

Octopi

2.

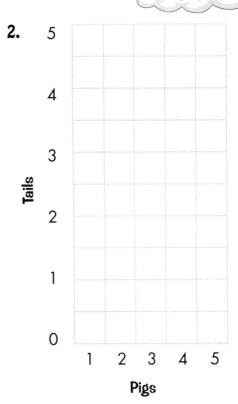

Tails

5
4
3
2
1
0

1 2 3 4 5

Pigs

For numbers 3 and 4, be sure to fill in the numbers and titles for each axis.
They have not been provided.

3.

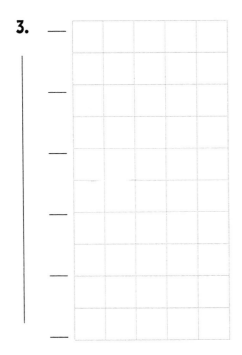

4.

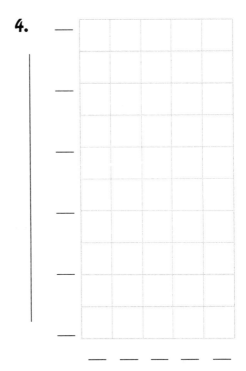

Tricks of the Trade

There are many short cuts for multiplication. Here are four — for the days when you can't use a calculator.

Tip #1   Multiplying by 9

To remember your 9 × table, just use your head, but even more, use your fingers!

1. Place your hands out on a table (or in your lap) with your fingers outstretched.
2. Take the number by which you are multiplying the 9. For example, if the question is 3 × 9, you take the number 3.
3. Counting from the left, locate your 3rd finger and hide it under your palm like this:

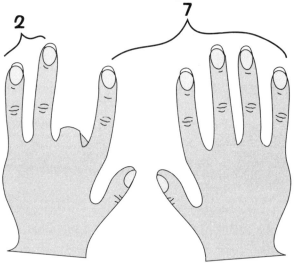

4. Look at what fingers are left and use them for each digit. So, your answer for this question is 27. Try a few others.

Tip #2   Multiplying by 10, 100, 1000 and so on

To multiply any number (without a decimal) by 10, just add a zero!

| For example, | 13 × 10 | just add a zero to the 13 | 130 |
| | 521 × 10 | just add a zero to the 521 | 5210 |

To multiply by 10 or any multiple of 10 (like 100, 1000, etc.), simply look at how many zeros are in the number, then add those zeros to the end of your other factor.

For example,	45 × 10	10 has 1 zero, so add 1 zero to 45	450
	21 × 100	100 has 2 zeroes, so add 2 zeroes to 21	2100
	6 × 1000	1000 has 3 zeros, so add 3 zeros to 6	6000

Tip #3   Multiplying by 11

Here's a fun one! If the sum of the numbers you are multiplying is less than 10, then look ahead for an easy answer.

1. Take the 1st digit of the number you are multiplying and place it at the beginning of your product.
2. Take the 2nd digit of the number you are multiplying and place it at the end of your product.
3. Then add your 2 numbers and place the sum in the middle of your product.
4. Voila! Your answer!

For example, 34 × 11	Product
1. Take the 3.	3
2. Take the 4.	3 4
3. Add them together.	3 + 4 = 7
4. Place the sum in the middle.	374

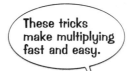

These tricks make multiplying fast and easy.

Tip #4   Multiplying by 5, and other multiples of 5

If you are multiplying by 5, simply add a zero to the number you are multiplying and divide it by 2.

For example,	14 × 5	add a zero	140	Divide by 2	70
Try some more.	21 × 5				
	38 × 5				

If you are multiplying by 25, simply add 2 zeros to the number you are multiplying and divide it by 4.

For example,	4 × 25	add 2 zeros	400	Divide by 4	100
Try some others.	8 × 25				
	12 × 25				

Quick Tips

In math, we're often looking for a quick common divisor. Here are some tricks to find a number that works.

Tip #1   When is a number divisible by 2?

…when it ends in an even number. For example, it ends in a 2, 4, 6, 8, or 0.

Circle the numbers that are divisible by 2.

   (32)   41   58   76   97   124   35

   45   22   65   70   882   402   30

Tip #2   When is a number divisible by 3?

… when the sum of the digits is divisible by 3. For example, 48 (4 + 8 = 12) is divisible by 3.

Circle the numbers that are divisible by 3.

   (21)   57   32   63   91   27   54

   38   74   42   95   84   112   243

Tip #3   When is a number divisible by 4?

… when the last two digits are divisible by 4. For example, 412 (last 2 digits = 12) is divisible by 4.

Circle the numbers that are divisible by 4.

   (232)   442   336   724   508   3304   212

Tip #4   **When is a number divisible by 5?**

... when the last digit is a 5 or a 0. For example, 415 (ends in a 5) is divisible by 5.

Circle the numbers that are divisible by 5.

(110)   31   575   234   213   790   645

Tip #5   **When is a number divisible by 10?**

... when the last digit is a 0. For example, 310 (ends in a zero) is divisible by 10.

Circle the numbers that are divisible by 10.

(230)   301   40   55   320   121   520

Tip #6   **When is a number divisible by 6?**

...when it is an even number and is divisible by 3. For example, 312 (even number and is divisible by 3) is divisible by 3. (This is simply the rules of divisibility for both 2 and 3 together.)

Circle the numbers that are divisible by 6.

38   74   (42)   95   84   112   243

Tip #7   **When is a number divisible by 9?**

...when the sum of the digits is divisible by 9. For example, 108 (1 + 0 + 8 = 9) is divisible by 9.

Circle the numbers that are divisible by 9.

(81)   57   32   63   91   27   54
230   306   45   55   325   121   522

Sports Extravaganza

Upper Fraser Public School's students love their sports. Here is a pie graph showing you which sports they love the most.

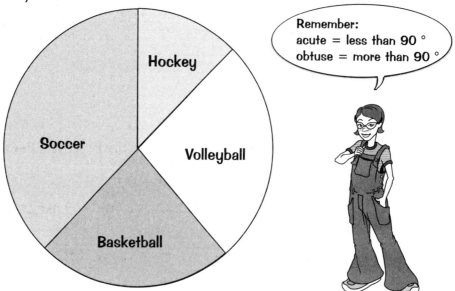

Remember:
acute = less than 90 °
obtuse = more than 90 °

1. Name the angles for each sport as either acute or obtuse. Circle the correct answer.

Soccer = 115°   acute or obtuse   Basketball = 80°   acute or obtuse

Volleyball = 100°   acute or obtuse   Hockey = 65°   acute or obtuse

2. Write each of the sports as a fraction using the angles to help you. Remember that a full circle is 360°. Then see if you can change the fraction to a smaller equivalent fraction. Look at the example to help you out.

Soccer $\dfrac{115}{360} = \dfrac{23}{72}$ Basketball

Divide both by 5.

Volleyball   Hockey

Fraction Factory

Now change your fractions into decimals at the Fraction Factory.
Look at the way to make the fraction for soccer.

> Numbers 5 and above, round up. Numbers below five, leave it.

Simply punch in the numerator, 115
the divide key, ÷
the denominator, 360
and then the equal key. =
0.3194444

Abracadabra, the decimal you've been looking for! However, there is still a little work. Round to the nearest hundredths, like this:

Look at the thousandths column to see whether you need to change the hundredths.
0.31**9**4444 changes to   0.32

3. Give it a try. Write decimals for the other 3 sports.

> Use a calculator for this one. You're allowed!

	Calculation	Decimal Rounded
Basketball	_____	_____
Volleyball	_____	_____
Hockey	_____	_____

4. Now it's not quite over yet. Change your decimal to a percentage.

Soccer   _0.32 = 32%_   Volleyball _____

Basketball _____   Hockey _____

5. Explain how fractions, decimals, and percentages are related.

_____

_____

_____

_____

Great Gridness

Now you can add percentages to our pie graph below, and then answer the following questions.

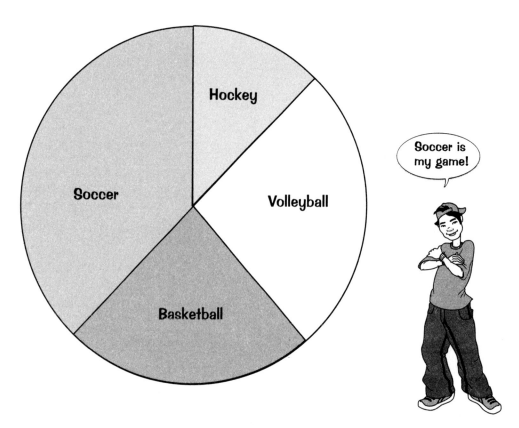

1. What percentage of students like soccer? _____

2. Which sport do the students like the least of the four? _____

3. If there were 100 students, how many would like volleyball? _____

4. If there were 200 students, how many would like volleyball? _____

5. If there were 100 students, how many would like hockey? _____

6. If there were 50 students, how many would like hockey? _____

7. If there were 100 students, how many would like basketball? _____

8. If there were 300 students, how many would like basketball? _____

9. If there were 60 students, estimate how many would like hockey. _____

10. If there were 80 students, estimate how many would like hockey. _____

11. Shade in the following grids to show the percentages of each sport.

Soccer

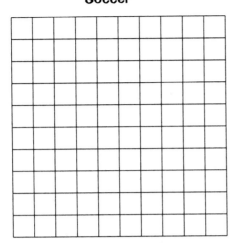

Hockey

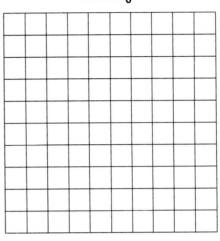

Basketball

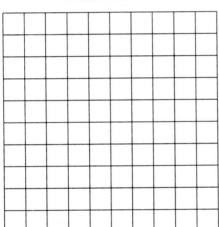

Volleyball

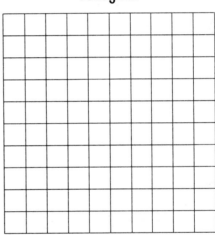

Explain how pie graphs and grids are useful for understanding information.

_____

_____

_____

_____

_____

In what other ways might you be able to present the information about Upper Fraser Public School's sports?

_____

_____

School Spirit

Paul, a student at Upper Fraser, visited his friend's school and saw the flags that they designed for their sports teams.

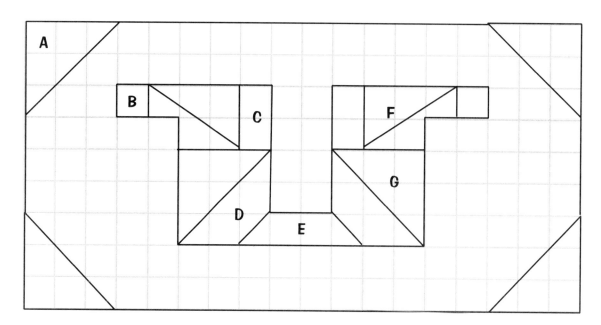

My mind is flagging from all these shapes!

Fill in the following chart using the flag above.

Shapes/Angles	Definitions	Letters with shape/angle
triangle		
quadrilateral		
right angle		
acute angle		
obtuse angle		

Paul thought that Upper Fraser school spirit might be even better with a flag of their own. Design a flag for Upper Fraser.

Fill in the following chart using the flag you designed.

Shapes/Angles	Definitions	Letters with shape/angle
triangle		
quadrilateral		
right angle		
acute angle		
obtuse angle		

Fun to Raise

The new flag may be fun to raise, but there are also funds to raise so that the school can take the sports teams on their trips. Using the thermometer and the instructions below, fill in the amount raised for their teams. Answer the questions below to help you with your thermometer reading.

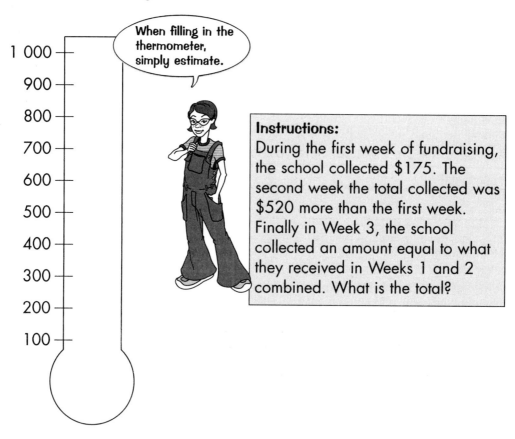

When filling in the thermometer, simply estimate.

1 000
900
800
700
600
500
400
300
200
100

Instructions:
During the first week of fundraising, the school collected $175. The second week the total collected was $520 more than the first week. Finally in Week 3, the school collected an amount equal to what they received in Weeks 1 and 2 combined. What is the total?

1. What was the amount raised in Week 1? _____

Week 2? _____

Week 3? _____

2. What was the total amount raised? _____

3. If their goal was to reach $2000, approximately what percentage of their goal did they reach?

That's a lot of door-knocking.

4. How does the thermometer help you to understand the percentage of 2000?

_____

_____

_____

5. Use greater than, less than, and equal signs to fill in the answers.

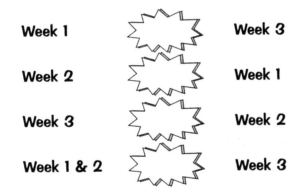

Week 1		Week 3
Week 2		Week 1
Week 3		Week 2
Week 1 & 2		Week 3

6. If Upper Fraser plans a bigger fundraiser next year and the total amount raised is 25% more than this year's fundraiser, estimate how much they will raise. Use pictures, numbers, and words.

A Camping We Will Go!

The Active Minds gang are going on a camping trip. Yippee!

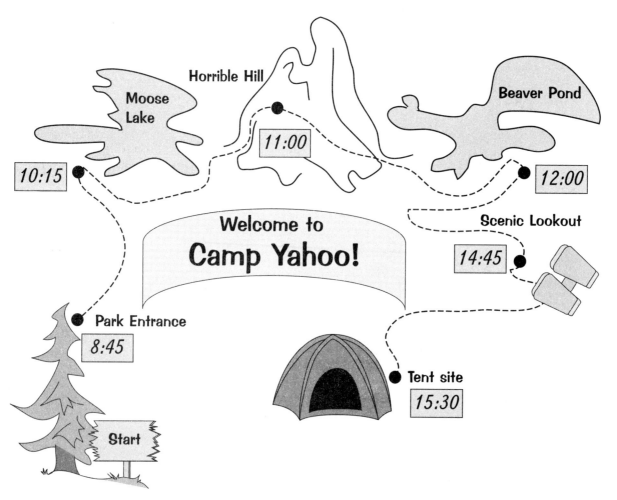

1. When did the gang arrive at Moose Lake? _____10:15_____

2. When did the gang climb up Horrible Hill? _____

3. When did they reach the Scenic Lookout? _____

4. What was the travelling time from Moose Lake to Beaver Pond? _____

5. What was the travelling time from Horrible Hill to Scenic Lookout? _____

6. What was the total travelling time to reach their tent site? _____

7. If the gang left at 7:30 a.m., at what time would they have arrived? _____

8. If the gang left at 10:30 a.m., at what time would they have arrived? _____

Direct Me, Please!

When camping we often use a compass to help us find our directions. Using this compass and the map of our trail, answer the following questions.

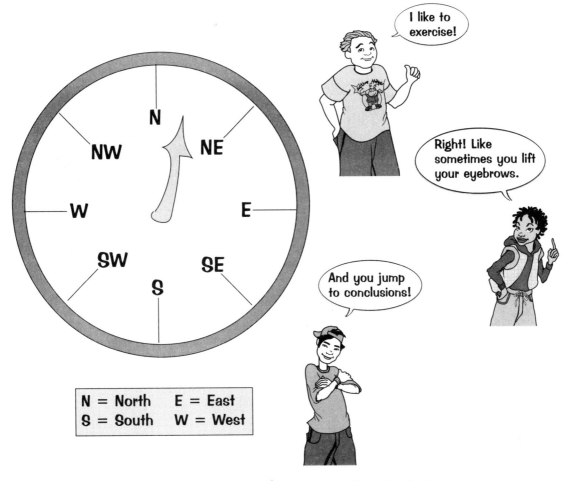

I like to exercise!

Right! Like sometimes you lift your eyebrows.

And you jump to conclusions!

N = North	E = East	
S = South	W = West	

1. The Tent Site is to the _____*east*_____ of the Park Entrance.

2. Moose Lake is to the _____ of the Park Entrance.

3. Moose Lake is to the _____ of Horrible Hill.

4. Horrible Hill is to the _____ of Beaver Pond.

5. Beaver Pond is to the _____ of Scenic Lookout.

6. Scenic Lookout is to the _____ of Moose Lake.

7. The Tent Site is to the _____ of Horrible Hill.

8. Beaver Pond is to the _____ of the Park Entrance.

9. Moose Lake is to the _____ of the Tent Site.

10. The Tent Site is to the _____ of Horrible Hill.

Dip, Dip, and Swing

1. During the trip, Francine and Suzy spend a lot of time canoeing the lakes at Camp Yahoo. To rent a canoe costs $14.50 per day. Estimate how much it will cost to rent a canoe for 5 days. Use pictures, numbers, and words to explain your answer.

2. If the canoe is shared between the two of them, how will you calculate the cost per person?

   _____

   _____

3. Estimate what that cost will be per person.

4. There are a total of 10 people on the trip. If they rent 5 canoes, the canoe rental gives them a 10% discount on all 5 canoes. What will the total cost be for all 10 people to canoe? *Remember that there are 2 people per canoe.

5. One day on the trip, Freddie went for a walk with 2 friends, but they arrived at a pond that they had to cross. They met 2 adults who had a small boat. The boat can hold 2 young people or 1 adult. How did all 5 people get across the river? How many trips did it take? Use pictures, numbers, and words to answer this question.

At the tent site, Freddie must work out where to fit all of the tents.
This exercise will help him plan.

Divide this into 2 equal parts that are exactly the same.

Divide this into 3 equal parts that are exactly the same.

Divide this into 4 equal parts that are exactly the same.

Divide this into 12 equal parts that are exactly the same.

Room and Board

To plan for the trip, the Active Minds gang needs to make a budget.

- Costs include the tentsite, the food, and your canoes.
- Total budget is $200.
- Calculate how you will spend your money.
- Calculate the amounts of each cost using pictures, numbers, and words.

Canoe	Tent sites	Food
costs 3/5 of the budget	costs 20 % of the budget	the rest of the budget

$200 doesn't go very far.

Bedbugs!

Unfortunately, the camp site has a few bedbugs! Each 2-person tent has 12 bedbugs that manage to creep their way in. Each three-person tent has 15 bedbugs!

> Use pictures, numbers, and words for your answers.

1. If there are two people in the 12-bug tent and three people in the 15-bug tent, which tent would you rather end up in? (Consider the ratio of bugs to people.)

2. If the tent site has a total of 45 bugs, what sized tents are on the site and how many of each size?

3. If the tent site has a total of 51 bugs, what sized tents are on the site and how many of each size?

> I'm glad I didn't have to count the bugs.

4. If the tent site has a total of 102 bugs, what sized tents are on the site and how many of each size?

Grub Time

It's dinner time and here are the camp's choices.

Make a list!

Meat	Potatoes	Vegetables	Drink
hamburger	baked	corn	orange juice
fish	french fries	peas	pop
	mashed	carrots	

What are all the different combinations that you can make with these categories?

- *hamburger* *baked potato* *corn* *orange juice*
-
-
-
-
-
-
-
-
-
-
-
-
-
-
-

Flipping Fish?

Francine caught a fish. Follow these instructions to move the fish around while it's frying.

1. Flip Fresh Fish (FF1) over the flip line to make FF2.

2. Slide your FF2 10 down and 4 to the right to make FF3.

3. Turn (rotate) FF3 a $\frac{1}{4}$ turn counter-clockwise and slide it 8 to the left to make FF4.

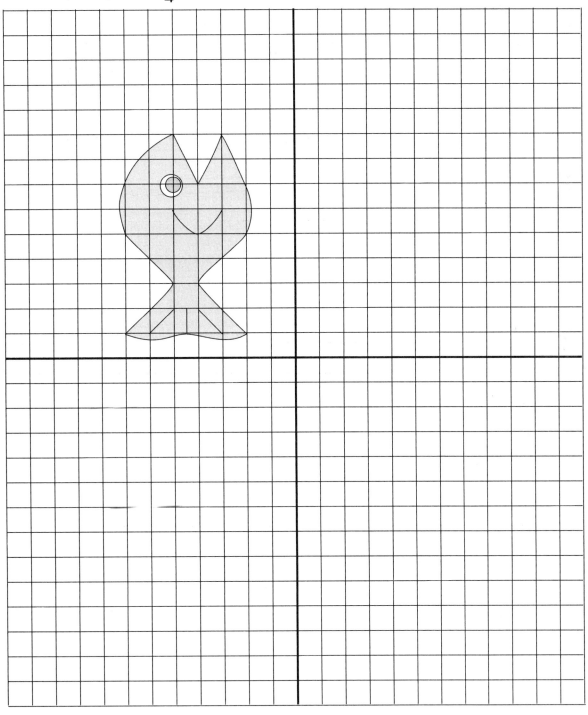

Put It to the Test!

Let's see if you remember your strategies and other helpful math tools!

Across

1. A _____ can help to organize information.

3. You can _____ by using your head, or by using a calculator.

4. A _____ can help to organize information.

5. If you do not understand the problem, you may have to _____ it again.

9. Exact answers are not always necessary. Instead, you should just _____.

10. Different ways to organize information include making a chart, graph, or a _____.

11. If you _____ ahead, problem solving is much easier.

12. Things often repeat themselves, so look for a _____.

13. Objects that help you to solve a problem are called _____.

Down

2. Drawing is fun and makes things easier to understand, so draw a _____.

6. If there is too much information, _____ the things you don't need.

7. When all else fails and you don't know what to do, just _____ _____.

8. If clues in a question are not in order from beginning to end you might need to _____.

Tips for Tests

Keep these tips in mind when taking your tests.

- Watch your time carefully. If you have 3 big questions to finish in 40 minutes, allow yourself about 10 minutes per question and then take some time to check over your answers.

- If a question is difficult and you can't answer it, don't waste too much time on it. Go to the next question that you can answer. Come back to that stumper of a question later.

- Understand what is being asked in a question before devising a plan of attack.

- Plan your problem solving, and then carry out the plan. Too many people do not think and plan before starting a problem.

- ALWAYS check over your answers. Many foolish mistakes come from simple errors that could have been corrected.

- For multiple choice tests, eliminate the answers that you know are impossible. That way you are considering fewer choices.

- Check the test rules. If you do not lose points for wrong answers on a multiple choice test, answer every question even if you are not certain of your answer. If you do lose points, don't guess!

- Pictures, numbers, and words help to make your answer complete.

- If there are 5 lines provided for an answer, try to fill all 5 lines.

- Practise communicating your written answers orally (or in your head) first. Then write them down clearly and completely. Reread your written answers to make sure that they make sense!

Review these tips often to help you out.

Problem-Solving Method

Understand the problem

Make a plan that will work for the problem

Carry out your plan carefully

Look back, and check your work

Show your answer in pictures, numbers, and words

Use your head first.

Strategies for Math Problem Solving

Read and reread the problem

Eliminate information you don't need

Circle or underline important information

Draw a picture

Make a chart, graph, or list

Estimate

Guess and check

Look for a pattern

Use manipulatives

Work backwards

Pick the strategies you need.

Test Taking Booster
Grades 5 & 6

This workbook belongs to: _____

Table of Contents

Read It Over and Over

To ace a test in class or on a provincial exam, you have to read the questions carefully. If you can't figure out a way to tackle the problem after the first reading, read the question again and again until you do.

1. Going on a trip.

Freddie and Hiro are going on a weekend trip to Banff. They're going to need to budget for their expenses. Together, they have $600 for the journey. The bus fare is $130 each for a return trip. They have decided to spend the rest of their money like this: 50% on accommodation; 30% on food and 20% on "other."

- How much do they plan to spend on food?
- How much do they plan to spend on accommodation?
- How much is left for "other" expenses?

Show all your calculations in the space below.

Two bus fares: $130 × 2 = $260.

Money left after bus fares: $600 − $260 = $340

We need cash for food.

Accommodation	Food	"Other"
$340	$340	$340
× .5	× .3	× .2
$170	$102	$68

They'll spend $170 on accommodation, $102 on food and $68 on other expenses.

(Check: $260 + $170 + $102 + $68 = $600)

Thirty percent is barely enough.

Now you try. Here are two questions where you have to read carefully.

2. **Francine's project.** Francine is putting together a big art project. She has a budget of $40 from her parents to pay for everything. She figures that the backing board for her project will cost $10. She wants to spend equal amounts of the remaining money on markers, paints and glue.

How much will Francine spend on paints? Show your work below.

3. **Don't forget the tax.** Francine picked out $10 of backing board, but forgot about sales tax and the GST. They added 15% to the price she had to pay. She decided to revise her budget, taking the amount she needed for the tax from her budget for glue.

What will Francine be able to spend on glue? Show your work.

I wish I were in Alberta.

Make a bar graph of Francine's *revised* budget. Each figure must now include the tax.

Because there's no sales tax!

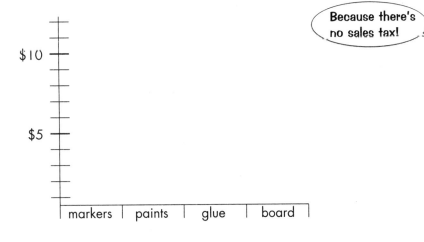

Underline What Counts!

If you have a big question, it helps to underline the important facts. Concentrate on the information you need and ignore the rest.

1. **Survey.** Freddie did a survey of the kids in his class. He wanted to have their votes on how the student council should spend the money they raised in a car wash. Ms. Effredi, the teacher, thought they should spend the money on <u>trees</u> to be planted in the front of the school. <u>Ten kids</u> voted with her. <u>Five kids</u> thought the money should go towards a <u>dance</u>. <u>Seven kids</u> wanted to sponsor a <u>foster child</u>. <u>Three kids</u> thought the money should go to help the <u>soccer</u> team. <u>Two kids</u> <u>were off sick</u> the day Freddie did his survey.

Of the <u>kids</u> in the class <u>who voted</u>, what <u>percentage</u> wanted to spend the money on trees? Show your work.

Kids who voted: $10 + 5 + 7 + 3 = 25$ *kids*
(Ms. Effredi and the absent kids don't count!)

Percentage who favour trees: $\dfrac{10}{25} = 0.4 = 40\%$

Now make a circle graph with labels to show all the responses from the kids who voted. Show your work.

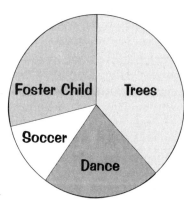

Underlining helps focus your attention!

Trees: $\dfrac{10}{25} = .4 \times 360° = 144°$

Dance: $\dfrac{5}{25} = \dfrac{1}{5} = .2 \times 360° = 72°$

Foster child: $\dfrac{7}{25} = .28 \times 360° = 100.8°$

The check makes sure your answer works!

Soccer: $\dfrac{3}{25} = .12 \times 360° = 43.2°$

(Check: $144° + 72° + 100.8° + 43.2° = 360°$)

Now you try. Here are two questions where you should underline the important information and question words. Then do the answers.

2. Hiro did a survey in his class. The results were a little different from Freddie's. Only eight kids voted for more trees. Ten were in favour of sponsoring a foster child. Nobody thought money should go to the soccer team, but six kids thought the basketball team needed new uniforms. Four kids voted for a dance. Two kids thought the money should go towards graduation.

 Make a circle graph of the results of Hiro's survey. Show your calculations.

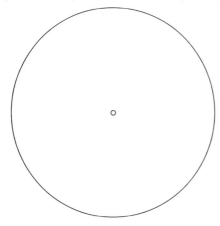

3. Francine is flying from Toronto to Vancouver over the March Break. The entire trip is 4300 kilometres. Her teacher asked her to do a line graph showing the trip she will take and the distance to some major cities her plane will pass over. Here's some data:

City	Distance
Thunder Bay:	1400 km
Regina:	2700 km
Winnipeg:	2100 km
Calgary:	3400 km
Montreal:	540 km
Halifax:	1460 km

Fill in the graph. Show your math.

Hey, two of these cities aren't on the route.

That's the trick!

Toronto [   ] **Vancouver**

Cross It Out

Some problems have more information than you need. You can focus better on what's important if you cross out the useless information.

1. Circus Camp. Suzy and Sandra are spending their summer holidays in Montreal this year at the Cirque Du Soleil's annual circus camp. ~~Suzy signed up because she thought it would be a fun way to improve her French. Sandra, though, has always dreamed of joining the circus. She saw the Moscow Circus when she was just seven years old and has never forgotten it!~~

Suzy is surprised at how many other kids are attending the camp. There are 60 kids in Level 1, 25 in Level 2, and another 20 in the advanced section. ~~Suzy goes off towards the clown tent to learn how to ride one of those funny mini bikes. Sandra bolts over towards the outdoor trampoline. It is quite a distance away, and it takes her almost twenty minutes to get there. Sandra wanted to be the first in line, but lots of kids have already arrived, and are waiting for their turn.~~ The instructor explains the rules: Each Level 2 student will be able to jump up and down for only 15 minutes at a time, ~~that is, providing they have completed a full, 10 minute warm up.~~ Only one person is allowed to use the equipment at a time. Sandra scans the line-up. There are five kids in front of her and the rest of the Level 2 kids behind her.

How long will Sandra have to wait to try the trampoline herself? How much longer will it take for all the Level 2 kids to jump? Show your work.

This question is way too long!

5 kids in front of Sandra: 5 × 15 minutes = 75 minutes.
It will be 75 minutes before Sandra can jump on the trampoline.

Think:

25 kids in Level 2. Total time: 25 × 15 minutes = 375 minutes
Sandra and 5 kids took 90 minutes.

$$375 - 90 = 285 \text{ minutes} \quad \frac{285}{60} = 4.75 \text{ hours}$$

It will take 4 hours and 45 minutes for the rest of the level two kids to jump.

Circus camp was cool.

Math—Finding relevant information

Now you try one. Cross out the useless information, then solve the problem.

2. Freddie is making a box planter for his mother. She wants to plant some herbs on the balcony of their apartment. Here are the dimensions of the planter:

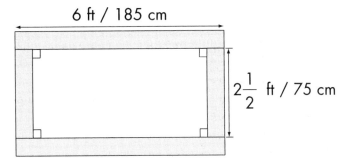

6 ft / 185 cm

$2\frac{1}{2}$ ft / 75 cm

Freddie is going to use 1 × 8 cedar to make the planter. He'll also need 2 × 2 cedar to support the corners. How much 1 × 8 cedar does Freddie need? If 1 × 8s only come in 4-foot and 8-foot sections, how many will he need of each? Show your thinking.

3. Here is a chart of lumber prices. Use it to figure out how much the wood for the planter will cost. (Note: 1 × 8 × 4 means a piece of 1 × 8 inch lumber that is 4 feet long.)

Size	Cost
1 × 8 × 4	$3.20
1 × 8 × 8	$5.80
2 × 4 × 8	$3.85
1 × 10 × 8	$8.70
2 × 2 × 4	$2.00

How come everything in Canada is metric except wood?

Maybe because we sell so much to the U.S.

Plan Ahead

You need a plan to tackle any problem Think first. Plan your approach — do you need to draw a picture? make a chart? do a graph? Think before you even start calculating!

---

1. Francine works at a summer camp. She thinks that the campsite should be reorganized so that it can be used more efficiently. Here's a diagram of the camp.

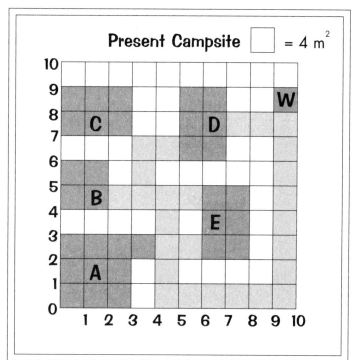

Present Campsite ☐ = 4 m²

A	= Food tent
B	= Craft tent
C, D, E,	= Sleeping tents
W	= Washrooms
☐	= Walkway

Calculate the percentage of the area used for tents and the washroom. Calculate the percentage of the area used for all activities, including walkways. Explain your thinking.

*The tents and the washroom are easy: just count the squares. 33 squares Here's my plan out of 100 = 33% But the question said **calculate** so...*

$$A = 3 \times 3 + 1 = 10 \qquad B = 2 \times 2 = 4 \qquad C = 2 \times 3 = 6$$
$$D = 2 \times 3 = 6 \qquad\qquad E = 2 \times 3 = 6 \qquad W = 1$$

Total = A + B + C + D + E + W
$$10 + 4 + 6 + 6 + 6 + 1 = 33 \qquad \frac{33}{100} = 33\%$$

For walkways I'm just going to count since they're only 1 square in width. 26 squares

Total space used, including walkways: 26 + 33 = 59
59% of total space
(Check by counting the white squares: 41 — it works!)

Now you try. Here are two more problems based on Francine's map of the camp.

2. Francine thinks that two of the sleeping tents could be put side by side. What does the revised camp look like. Will there be any more unused space? Explain your reasoning.

Start by drawing the revised camp.   Then explain.

<table>
<tr><td></td><td></td><td></td><td></td><td></td><td></td><td></td><td></td><td></td></tr>
<tr><td></td><td></td><td></td><td></td><td></td><td></td><td></td><td></td><td></td></tr>
<tr><td></td><td></td><td></td><td></td><td></td><td></td><td></td><td></td><td></td></tr>
<tr><td></td><td></td><td></td><td></td><td></td><td></td><td></td><td></td><td></td></tr>
<tr><td></td><td></td><td></td><td></td><td></td><td></td><td></td><td></td><td></td></tr>
<tr><td></td><td></td><td></td><td></td><td></td><td></td><td></td><td></td><td></td></tr>
<tr><td></td><td></td><td></td><td></td><td></td><td></td><td></td><td></td><td></td></tr>
<tr><td></td><td></td><td></td><td></td><td></td><td></td><td></td><td></td><td></td></tr>
<tr><td></td><td></td><td></td><td></td><td></td><td></td><td></td><td></td><td></td></tr>
</table>

Now you could recalculate all the areas, but you don't have to.
Think and then explain why.

_____

_____

_____

_____

3. Francine thinks that the food tent could also be used for crafts. If the craft tent is taken down, how much more space is available for other activities? Show your work.

Picture This!

Use pictures, charts and words to solve a problem. Sometimes it's easier to "see" the answer if a diagram is right in front of your eyes.

1. **Tree planting.** Hiro led a project to plant trees behind the school. He knows that trees are good for the environment and decided that five rows of pine trees would also be a good wind break. In the first row south of the school, the group planted four trees. There are twice as many trees in the next row. In the third row, the group planted two more trees than in the second row. The fourth and fifth rows both have three times as many trees as row 1.

A chart makes it easy to see this:

A chart makes this easy!

How many trees were planted altogether?

That's easy. Just count: *44.* Or calculate:
4 + (2 × 4) + (2 × 4) + 2 + 2(3 × 4) = 46

If there are 12 places in each row to plant trees, what percentage of the third row is planted?

$$\frac{10}{12} = .8333 = 83\%$$

Which row has the most trees? How many are there?

Rows 4 and 5 each have 12 trees.

But planting trees is hard.

What is the relationship between the number of trees in row 1 and the number in row 5?

There are three times more trees in row 5 than in row 1.

Now you try a couple. You'll need to use your drawing and charting skills.

2. The owners of an amusement park collect data on the people who visit the park. They found that five-year-olds spend the least money and 18-year-olds spend the most. The average five-year-old spent $5. The average 18-year-old spent five times that amount. The owners also got some other averages: 10-year-olds spent $13; 12-year-olds spent $17; 11-year-olds spent $14.50.

 Make a chart of this data, arranged by age.

Age	Money Spent

 Turn your chart into a line graph on this graph paper.

Don't forget to label the axes!

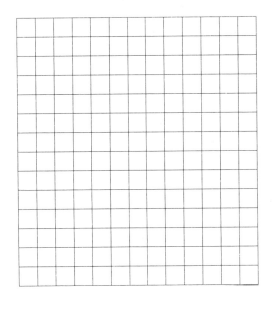

3. From the line graph, estimate the amount of money the average 13-year-old spends at the amusement park. Explain your reasoning.

_____

_____

_____

Explain Yourself!

On many math tests, it's not enough to come up with the right answer. You have to **EXPLAIN** how you got it. This means you have to think about how you think — and then get it down on paper.

1. Josie and Alex played a game at the school fair. This is how the game worked. Players had to close their eyes and toss a penny onto a square game board shown below. (If the penny landed on a line, the player tossed again.) If the penny landed on the white square, the player won a prize. If the penny landed on any other colour, it was game over.

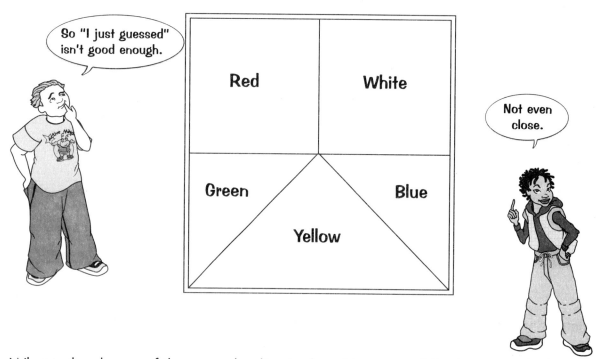

So "I just guessed" isn't good enough.

Not even close.

What is the chance of the penny landing in the white section? Explain your thinking.

I can see that white is a quarter of the whole game board. I can also measure to show that it's $\frac{1}{4}$. So the chance of the penny landing in the white square is one in four.

What is the chance of the penny landing in the yellow section? Explain your thinking.

The yellow section looks bigger than the others, but if blue and green are put together, they are as big as red or white. So the yellow section must have the same area as either the red or white section. That means it's $\frac{1}{4}$ of the total area, so the chance of a penny landing there is still one in four.

Now you try some. Here are three more problems where you have to explain your thoughts. Check your answers with the answer key on page 47.

2. Look at the game board again. What is the chance that the penny will land in the green section? Explain your thinking.

_____

_____

_____

_____

_____

_____

3. Last week in a basketball game, Hiro scored 32 points and Freddie scored 8. They're going to play again on Friday. If Hiro is injured and doesn't score any points in that game, how many points does Freddie need to match Hiro's 2-game total? Explain your thinking.

_____

_____

_____

_____

_____

_____

4. Hiro's score of 32 points was half the points scored by his entire team. His team finally beat the other team by 5 points. What were the scores for each team? Explain your thinking.

_____

_____

_____

_____

_____

Check It Out!

Sometimes the only way to solve a problem is to try a few different answers until one works. This isn't guesswork — it's just another way to find the answer.

The umbrella has changed its position. Did it **slide**, **flip** or **turn**? Explain your thinking.

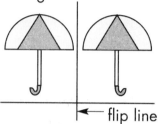

←— flip line

One way to solve the problem is to try the 3 answers out. If the umbrella made a **slide**, it would look like this:

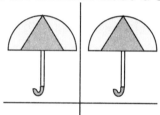

Just keep trying until it works!

If the umbrella did a **flip**, it would look like this:

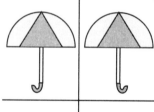

If the umbrella did a **turn**, it would look like this:

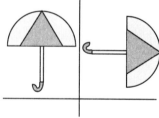

That's perseverance.

You can see that the "flip" answer looks right. So you write:

The umbrella did a flip because it is still upright but now the handle points to the right, not the left.

Now you try some. Try out each suggested answer to see which solves the problem.

2. Francine and Suzy are potting small tropical plants at a nursery. If they can each pot 40 plants an hour, how many plants will they have in pots at the end of an eight-hour day?

Ⓐ 80

Ⓑ 320

Ⓒ 640

Ⓓ 1020

3. Hiro and Freddie are shooting baskets. Hiro sinks every other shot. Freddie sinks about one shot in five. If Hiro shoots for 10 minutes, how many minutes must Freddie shoot to get the same number of baskets?

Ⓐ 20

Ⓑ 25

Ⓒ 45

Ⓓ 50

4. If we flip this Christmas tree on the flip line, how will it look?

Tree

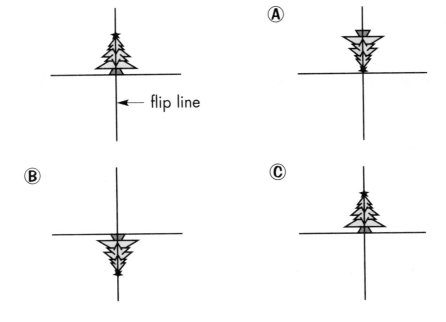

Working Backwards

Often the best way to check your answer is to work the problem backwards. Use your answer and see if it works with the facts at the start.

1. Does it fit? The school board wants to deliver a flyer on provincial test results to all the schools in the district. There are 60 schools, so 60 bundles of flyers must be delivered. The bundles are 5 cm high and have to fit in boxes as shown below.

Bundle of Flyers

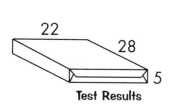

Test Results

Packing Box

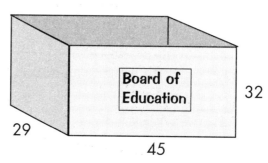

Bundles cannot stick out over the top of the packing box. How many bundles can fit into a box? If there are 60 bundles, how many boxes are needed?

Start by drawing a picture of the bundles stacked up inside the box:

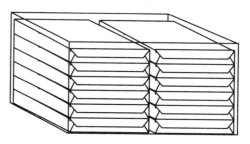

How many bundles are in each stack?

$$\begin{array}{r} 6\ R2 \\ 5\overline{)32} \\ \underline{30} \\ 2 \end{array}$$

6 bundles in a stack

with 2 stacks there will be 12 bundles in a box

How many boxes are needed:

$$\begin{array}{r} 5 \\ 12\overline{)60} \end{array}$$

5 boxes

Now go back and check your answers:

6 bundles × 5 cm = 30 cm stack. Yes! That will fit.

5 boxes × 12 bundles = 60 bundles. Yes! That's right.

Now you try a few. We've given you an answer. Your job is to work backwards and make sure it's right.

2. Suppose the bundles on page 16 were 8 cm high. How many boxes would be needed then? Is the answer 8 boxes?

3. Freddie and Hiro are both saving money for a trip next summer. During the school year, Freddie saves $5 each week. Hiro saves $7. After 15 weeks, how much money will each of them have saved? Is the answer Freddie $75, Hiro $105?

4. Francine charges $4 per hour for babysitting. Suzy charges $4.50 per hour. Last week, they both babysat for 12 hours. How many more hours must Francine babysit to have her earnings equal Suzy's? Is the answer 1.5 hours?

I've got to raise my fees!

Read, Read, Read

When you do tests in reading comprehension, the best way to understand a passage is by doing three steps.
1. Think about the piece before you read it (make predictions by using the title and any illustrations).
2. Read the passage carefully, at a comfortable speed.
3. Go back and reread to find what you need to answer any questions.

Here's a quick example. This short article is about the *Titanic*. You already know something about that tragic story from the movie. Here are more facts:

> The *Titanic* was one of the biggest and most luxurious ships in the world. The ship was 269 metres long and 28.2 metres wide at its widest point. The hull was double-bottomed and divided into 16 compartments that were thought to be watertight. Four of these compartments could fill with water and still not affect the liner's flotation. The *Titanic* was considered unsinkable.
>
> Just before midnight on April 14, the ship hit an iceberg about 650 km south of Newfoundland. At least five of its watertight compartments were torn open. Four of these five compartments filled with water and pulled down the front of the ship. The ship sank at 2:20 AM on April 15, 1912. Because there weren't enough lifeboats aboard the ocean liner for all the passengers, some 1500 people died on that tragic night at sea.

Now look back to find the answers to these questions.

1. Why was the *Titanic* considered unsinkable?

The Titanic was thought to be unsinkable because it had a double hull and 16 compartments that were watertight.

2. What does the word "watertight" mean? _____

_____

3. Did the ship sink during the day or at night? _____

_____

4. Why did so many passengers die if there were lifeboats? _____

_____

_____

Now you try. Here's an article about the history of the Barbie doll. Read it and answer the questions.

In March 1959 the first Barbie doll was displayed at a toy fair in New York City. The doll had been first created by Ruth Handler in 1945 and named after her daughter, Barbara. While raising her daughter and her son Kenneth, Handler noticed how much her daughter liked to play "pretend" with paper dolls. She decided to invent a three-dimensional doll for her to play with. The result became the world's most famous doll — Barbie.

In 1961 Handler's son's name became immortal when the Ken doll, Barbie's male companion, was introduced. More than 800 million dolls in the Barbie line have been sold around the world. The Barbie group now includes four younger siblings, a number of friends and a wealth of accessories—each sold separately.

Barbie may have begun life as a teenage fashion model, but over the years she has taken on other jobs. Barbie has been a ballerina, a registered nurse, an airline stewardess, a surgeon and a U.S. Air Force pilot. In 1992 she ran for President but unfortunately lost. The United States would be a different place had Barbie and Ken ended up in the White House.

1. What person is the Barbie doll named after?

_____

_____

2. Was the Ken doll invented at the same time?

_____

_____

3. About how many Barbies have been sold throughout the world?

_____

_____

4. Barbie is not just a fashion model. What are three other jobs that Barbie has held?

_____

_____

Getting the Big Ideas

Some questions about a piece of writing will be on the big ideas. You might have to think about the whole article or go back to a specific section to come up with an answer.

My teacher, Ms. Sharp, was in a hurry to go to her hairstylist after school on Thursday. She was a little late leaving school, then she realized she'd be even later for her appointment because of heavy traffic, so she put her foot down hard on the accelerator as soon as she reached some clear highway.

Only a minute later, she saw flashing lights in her mirror. It was the RCMP. She immediately pulled over to the curb and the officer approached her.

"Where are you going in such a hurry?" asked the officer.

"I'm sorry. I was late for an appointment and I didn't want to be any later than I already am."

"An appointment?" asked the officer. "Are you on the way to the doctor's, or is it something else really urgent?"

Ms. Sharp was embarrassed. "Not really. I … well, I have an appointment to have my hair cut."

The officer looked at my teacher and then at her hair. He thought for a second and then smiled. "You're right, it's an emergency so I'll let you off without a ticket this time. Just leave a little more travel time in the future."

That's when my teacher blushed. Was her hair really that awful?

Start with these factual questions:

1. Who is telling the story?

The narrator is a student in Ms. Sharp's class.

Factual questions are easy!

2. Why did the RCMP officer pull over Ms. Sharp?

_____

_____

3. Did Ms. Sharp get a ticket? _____

_____

_____

Now let's try some of the "big idea" questions:

4. Why was Ms. Sharp in such a hurry?

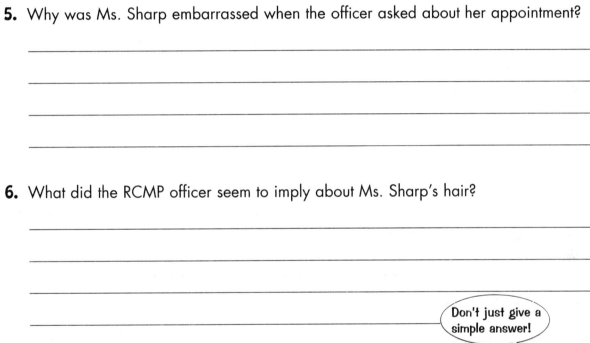

A simple answer might be:

She was late for her hairstylist appointment.

A better answer would be:

*Ms. Sharp was delayed leaving school and by heavy traffic.
She wanted to get to her hair appointment on time.*

5. Why was Ms. Sharp embarrassed when the officer asked about her appointment?

_____

_____

_____

_____

6. What did the RCMP officer seem to imply about Ms. Sharp's hair?

_____

_____

_____

_____

Don't just give a simple answer!

Now you have to think about the whole story…

7. What best describes the intention of the author of the story?

Ⓐ to give an example of dangerous driving

Ⓑ to tell a humorous story about his or her teacher

Ⓒ to make fun of Ms. Sharp

Ⓓ to describe the current state of law enforcement

Use Your Magnifying Glass

Some questions refer to small details in the reading selection. If you're allowed to do so, look back to check the facts.

In-line Skates

Many people think that in-line skates are a brand new idea, but they actually date back to 1760. The world's very first skates were invented by an Englishman named Joseph Merlin who was a craftsman, an inventor and a bit of a show-off. To make a grand entrance at a party, Merlin invented a pair of shoes with wheels. His plan was to come in, playing his violin, to amaze the guests. Instead, Merlin skated out of control across the ballroom and slammed into a mirror, smashing both the mirror and his violin!

Merlin's first skates had only two wheels so they required that the rider have a good sense of balance. An American inventor, James Plimpton, had the idea of using four wheels on each skate. This improvement in 1863 made skates easier to steer and control movement. Plimpton later opened the world's first roller rink in 1867.

The modern in-line skate was invented in 1823. That skate used five wheels in a single line to make is easy for a skater to steer. The in-line design, however, did not really catch on until 1979 when a 19-year-old hockey player name Scott Orson tried on a pair and showed them to his teammates. They were a hit! Orson went on to refine the skates, improving the wheels and bearings and coming up with a brake. Orson sold many pairs from his basement before forming the company that ultimately became Rollerblades.

Go back and check the story to answer these questions:

1. Who is credited with inventing the first roller skate?

_____

_____

_____

_____

2. What happened when Merlin showed the skates in public for the first time?

_____

_____

_____

3. When did the four-wheeled skate first appear?

Ⓐ 1760   Ⓑ 1863

Ⓒ 1867   Ⓓ The article doesn't say.

4. James Plimpton had two good ideas. What were they?

_____

_____

_____

5. Scott Orson became interested in in-line skates

Ⓐ because regular skates didn't fit his feet

Ⓑ because he could use them to train off season to play hockey

Ⓒ because they worked on ice and sidewalks

Ⓓ because he was a natural inventor

Okay, this last question isn't just detail!

6. Orson made improvements to the skates. What were they?

_____

_____

_____

7. How old was Orson when he first tried in-line skates?

_____

_____

8. Were Orson's improvements successful? How do you know?

_____

_____

_____

Know Your Characters

When you read a story, you have to know your characters. Easy questions just ask for the facts. Tougher questions need you to get "inside" characters to understand how they feel or why they do something.

Read this story about the time Hiro meets his idol, Canadian astronaut John Gaston, then tackle the thinking questions that follow. We've done the first question to show you how.

Spaced Out

Hiro was nervous. The famous Canadian astronaut John Gaston was coming to their school that afternoon. Hiro had been chosen to greet the astronaut, show him around the school and introduce him at the assembly.

"Just relax," Francine told him. "He's probably just a very nice guy."

"He might even be funny, like me," Freddie added.

Hiro had a frown on his face. None of his friends took things as seriously as he did. They didn't work hard at their homework, or study that hard for tests, or really put all their heart into projects and presentations. Hiro was different. His science fair project was easily the best in the school and one of the top five in the city. He finished near the top in the provincial math contest. He was usually very confident in what he could do — except today.

"You guys don't understand," Hiro told his friends. "It's like John Gaston is my idol. I mean, when I grow up and get out of school, I want to be just as successful as he is."

Freddie shook his head. "Sounds like a lot of work to me."

Francine was more sympathetic. "Just be yourself, Hiro. There's no reason to get uptight."

After lunch, Hiro was bouncing on the balls of his feet as he waited for John Gaston to arrive. Suddenly he saw the special Canadian Aerospace van pull into the parking lot. The passenger door opened and out came John Gaston, the first Canadian to walk on the moon! He walked to the entrance where Hiro was supposed to greet him.

"Uh, Mr. G-G-Gaston ..." Hiro stuttered for the first time in his life....

1. How does Hiro see himself as "different" from the other kids in the Active Minds Gang? Show his uniqueness through examples in the story.

Hiro thinks that his friends don't take their studies seriously enough. They don't work on their homework assignments or prepare themselves properly for tests or put their heart into either their projects or their class presentations. Hiro is ambitious and works very hard to be successful. His science project, for example, was one of the top five in the city. He also received one of the highest grades on the provincial math contest.

2. Hiro is normally very confident. But the idea of meeting his idol, astronaut John Gaston, sends him into a nervous tizzy. Why do you think he is so anxious?

_____

_____

_____

_____

_____

3. If Hiro could be convinced that Gaston was "just a very nice guy," do you think that would change Hiro's attitude towards meeting his astronaut idol? Why or why not?

_____

_____

_____

_____

_____

4. Freddy and Francine respond very differently when Hiro explains to them that his ultimate goal in life is to be "just as successful as John Gaston." Explain what Freddie and Francine's comments reveal about their character.

_____

_____

_____

_____

_____

5. What would your advice to Hiro be? Can you think of something else to say to Hiro that will calm him down and cheer him up before his big meeting?

_____

_____

_____

_____

Active Minds

Respond, Please

When you answer questions about something you read, you can't just write a word or two. A response should always be a complete sentence, even for a simple factual question. If the question is more complex, answer in a paragraph or more!

Read through this article about Lego. We'll give you a bad response to each question. Your job is to write a good one.

What's wrong with a one-word answer?

It's like answering somebody with a burp.

Lego was invented just after World War II by a Danish carpenter named Ole Kirk Christiansen. After learning woodworking, Ole built houses and furniture, but his real love was building toys and doll houses. He created a company to manufacture his wooden toys and called it Lego from the Danish words *leg godt* that mean "play well."

The first Lego bricks were made in 1949, but it wasn't until 1958 that the company came up with the present design that allows the bricks to stay together but come apart with just a tug and a twist. They were a tremendous success.

Ole and his son Godtfred were in charge of the company until 1979. They felt very strongly that Lego blocks shouldn't represent a particular object — a car or building or space station. They thought kids should be free to create their own objects using their imaginations. But parents and kids around the world kept asking for "suggestions" on what to build, so finally the company gave in.

Today, Lego kits are available to build motorized cars, sophisticated racing vehicles, outer space habitations, ocean liners and hundreds of other items. They come in large versions (Duplo) for babies and complex versions (Technics), which challenge adults. They also have step-by-step instructions on how to build the particular object pictured on the package. But after that one object is built and disassembled, and the instructions are lost under the couch, kids still use the pieces to make whatever they can imagine. Ole and Godtfred Christiansen would be happy about that.

1. When were the first Lego blocks made?

Bad answer: *1958.*

Better answer: *Lego blocks were first made in 1949, but the current design wasn't used until 1958.*

2. Did the idea for Lego blocks come from other plastic toys?

Bad answer: *No, from wood.*

Your better answer: _____

_____

_____

_____

I'm good at bad answers!

3. What kinds of things can be made from Lego pieces?

Bad answer: *Lots of stuff.*

Your better answer: _____

_____

_____

_____

4. Why did the company start selling kits with instructions to make particular toys?

Bad answer: *Because people asked them to.*

Your better answer: _____

_____

_____

_____

5. The article ends by saying "Ole and Godtfred Christiansen would be happy about that." What would they be happy about?

Bad answer: *They'd be happy kids bought Lego.*

D'oh!

Your better answer: _____

_____

_____

_____

Story Time!

The easiest kind of writing for most kids is creating a story. If you can work just from your imagination, then all it takes is ideas, organization and a few rewrites. On a test, sometimes you have to create a story from characters and situations that get handed to you. That's harder!

1. Look back at Hiro's situation on page 24 and finish the story.

First: Think it through.

How do I want to end the story? Should Hiro stay tongue-tied, or will something happen to give him confidence?

Second: Plan it out.

You can use a web or an outline or some other way to sketch out your idea.

Hiro scared -- Astronaut sees this --- Astronaut tells story -- Friendship

Third: Create a rough draft.

If you have time, get your words down in a rough form. Fix it later.

Hiro was so scared that he was ~~trem~~ shaking. The astronaut noticed this when he shook Hiro's hand. ~~"What's the matter," he asked Hiro. "Are you afraid of me."~~ John Gaston had seen this kind of thing before, and he knew just what to do.
"I remember when I was in school," he began. (continues)

Fourth: Edit it and make a clean copy.

We've already done some editing on the rough copy above. Here's the first part of the submitted story:

Hiro was so scared that he was shaking. The astronaut noticed this when he shook Hiro's hand. John Gaston had seen kids acting like this before, and he knew just what to do.
"I remember when I was in school," he began. "I sometimes had to introduce people and I always got nervous. It seemed as if I couldn't find anything to say.
"Really?" Hiro asked. Suddenly he found his voice...." (continues)

28   Writing strategies—Fiction

Now you try. Remember to think first, plan your story, write a rough version, then do a good copy. You can use the story-starter on page 28 or start your own version.

Remember to include some dialogue.

Yeah, right!

I wasn't that nervous.

Make Your Point!

On many tests, you'll be asked to present an opinion and then support your ideas. Here's how to do it.

1. The school council plans to build a playground for your school. **Plan A** gives a bigger playground but cuts down 40 trees at the back of the school. However, there is a large forest not far from the school. **Plan B** gives a playground that's a third the size of that in **Plan A** but big enough for the usual playground equipment. Plan B does not require any trees to be cut, but it puts the playground right beside the teacher parking lot.

Write a 100- to 150-word essay supporting either **Plan A** or **Plan B**.

First: Think it through.

What side do I take? Plan B. Why? No trees would be cut. The playground would be big enough. Teachers are careful drivers — there's no danger to kids in this design.

Second: Plan it out.

Introductory paragraph. Paragraph with reasons why. Paragraph with strong closing.

Third: Create a rough draft.

> *The school can give us a new playground and do something about our environment. How? By choosing Plan B over Plan A, which is dumb and destructive. Let's set an example! C'mon!*
> *To start with, what counts more? Trees or some useless space for hopscotch. The Plan B playground is plenty big enough for team sports. It has stuff for kids at lunch, too. The thing is, we have to start doing something to save trees in our community. School is a good place to start.... (continues)*

Fourth: Edit it and make a clean copy.

> *The school council has a choice to make on the new playground. It can choose Plan A, which is destructive to our environment. Or it can choose Plan B, which makes a statement about conservation. I hope they have the courage to choose Plan B.*
> *The Plan A playground may be bigger, but the Plan B playground is big enough for team sports. It has climbers for kids to use at lunch, too. Most important, Plan B give us a chance to start doing something to save trees in our community. School is a good place to make a statement. ... (continues)*

Now you try. Take the other point of view. Think, create and revise an opinion article saying that **Plan A** is better.

Plan in this space:

My opening:

Reason 1   Reason 2   Reason 3

My closing

Rough draft here:

_____

_____

_____

_____

_____

_____

_____

_____

_____

_____

_____

_____

_____

Do the finished draft on your computer or on a fresh piece of paper.

Research the value of trees to our environment. The Internet or your school library will have resources. Then write an article on the importance of those 40 trees.

So Prove It!

In the upper grades, it's not enough to say what you think. You have to prove your point. That means explaining why you think something or choosing proof from the text.

Read this story about Freddie and Hiro going camping, then use parts of it to prove your answers to the questions.

I planned ahead.

So did I!

Freddie and Hiro were ready to go camping in Algonquin Park. Freddie had planned the food, making sure there was enough food for four meals a day, totalling about 4000 calories for each of them. He put all the food supplies in a *wannigan*, the name loggers gave to the portable kitchens that travelled with them.

Hiro looked after the shelter and maps. He had a compass, of course, but also knew how to find north by using Polaris, the pole star, and making his watch into a compass. For shelter, Hiro brought a light-weight tent and two sleeping bags. Then he arranged for his dad to drop them off and pick them up at the same location two days later.

"Just in case of emergency," Hiro told his friend, "I'm bringing a copy of Coles Notes *Wilderness Survival*. It explains how to deal with insects, snakes, poisonous plants and bears."

"I'm ready for emergencies, too," Freddie replied. He reached proudly into his pack and showed Hiro what he'd brought: six O'Henry bars and a cellular phone!

1. Do you think that Freddie and Hiro are prepared for the trip? Prove your view with specific examples from the story.

Yes, Freddie and Hiro both prepared for the trip. Freddie had bought enough food for four meals a day and a wannigan to cook it. Hiro brought a map, a compass and a book on wilderness survival. Even Freddie's chocolate bars would be a good idea in case the boys got stuck somewhere.

2. Freddie brought a cellular phone in case of emergency. Is this a good idea?

A cellular phone might or might not be a good idea. It would depend on where they were camping in the park. If they were close to a major town, the cell phone might work. If they were outside of cellular range, it would be pretty useless.

Now you try one on your own. Read this article on potato chips and use details to prove your point in the questions that follow.

Potato chips were invented because an angry guest at the Moon Lake Lodge sent back his french fries. He demanded that the staff in the kitchen make them "thinner, saltier and crispier."

Chef George Crum was insulted. When his second and third orders of french fries were rejected, he grabbed a potato and cut it into slices so thin you could see through them. Then he soaked the slices in cold water, fried them quickly and covered them with salt. He thought that the customer would hate the overcooked, over-salted fries.

Amazingly, the guest loved them. So did everyone else at the lodge. Soon "George Crum's Saratoga Chips" appeared on the menu and became incredibly popular. Today, Canadians spend almost half a billion dollars each year on potato chips, eating some 300 000 kg each day!

1. Were potato chips invented after much trial and error?

_____

_____

_____

I love potato chips!

2. How are potato chips cooked differently from french fries?

_____

_____

_____

_____

3. Do Canadians eat too many potato chips? Explain your reasoning.

_____

_____

_____

_____

The Fixer-Upper

Once you write and rewrite an essay answer, you have to proofread for mistakes. You should check spelling, grammar and the clarity of your ideas. This can count for 20% or more of your mark.

Here's the first part of an essay that Freddie wrote on a take-home assignment. Francine was his partner for peer editing. In the first two paragraphs, she found 8 spelling errors, 5 punctuation errors, some word errors and a few places where Freddie repeated himself.

> *I don't think that junk food should be sold in the school cafteria. Right now, we already have too much food with bad nurishment. They sell hot dogs and french fries and pizza slices for lunch. Do kids really need to eat fries and cheesies for desert.*
>
> *Also, I think school has to make a statement about what kids should eat. How can we teach kids about nutrishun in class and then give them junk to eat in the cafeteria? It's hippocritical. It's disgusting. It's revolting. Its bad enough that kid's bring junk food to school in their lunch boxes. But if we start selling it, the school is kind of giving junk food a stamp of apparrell!*

Here's how it looked after Francine's help:

> *I don't think that junk food should be sold in the school cafeteria. We already have too much food with little or no nourishment. The cafeteria sells hot dogs and french fries and pizza slices for lunch. Do kids really need to eat cheesies for dessert?*
>
> *Also, I think school has to make a statement about what kids should eat. How can we teach kids about nutrition in class and then give them junk to eat in the cafeteria? It's hypocritical!*
>
> *It's bad enough that kids bring junk food to school in their lunch boxes. But if we start selling it, the school is giving junk food a stamp of approval!*

Thanks for the edit.

No problem.

Now you can help Freddie. Here's another of his essays. There are at least 4 spelling errors, 5 punctuation errors, 2 grammar errors and a few spots that just aren't clear. Start by marking the obvious errors.

> *Our school newspaper needs some help. To start with, it doesn't really got any news! The last issue had an article about the soccer team that came out two months after the end of season. There was something about Ms. Murphy going on pregnency leave, but by the time it came out Ms. Murphy was back teaching!*
> *Remember, the first part of "news" is "new."*
>
> *Second, there's not enough fun stuff for kids. Most of the articlas seem to be for parents and not for students. Do kids really care about "The Principle's Message?" We hear the principle every day on the intercom! Do kids care about "The School Council report?" No! We want some television reviews, and some articles on new discs and groups. I would rather read about the BackStreet Boys than the "School Council report" and I don't even like the BackStreet Boys!*

Did you find at least 10 errors? Now pretend you are Freddie, and use your own suggestions to rewrite it. You can smooth out the style while you're rewriting.

_____

_____

_____

_____

_____

_____

_____

_____

_____

My style is smooth already!

Oh yeah?

Filling Those Blanks

Some tests ask you to "fill in the blanks" to give your answers. These can be simple — where you only need to reread the article or story. Or they can be hard — where you have to think a little and then put down your ideas.

Read this passage about television and answer the questions by filling in the blanks.

> There was no single person who invented television, but historians give a lot of credit to an unemployed Scottish engineer named John Logie Baird. In 1923, Baird began working on a way to transmit pictures in the same way radio could transmit sounds. He used a fan motor, a tea chest, the lens from a bicycle light and a bunch of spare radio parts to build the world's very first TV. The following year, he transmitted a flickering image of a cross onto a white sheet — TV was born!
>
> It wasn't until 1929 that the British Broadcasting System did the first real television broadcast. At first, they used Baird's invention, but soon other people were coming up with better ways of transmitting pictures.
>
> Early television screens were designed to match early movie screens — they were 1.3 times wider than they were tall. Movies changed from the 1:1.3 ratio in the 1950s to make the movie-going experience more exciting. Cinemascope movie screens had a ratio of 1:1.8 so they were very wide. It took television makers almost 50 years to catch up. Now, new HDTVs use the modern movie screen ratio and have surround sound. This gives viewers at home almost the same experience as people in theatres.

Pretty dull show.

We'll start with some easy, factual questions:

1. The first TV image of a flickering cross was sent in ___1924___.

2. The man credited with inventing the first TV

   was a Scot named _____.

3. Early television and movie screens both had a

   height to width ratio of _____.

Now let's try some more creative "fill in the blanks."

4. Three items that John Logie Baird used to build his first TV included _____,

_____ and _____.

5. Baird thought that television could transmit pictures the same way that _____
could transmit sounds.

6. The very first TV did not use a lens from a camera or telescope, it was a lens

borrowed from a _____.

7. Movies changed to a wider screen to make the movie-going experience

more _____.

8. Today, HDTV uses _____ and _____ to try to match
movie theatres.

9. When John Logie Baird died in 1946, his early television methods had been

entirely replaced by those of other inventors. He probably felt _____ at the

treatment his invention received.

10. Television was the biggest advance in entertainment since _____.

11. Compared to early television, modern TVs are _____

_____.

12. A good title for this article would be _____.

I've always wanted to be on TV!

Eliminate the Ridiculous

When you take a multiple-choice test, you can make things easier if you eliminate one or two of the choices. Usually, one choice is way off. Another choice will be impossible. Then you only have to decide between two possible options.

---

1. Francine went to buy two litres of milk at the corner store. The carton of milk cost $2.50. Francine had $1.50 left when she left the store. How much money had she taken to the store originally?

   Ⓐ two quarters *This is dumb. You can't buy milk for 50 cents!*

   Ⓑ $5.00

   Ⓒ $1.50 *This is a trick answer. She had $1.50 when she left the store!*

   Ⓓ $4.00

So the choice is really between answers Ⓑ and Ⓒ. $1.50 change + $2.50 for the milk = $4.00. That fits the question, so the answer is Ⓓ.

2. Freddie loves chocolate-covered almonds. They cost 65 cents per 100-gram package. Freddie did so well on a test that his mom let him buy more almonds than usual. He ended up with a nickel in change from the toonie his mom gave him. How many packages did Freddie buy?

Cross out the dumb answers first:

   Ⓐ 1   Ⓑ 2   Ⓒ 3   Ⓓ 15

Think: It couldn't be just one package, because that only costs 65 cents. And it couldn't be 15 packages because that would cost a lot! That leaves two possible answers.

The right answer is: _____

3. An English pound (£) is worth about 2.5 times more than the Canadian dollar. If it costs about $7.50 to go to a movie in Canada, how many pounds should it cost to go to a movie in Britain?

Cross out the impossible answers first:

   Ⓐ £1   Ⓑ £3   Ⓒ £7.50   Ⓓ £2.50

The correct answer is: _____.

Now to practice! For these questions in math and reading, you don't have to come up with the RIGHT answer. Just cross out the two impossible choices.

The IMAX movie was developed by three Canadian movie-makers in the late1960s. The inventors wanted to make pictures so clear and so big that the viewer would get swallowed up in them. They decided to shoot IMAX movies on 70 mm film that was twice as wide as that used for movies in ordinary theatres. Then they invented a new kind of theatre using screens 30 metres across, with seats that are steeply set up so no person is sitting more than 15 metres from the screen.

4. The IMAX movie is a _____ invention.

    Ⓐ American   Ⓑ ~~European~~   Ⓒ Canadian   Ⓓ ~~ancient~~

5. How wide is the film for a movie in an ordinary theatre?

    Ⓐ 8 mm   Ⓑ 35 mm   Ⓒ 70 mm   Ⓓ 150 mm

6. IMAX uses a bigger film because

    Ⓐ it's less expensive   Ⓑ there are no sprocket holes

    Ⓒ it permits a bigger picture   Ⓓ it's more fun to use a big camera

7. Imagine yourself in an IMAX theatre. Use the dimensions given in the article. Put yourself in the middle of the theatre. Which distances are correct for (a) and (b)?

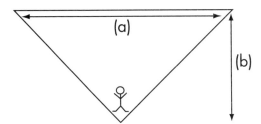

    Ⓐ 70 mm, 15 m

    Ⓑ 1960 mm, 1 m

    Ⓒ 30 m, 15 m

    Ⓓ 30 m, 30 m

8. Hiro is about 2 m tall. How many people of Hiro's size would need to lie down to match the width of an IMAX screen?

    Ⓐ 2

    Ⓑ 7.5

    Ⓒ 15

    Ⓓ 60

I'd call that lying down on the job.

Estimate First!

When you have a choice of answers, it's best to estimate first. Usually one or two of the choices will be way out of range. That brings you closer to the right answer.

1. Here's a layout for the garden that Freddie's mother wants to plant.

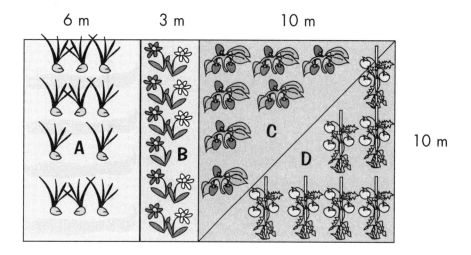

Freddie is going to use a rototiller to get the soil ready. If it takes him two hours to rototill section A, how long will it take him to do section B?

    Ⓐ 10 minutes   *No, just by looking you can see that's impossible.*

    Ⓑ 20 minutes   *Maybe. But B looks like $\frac{1}{2}$ of A, so 20 minutes is too short.*

    Ⓒ 60 minutes   *Looks good.*

    Ⓓ 4 hours   *Crazy. B is smaller than A. It couldn't take longer.*

So even without doing the math, you can see the only possible answer is Ⓑ.

2. Freddie is going to put a small fence between areas C and D. From the diagram, figure out how much fence he has to buy.

    Ⓐ 5 cm   *No. That would be the length of a finger.*

    Ⓑ 5 m   *No. That's smaller than the sides.*

    Ⓒ 50 m   *No. That's bigger than the C + D combined perimeter.*

    Ⓓ 14.14m   *Got to be this one. That's about $\sqrt{200}$ m.*

Now you try. You don't even need math to find the right answer. Just estimate the answer and only one choice will be possible.

3. It takes Freddie 3.5 hours to plant flowers in section A. How long will it take him to plant flowers in section C?

   Ⓐ 25 minutes   Ⓑ 1 hour 12 minutes

   Ⓒ 2 hours 55 minutes   Ⓓ 6 hours

4. After Freddie plants vegetables in section B, his mother wants a fence around that area. How much fence does Freddie need?

   Ⓐ 26 m   Ⓑ 13 m

   Ⓒ 30 m   Ⓓ 72 m

5. The flower seeds for section C cost $12.00. How much will the seeds for sections A and D cost?

   Ⓐ $6.00   Ⓑ $12.42

   Ⓒ $36.00   Ⓓ $26.40

6. Freddie's mom decided she wanted more vegetables than Freddie could plant in section B. If she expands it by taking 2 m × 10 m from section A, how will the size of the two sections compare?

   Ⓐ Sections A and B will be the same size.

   Ⓑ Section A will be bigger.

   Ⓒ Section B will be bigger.

   Ⓓ Section A will not longer exist.

Gardening is hard work! But my mom loves veggies!

Good, Better, Best

The teachers who set multiple choice tests usually give you one dumb choice, one not-very-close choice and two possible choices. Of the two possible choices, your job is to pick the **better** one.

Read this selection and answer the questions that follow:

People read books and magazines, but did you ever read somebody's shirt? Of course you have! Most T-shirts today come with messages and designs — and we see dozens of them every day.

Companies began putting messages on T-shirts as far back as the 1930s. They are perfect to carry messages because they are inexpensive and they're easy to print on. The very first logos on T-shirts promoted movies and small businesses. Today, T-shirts often advertise big companies, computer programs, rock concerts. Sometimes a T-shirt will even show an idea like "Peace," "Love," or "Random Acts of Kindness."

You can also design your own T-shirt to put out a message that you think is important. You'll need a plain cotton T-shirt, some fabric crayons or paints, some cardboard and a paper and pencil.

Here's what you do. First, take some time to plan your design or logo. It's best to sketch your design on paper to make sure it fits the shirt. Second, put the cardboard inside your T-shirt to keep your design from bleeding to the other side. Finally, get out your fabric crayons or paint and start working. You can work directly on the T-shirt or cut out your design and trace it on the shirt before you start.

1. Why did companies begin putting messages on T-shirts?

Ⓐ The T-shirt was a new invention. *Dumb! T-shirts are old.*

Ⓑ Coca Cola started it all. *No. Small companies were first.*

Ⓒ The designs lasted a long time. *Possible.*

Ⓓ T-shirts are cheap and easy to print. *Best answer!*

By eliminating two of the possible choices right away, you just have to choose between a "close" answer and the "best" answer. That's not so hard.

Now you try. For each question, fill the space by deciding how close the answer might be. Label the answers: "Dumb," "Not very close," "Possible" and "Best."

2. The best title for this reading selection would be:

Ⓐ T-shirts in History   *Possible*

Ⓑ T-shirt Designs and Slogans   *Best*

Ⓒ Modern Fabric Design   *Not very close*

Ⓓ The Model T   *Dumb*

That last question is tricky.

3. What three items do you need to design and print your own T-shirt?

Ⓐ fabric crayons, cardboard, pencil   _____

Ⓑ T-shirt, fabric crayons, cardboard   _____

Ⓒ T-shirt, stencil, model paint   _____

Ⓓ T-shirt, cardboard, car spray paint   _____

4. Why would you need cardboard to make your own T-shirt?

Ⓐ to make the shirt stiff   _____

Ⓑ to wash the shirt   _____

Ⓒ to practice the design   _____

Ⓓ to stop the design from bleeding through   _____

My mom does get mad!

5. What happens when you wash a T-shirt you make yourself?

Ⓐ the design washes off   _____

Ⓑ the wash water turns red   _____

Ⓒ your mom gets mad   _____

Ⓓ the article doesn't say   _____

But the article doesn't say.

So that's the best answer.

Test It Out!

When you have multiple choice answers in math, the fastest way to get an answer is to eliminate the dumb ones, then check the two good ones to see whether they solve the problem. Only one will work.

1. Francine's sister's band Foofarah! has made a new CD. In January, they sold 200 CDs at the launch. In February, after a good review, they sold 500. If they want to sell 1500 discs by the end of the year, how many do they need to sell each month from March to December?

    Ⓐ 10   *Dumb. Not even worth checking.*

    Ⓑ 50   *Maybe. 50 × 10 months = 500 copies + 200 + 500 = WRONG!*

    Ⓒ 150   *Unlikely. The answer will be a little over 50. I'll try Ⓓ first.*

    Ⓓ 80   *Bingo! 80 × 10 months = 800 copies + 200 + 500 = 1500.*

Of course, you could always calculate the answer.

But checking the supplied choices is way faster!

2. The last disc the band made sold 1848 copies over two years. How many copies did it sell each month?

    Ⓐ 25   *Dumb. That's only about 300 copies a year.*

    Ⓑ 55   *Closer.*

    Ⓒ 75   *This one is worth calculating. 75 × 24 = 1800. Nope!*

    Ⓓ 77   *Don't even have to do the math — this has to be it!*

3. Francine's sister is one member in the four-person band. They share the money they make equally, but first the discs have to be paid for. If the discs cost $2 each to make, how much will Francine's sister get if they sell 1500 copies at $12.00 each?

    Ⓐ $120   Ⓑ $1500

    Ⓒ $3750   Ⓓ $18,000

Two of these answers are dumb!

Now you try some. See how fast you can do these four problems.
Start your timer now!

4. When they put all their books together, Hiro, Suzy and Freddie have 460 different books. Hiro has twice as many books as Freddie. Suzy has 50 more than Hiro. How many books does Freddie have?

Ⓐ 12   Ⓑ 52

Ⓒ 62   Ⓓ 82

5. Hiro is a very fast reader. He checked himself and saw that he could read 300 words per minute. If there are 400 words on the average page of a book, how long would it take him to read Stephen King's latest 240-page book?

Ⓐ about 2 hours   Ⓑ 4 hours 10 minutes

Ⓒ about $5\frac{1}{2}$ hours   Ⓓ about 10 hours

6. Freddie is not a fast reader. He calculates that it takes him twice as long to read anything as it does Hiro. Hiro, as we know, reads at 300 words a minute. If it takes Hiro 3 hours to read *A History of Canada*, how long will it take Freddie to read the same book?

Ⓐ 1 hour   Ⓑ 2 hours

Ⓒ 3 hours   Ⓓ 6 hours

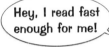

Hey, I read fast enough for me!

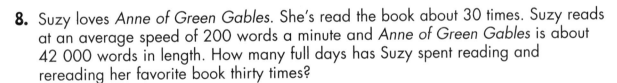

7. How long is *A History of Canada*?

Ⓐ 30 000 words   Ⓑ 47 500 words

Ⓒ 50 000 words   Ⓓ 54 000 words

8. Suzy loves *Anne of Green Gables*. She's read the book about 30 times. Suzy reads at an average speed of 200 words a minute and *Anne of Green Gables* is about 42 000 words in length. How many full days has Suzy spent reading and rereading her favorite book thirty times?

Ⓐ about a day   Ⓑ 4 days, 9 hours

Ⓒ just under 8 days   Ⓓ 16 days, 5 hours

I just love that book!

The Test-taking Puzzle

Let's check to see how much you've learned about test-taking. All the words are in this crossword.

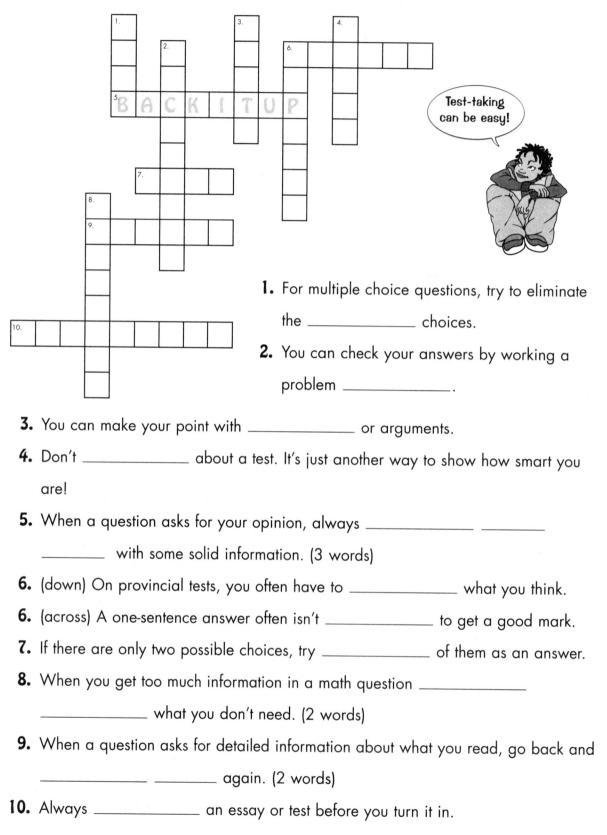

Test-taking can be easy!

5. B A C K I T U P

1. For multiple choice questions, try to eliminate the _____ choices.

2. You can check your answers by working a problem _____.

3. You can make your point with _____ or arguments.

4. Don't _____ about a test. It's just another way to show how smart you are!

5. When a question asks for your opinion, always _____ _____ _____ with some solid information. (3 words)

6. (down) On provincial tests, you often have to _____ what you think.

6. (across) A one-sentence answer often isn't _____ to get a good mark.

7. If there are only two possible choices, try _____ of them as an answer.

8. When you get too much information in a math question _____ _____ what you don't need. (2 words)

9. When a question asks for detailed information about what you read, go back and _____ _____ again. (2 words)

10. Always _____ an essay or test before you turn it in.

Answer Key

Some of the pages in this workbook contain creative activities and spaces for open-ended responses. Other activities ask students to explain their thinking or show all their work but we cannot provide such complete answers in this space. Only simple solutions and numerical answers are provided here.

Page 3
2. $10.00
3. $8.50

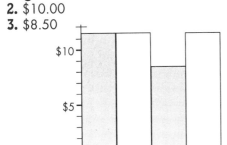

Page 5
2.

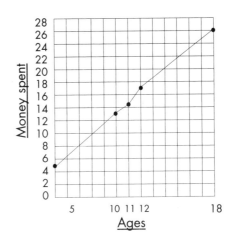

Trees: 8 ÷ 30 = 27% = 97 degrees
Foster Child: 10 ÷ 30 = 33% = 119 degrees
Basketball: 6 ÷ 30 = 20% = 72 degrees
Dance: 4 ÷ 30 = 13% = 47 degrees
Graduation: 2 ÷ 30 = 7% = 25 degrees

3. Francine's Trip: 1 cm = 500 km
NB. Montreal and Halifax are in the wrong direction!

Toronto		Winnipeg	Calgary	
	Thunder Bay	Regina		Vancouver

Page 7
2. 2 sections each 1 × 8 × 4 and 1 × 8 × 8 ft.
3. $20.00 (Don't forget the 2 × 2!)

Page 9
2. Illustrations will vary. The used-up area doesn't change simply by moving the tents, so it isn't necessary to recalculate the area. There will be no additional unused space.
3. 4% more space will be available.

Page 11
2. Amusement Park Data:

Age	Money Spent
5	$5.00
10	$13.00
11	$14.50
12	$17.00
18	$25.00

3. A 13-year-old spends about $18.00

Page 13
2. Green is half the size of red, so it's one eighth of the board. There is a one in eight chance of the coin landing there.
3. Hiro has 32 points, Freddie 8, so Freddie needs 32 – 8 to catch up. Freddie will need 24 points to match Hiro.
4. Hiro scored 32 points, which is half the team total. So the total is 32 × 2 or 64. Their total, 64, is five points higher than the other team. 64 – 5 = 59. So the score was 64 to 59.

Page 15
2. c   **3.** b   **4.** c

Page 17
2. No. 10 boxes would be needed.
3. Yes.   **4.** Yes.

Page 18
2. Watertight means waterproof.
3. The ship sank in the early morning, at 2:20 am.
4. So many people died because there were not enough lifeboats for all the passengers.

Page 19

1. The Barbie doll is named after Ruth Handler's daughter.
2. No, the Ken doll was invented in 1961, two years after Barbie.
3. More than 800 million Barbies have been sold worldwide.
4. Barbie has also "worked" as a ballerina, a registered nurse and a surgeon.

Page 20 – 21

2. The RCMP officer pulled Mrs. Sharp over because she was driving too fast.
3. No, Mrs. Sharp did not get a speeding ticket.
5. Mrs. Sharp was embarrassed because she knew that she shouldn't be putting lives at risk by speeding on the highway, just to be on time for a silly hairdressing appointment.
6. By letting Mrs. Sharp off this time, the officer was implying that her hair was, indeed, a disaster, and that she should speed to get it fixed.
7. b

Pages 22 – 23

1. Joseph Merlin is credited with inventing the first pair of roller skates in 1760.
2. Merlin lost control of his skates, crashed into a mirror and broke his violin.
3. b
4. Plimpton added two more wheels and opened the world's first roller rink in 1867.
5. b
6. Orson improved the wheels, the bearings and added brakes.
7. Orson was nineteen when he first tried in-line skates.
8. Orson's improvements were successful. He formed a company called Rollerblades because his skates were so popular.

Page 25

2. Hiro is nervous because the astronaut is very famous. As well, Hiro idolizes the astronaut so he's probably afraid that he'll do or say something awkward.
3. Hiro would still be nervous, but less so, if he could see the astronaut as an ordinary person. For instance (answers will vary).
4. Freddie's comment shows him to be lazy, unwilling to work for what he wants. Francine is sympathetic to Hiro but wants him to see famous people in an ordinary way.
5. Answers will vary.

Page 27

2. Ole Kirk Christiansen created his Lego company because he'd always loved manufacturing wooden toys and dollhouses.
3. Lego pieces can create many things: for instance motorized cars, racing vehicles, outer space habitations and ocean liners.
4. Lego started selling instructions on how to make specific objects because people seemed to want ideas about what to build.
5. Ole and Godtfred would be happy to know that, when people lose their building instructions, they continue to build Lego structures from their imaginations.

Page 33

1. No. Potato chips were invented almost by accident. Chef, George Crum responded to a customer's complaint about his thick French fries. Insulted, Crum sliced his fries very thinly, over-cooked them and then drowned them in salt to come up with potato chips.
2. Potato chips are sliced very thinly, soaked in cold water, fried very quickly and then loaded with salt.
3. Canadians eat approximately 300 000 kg of potato chips each day and that amount costs half a billion dollars each year!

Pages 36 – 37

2. John Logie Baird
3. 1:1.3
4. fan motor; tea chest; bicycle light lens
5. radio
6. bicycle light
7. exciting
8. modern movie screen ratios; surround sound
9. upset/snubbed
10. radio or movies
11. are more exciting because they try to imitate the movie-going experience through modern movie screen ratios and surround sound.
12. answers will vary

There are 12 mammals on the cover.

Pages 38 – 39
2. c   **3.** b   **5.** a and d   **6.** a and d
7. a and b   **8.** a and d

Page 41
3. c   **4.** a   **5.** d   **6.** c

Page 43
3. Not very close, Best, Possible, Dumb
4. Possible, Dumb, Not very close, Best
5. Possible, Not very close, Dumb, Best

Page 44 – 45
3. c   **4.** d   **5.** c   **6.** d
7. d   **8.** b

Page 46

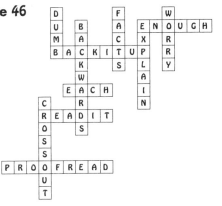

Page 51

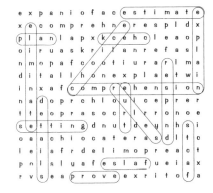

Page 52
2. 10:50 am
3. 11:15 am.
4. Freddie should not give up, but if he's out of time, he should return to the questions that are worth a lot and recheck them.
5. 30 min.   **6.** 40 seconds
7. 12.5 min. on paragraph; 1.25 min. on each multiple-choice
8. Answers will vary. Possible: outline —15 min; writing each paragraph —30 min; proofreading —15min.

Page 54
1. a   **2.** b or d   **3.** b
4. c   **5.** d   **6.** b
7. a   **8.** b   **9.** c
10. d

Pages 56 – 57
textbook - never; computer - never
answer key - never; eraser - always
protractor - sometimes; dictionary - sometimes
your mom - never
2. a   **3.** b   **4.** c
5. a   **6.** b   **7.** a
8. c   **9.** b   **10.** a

Pages 63 – 64
1. c   **2.** c   **3.** b
4. d   **5.** a   **6.** a
7. b   **8.** d   **9.** d
10. d   **11.** a   **12.** d
13. d   **14.** c   **15.** b
16. d   **17.** a   **18.** a

Page 65
1. likes to be in the "in" crowd; she lies
2. Carrie
3. fifty dollars
4. out-of-focus screen; sticky keyboard; wonky colours
5. exaggerates to the point of lying
6. antique Barbies
7. her computer is being repaired
8. they know Sherri was lying
9. alone
10. an old, junky, fifty-buck computer

Pages 68 – 69
1. b   **2.** c   **3.** c
4. MAK; $82.50, Compact; $150.00, Bargain, $161.67
5. a   **6.** b   **7.** a

Pages 72 – 74
1. c   **2.** a   **3.** b
4. c   **5.** c   **6.** d
7. d   **8.** b   **9.** d
10. a   **11.** a   **12.** c
13. b   **14.** d   **15.** b
16. a   **17.** a   **18.** d
19. c   **20.** b   **21.** b
22. c   **23.** d   **24.** a
25. d

Page 75
1. gnarly, sick; hotdog, shinny, etc.
2. Unlike regular sports, extreme sports are more dangerous and have more of an entertainment quality to them. For example, extreme skateboarding and snowboarding each have a high element of risk to them and involve lots of showy moves.
3. Public displays are a good idea because they are entertaining, bring a community together and give the kids who do them a sense that their street sports are valuable and appreciated.

Pages 76 – 77
1. d	2. c	3. a
4. d	5. b	6. a
7. b	8. c	9. a
10. b	11. 9.6 km/h	
12. 8 km/h		

Pages 78 – 79
1. b	2. d	3. d
4. d	5. d	

Pages 83–84
1. d	2. b	3. a
4. b	5. d	6. b
7. a	8. a	9. b
10. d	11. d	12. d
13. b	14. a	15. d

Page 85
1. F	2. F	3. T
4. F	5. T	6. F
7. T	8. T	9. F
10. F	11. F	12. T
13. F	14. F	15. T

Page 86
1. Repetition shows us that Ian is in the process of realizing his miraculous hit.
2. It puts a lot more pressure on a batter, but sometimes that pressure works — as it did for Ian — even if he is terrified.
3. A gym teacher should encourage weaker athletes, give them extra help and teach other kids to be encouraging too.
4. Ian doesn't really like baseball because he's not good at it. For example, he makes fun of the baseball diamond by joking that Flossie Slocum Park must be named after a dog.

5. Ian and Trevor will probably be tense together now, because Trevor caught Ian's one miraculous hit to put him out. But they might also share the quiet secret that they were nerds who, once in their lives, both made good plays.

Pages 88 – 89
1. b	2. b	3. a
4. d	5. b	6. a
7. b	8. d	9. c

Pages 90 – 91
1. b	2. d	3. a
4. a	5. b	6. d
7. d	8. c	9. d
10. a		

11. Overall, Bob's statistics are better so I'd pick him for my team over Christine.

Page 92
1. c	2. a	3. b
4. a		

5. b. I used the formula $c^2 = a^2 + b^2$.
6. d. The distance is 150 m + 300 m to walk around the field. That's 450 m. It's only 335m to cut across, so the ratio is $335 \div 450 = 0.745$. The time would have the same ratio. 4 minutes × 0.745 = 2.97 minutes or just under three minutes.
7. b. The distance to the playground from the batting cage is about 200 m.

Page 94
1. eliminate
2. estimate
3. answer
4. guess
5. skip
6. work
7. spelling; punctuation
8. explain
9. extra
10. planning; checking

Good work, guys!

Page 95
1. d
2. d
3. d
4. d
5. d
6. d

Another Test Puzzle

Here's a word search with some test-taking vocabulary.

```
e x p a n i o f a c e s t i m a t e
x e c o m p r e h n e r e s p l d x
p l a n l a p x k c e h c l e a o p
o i r u a s k r i l a n r e f a s l
n m o p a f c o o t i u r a r l m a
d i t a l l h o n e x p l a e t w i
i n x a f c o m p r e h e n s i o n
n a d o p r c h l o u i c e p r e r
t t e o p r a s o c r l r r o n o e
s e t t i n g d n u t d e y n h s i
o a a c h i o c a t e r a s d l t c
l e i a f r d e l i m o p r e a c t
p o l s l u a f e s l a f u e i a x
r v s e a p r o v e e x r i t o f a
```

choice	check	comprehension	details
eliminate	estimate	explain	facts
false	plan	prove	respond
rules	setting	true	

Watch Your Watch!

When you take a big test, the first thinking you should do is a little math. Figure out how much the questions are worth, then calculate the time you should take for each answer.

Here are some questions to practice your timing skills:

1. Freddie is taking a big test on a unit in science. The teacher is allowing one hour for the test. There are 10 short-answer questions worth 3 marks each; 2 lab questions worth 10 marks each; and an essay worth 50 marks. How long should he spend on each part?

Think: I need 5 minutes to plan my attack and 5 minutes to proofread and check answers.

$$60 \text{ min} - 10 \text{ min.} = 50 \text{ min.} \qquad 50 \text{ min} = 100 \text{ marks}$$

Essay is 50 marks. $\dfrac{50}{100} = \dfrac{1}{2}$ $50 \text{ min} \times \dfrac{1}{2} = 25$ minutes.

Lab questions are 20 marks. $\dfrac{20}{100} = \dfrac{1}{5}$.$50 \text{ min.} \times \dfrac{1}{5} = 10$ minutes.

That's 5 minutes for each lab question.

Ten short answers at 3 marks each = 30 marks. $\dfrac{30}{100} = \dfrac{3}{10}$

$50 \text{ min.} \times \dfrac{3}{10} = 15$ minutes, about 1.5 minutes each question.

2. If the test starts at 10:20 AM and Freddie does the questions in order, when should he be starting the essay?

3. What time should Freddie start going over his answers?

At least I never give up!

4. If Freddie really gets into trouble and can't finish on time, what should he do?

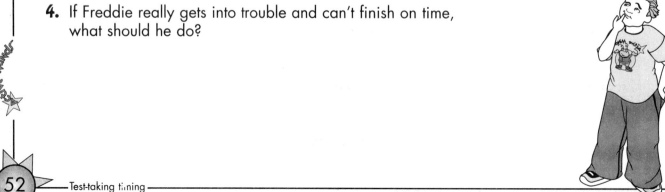

5. Francine is taking the provincial assessment in math. The time permitted for the first section is 2 hours. The teacher is going to go over the question material for about 30 minutes at the beginning of the time period. If there are 3 pages of questions, about how long should Francine spend on each page? (Don't worry about the review time for this one.)

6. Hiro is doing a long multiple-choice test. There are 75 questions to be done in 60 minutes. Hiro wants to leave the last 10 minutes to go back over his answers and tackle questions any that he missed. About how long does he have for each question?

7. Suzy's teacher gave the class a test worth 24 marks. The kids have only 30 minutes to do the entire test! There are 12 multiple-choice questions and a short one-paragraph answer, worth 12 marks. If Suzy allows the last 5 minutes to go over everything, about how much time should she spend on the paragraph? How much time on each multiple-choice question?

8. Freddie's teacher, Mr. Givens, is giving the class a big essay to do as a unit test. The essay is supposed to be about 200 words long. It should also be 3 paragraphs in length. Mr. Givens hates spelling errors, so kids are allowed to use a dictionary to proofread their work.

If Freddie has two hours to do the essay, and not enough time to do a rough draft and a finished draft, how should he organize his time?

Planning, outline: _____ minutes

Writing each paragraph: _____ minutes

Proofreading: _____ minutes

Total time: _____

(120 minutes total time)

Be Test Smart!

Kids do all sorts of silly things on tests that cost them marks. Here's a quick quiz on how to avoid dumb stuff. See if you're test-ready.

1. Kids throw away the <u>most</u> marks by

   Ⓐ Not answering questions fully

   Ⓑ Bad spelling

   Ⓒ Lousy math

   Ⓓ Not organizing their time

2. The dumbest thing you can do on a test is

   Ⓐ Daydream

   Ⓑ Forget to study

   Ⓒ Guess

   Ⓓ Give up

3. If you come across a question that's too hard, you should

   Ⓐ Give up

   Ⓑ Skip it the first time, come back at the end

   Ⓒ Guess

   Ⓓ Leave it blank

4. When you figure out how to spend time on a test, always

   Ⓐ Go as fast as you can

   Ⓑ Ask your friends how they do it

   Ⓒ Leave 5 to 10 minutes to go over your answers

   Ⓓ Leave stuff till the end

5. If you finish a test early, you should

   Ⓐ Ask if you can leave early

   Ⓑ Take out a book and read

   Ⓒ Work on your homework

   Ⓓ Check your answers for errors

6. If a friend asks you for an answer on a test that you're supposed to do on your own, you should

   Ⓐ Tell the teacher

   Ⓑ Ignore the request

   Ⓒ Whisper the answer

   Ⓓ Write the answer down and pass it over

7. On a provincial assessment, you often have several days to do the work. The best approach is to

   Ⓐ Space the work out over the time you're given

   Ⓑ Relax and do your work on the last day

   Ⓒ Work as fast as you can to finish early

   Ⓓ Take it home and ask your parents for help

I always take all the time the teacher allows

8. On a multiple-choice test in math, you don't always have to calculate the right answer. Why not?

Ⓐ   Why trust your own math?

Ⓑ   Two of the answers are often impossible.

Ⓒ   The questions are just tricks, anyhow.

Ⓓ   Your teacher will help you.

9. In math, it's always a good idea to _____ before you calculate an answer.

Ⓐ   Ask the teacher for help

Ⓑ   Check your calculator

Ⓒ   Estimate

Ⓓ   Guess

10. If you're really stuck and you can see the answers of someone sitting up ahead of you, you can always

Ⓐ   Peek at that person's answers

Ⓑ   Figure how smart the person is, then peek at the answers

Ⓒ   Do your own answer, then see if it matches that person's answers

Ⓓ   Ignore the view; go to another question and come back to the tough one

11. We all have problems taking tests. Tick off which problems below affect you.

☐ I get nervous   ☐ I don't gauge my time

☐ I'm in too much of a hurry   ☐ I don't study enough

☐ I don't go over my answers   ☐ I don't focus on the questions

☐ I don't proofread my work   ☐ I keep bugging the teacher for help

☐ I get scared without a calculator or the book

Write your own special problem(s): _____

_____

_____

_____

_____

Know the Rules

Every test has rules. Sometimes a provincial test goes on for a week or more. Some multiple-choice tests are only 10 minutes long. For some tests it's smart to guess. For other tests, you'd better know the answers. It all depends on the rules.

Here are some "rule" questions to help you get top marks.

1. **Bring what you need** — and what you're allowed. You can often bring helpful items to a test. Mark these items to show you can bring them whether ... always, never, sometimes.

   pencil ___*always*___   eraser _____   notes _____

   protractor ___*sometimes*___   textbook _____   dictionary _____

   computer _____   your mom _____   answer key _____

2. **Calculate the odds.** Some multiple-choice tests have no penalties for wrong answers. If there's no penalty, then what should you do when you hit a question you just can't answer?

   (A) guess   (B) guess if you can narrow to two choices

   (C) leave it blank   (D) always choose answer (D)

3. Some multiple-choice tests give a reasonable penalty for guessing. If you lose $\frac{1}{2}$ the value of the question for every wrong answer, then what should you do when you hit a question you just can't answer?

   (A) guess   (B) guess if you can narrow to two choices

   (C) leave it blank   (D) always choose answer (D)

4. Some multiple-choice tests give a big penalty for guessing. If you lose the entire value of the question for every wrong answer, then what should you do when you hit a question you just can't answer?

   (A) guess   (B) guess if you can narrow to two choices

   (C) leave it blank   (D) always choose answer (D)

5. If the penalty for a wrong answer is small, and you're not sure about the right answer, what should you do?

   (A) guess   (B) guess if you can narrow to two choices

   (C) skip the question   (D) always choose answer (D)

6. Show your work. On many tests, it's not enough to give the right answer. If the teacher says "show your work" and you hit a question you just can't answer, you should

(A) guess the answer   (B) try anyhow, even if you get the wrong answer

(C) skip the question   (D) make up some numbers

7. Show your writing process. On many language arts tests, you have to show the stages in your writing, not just a finished essay. The stages would include

(A) points/ideas, rough, finished   (B) outline, finished

(C) rough, finished   (D) date, finished version

8. Show your thinking. On many tests, you have to explain how you thought your way to the answer. Usually, this can be done

(A) in a word or two   (B) by filling a blank

(C) in a few sentences   (D) in a 3-paragraph essay

9. Figure the marks. If you're doing a 30-mark essay and the instructions say "up to 20% can be deducted for spelling and grammar errors," those errors could cost you

(A) 5 marks   (B) 6 marks

(C) 10%   (D) lots

> Play by the rules and you'll be the winner!

10. Use your strengths. If you're good at multiple choice and bad at essays, where should you spend more time on a test?

(A) the essay   (B) the multiple choice

(C) even amounts of time   (D) short answers

Explain why: _____

11. What's the worst mark you ever got on a test? _____ What went wrong?

Usually it's more than one thing: _____

_____

12. What was the last difficult test where you did really well? _____

What did you do that gave you the good mark? _____

_____

Active Minds Answer Sheet

Many standardized tests require that you put your answers on a separate answer sheet like this one. Use this one to record multiple-choice answers for the three practice tests that follow. (Note: Some pages will ask for longer answers. Those answers should be written right on the page.)

Pages 63 – 64
1. Ⓐ Ⓑ Ⓒ Ⓓ
2. Ⓐ Ⓑ Ⓒ Ⓓ
3. Ⓐ Ⓑ Ⓒ Ⓓ
4. Ⓐ Ⓑ Ⓒ Ⓓ
5. Ⓐ Ⓑ Ⓒ Ⓓ
6. Ⓐ Ⓑ Ⓒ Ⓓ
7. Ⓐ Ⓑ Ⓒ Ⓓ
8. Ⓐ Ⓑ Ⓒ Ⓓ
9. Ⓐ Ⓑ Ⓒ Ⓓ
10. Ⓐ Ⓑ Ⓒ Ⓓ
11. Ⓐ Ⓑ Ⓒ Ⓓ
12. Ⓐ Ⓑ Ⓒ Ⓓ
13. Ⓐ Ⓑ Ⓒ Ⓓ
14. Ⓐ Ⓑ Ⓒ Ⓓ
15. Ⓐ Ⓑ Ⓒ Ⓓ
16. Ⓐ Ⓑ Ⓒ Ⓓ
17. Ⓐ Ⓑ Ⓒ Ⓓ
18. Ⓐ Ⓑ Ⓒ Ⓓ
19. Ⓐ Ⓑ Ⓒ Ⓓ
20. Ⓐ Ⓑ Ⓒ Ⓓ

Pages 72 – 74
1. Ⓐ Ⓑ Ⓒ Ⓓ
2. Ⓐ Ⓑ Ⓒ Ⓓ
3. Ⓐ Ⓑ Ⓒ Ⓓ
4. Ⓐ Ⓑ Ⓒ Ⓓ
5. Ⓐ Ⓑ Ⓒ Ⓓ
6. Ⓐ Ⓑ Ⓒ Ⓓ
7. Ⓐ Ⓑ Ⓒ Ⓓ
8. Ⓐ Ⓑ Ⓒ Ⓓ
9. Ⓐ Ⓑ Ⓒ Ⓓ
10. Ⓐ Ⓑ Ⓒ Ⓓ
11. Ⓐ Ⓑ Ⓒ Ⓓ
12. Ⓐ Ⓑ Ⓒ Ⓓ
13. Ⓐ Ⓑ Ⓒ Ⓓ
14. Ⓐ Ⓑ Ⓒ Ⓓ
15. Ⓐ Ⓑ Ⓒ Ⓓ
16. Ⓐ Ⓑ Ⓒ Ⓓ
17. Ⓐ Ⓑ Ⓒ Ⓓ
18. Ⓐ Ⓑ Ⓒ Ⓓ
19. Ⓐ Ⓑ Ⓒ Ⓓ
20. Ⓐ Ⓑ Ⓒ Ⓓ
21. Ⓐ Ⓑ Ⓒ Ⓓ
22. Ⓐ Ⓑ Ⓒ Ⓓ
23. Ⓐ Ⓑ Ⓒ Ⓓ
24. Ⓐ Ⓑ Ⓒ Ⓓ
25. Ⓐ Ⓑ Ⓒ Ⓓ

Pages 78 – 79
1. Ⓐ Ⓑ Ⓒ Ⓓ
2. Ⓐ Ⓑ Ⓒ Ⓓ
3. Ⓐ Ⓑ Ⓒ Ⓓ
4. Ⓐ Ⓑ Ⓒ Ⓓ
5. Ⓐ Ⓑ Ⓒ Ⓓ
6. Ⓐ Ⓑ Ⓒ Ⓓ

Pages 83 – 84
1. Ⓐ Ⓑ Ⓒ Ⓓ
2. Ⓐ Ⓑ Ⓒ Ⓓ
3. Ⓐ Ⓑ Ⓒ Ⓓ
4. Ⓐ Ⓑ Ⓒ Ⓓ
5. Ⓐ Ⓑ Ⓒ Ⓓ
6. Ⓐ Ⓑ Ⓒ Ⓓ
7. Ⓐ Ⓑ Ⓒ Ⓓ
8. Ⓐ Ⓑ Ⓒ Ⓓ
9. Ⓐ Ⓑ Ⓒ Ⓓ
10. Ⓐ Ⓑ Ⓒ Ⓓ
11. Ⓐ Ⓑ Ⓒ Ⓓ
12. Ⓐ Ⓑ Ⓒ Ⓓ
13. Ⓐ Ⓑ Ⓒ Ⓓ
14. Ⓐ Ⓑ Ⓒ Ⓓ
15. Ⓐ Ⓑ Ⓒ Ⓓ

Page 85
1. Ⓣ Ⓕ
2. Ⓣ Ⓕ
3. Ⓣ Ⓕ
4. Ⓣ Ⓕ
5. Ⓣ Ⓕ
6. Ⓣ Ⓕ
7. Ⓣ Ⓕ
8. Ⓣ Ⓕ
9. Ⓣ Ⓕ
10. Ⓣ Ⓕ
11. Ⓣ Ⓕ
12. Ⓣ Ⓕ
13. Ⓣ Ⓕ
14. Ⓣ Ⓕ
15. Ⓣ Ⓕ

Pages 88 – 89
1. Ⓐ Ⓑ Ⓒ Ⓓ
2. Ⓐ Ⓑ Ⓒ Ⓓ
3. Ⓐ Ⓑ Ⓒ Ⓓ
4. Ⓐ Ⓑ Ⓒ Ⓓ
5. Ⓐ Ⓑ Ⓒ Ⓓ
6. Ⓐ Ⓑ Ⓒ Ⓓ
7. Ⓐ Ⓑ Ⓒ Ⓓ
8. Ⓐ Ⓑ Ⓒ Ⓓ
9. Ⓐ Ⓑ Ⓒ Ⓓ

Pages 90 – 91
1. Ⓐ Ⓑ Ⓒ Ⓓ
2. Ⓐ Ⓑ Ⓒ Ⓓ
3. Ⓐ Ⓑ Ⓒ Ⓓ
4. Ⓐ Ⓑ Ⓒ Ⓓ
5. Ⓐ Ⓑ Ⓒ Ⓓ
6. Ⓐ Ⓑ Ⓒ Ⓓ
7. Ⓐ Ⓑ Ⓒ Ⓓ
8. Ⓐ Ⓑ Ⓒ Ⓓ
9. Ⓐ Ⓑ Ⓒ Ⓓ
10. Ⓐ Ⓑ Ⓒ Ⓓ

Pages 92 – 93
1. Ⓐ Ⓑ Ⓒ Ⓓ
2. Ⓐ Ⓑ Ⓒ Ⓓ
3. Ⓐ Ⓑ Ⓒ Ⓓ
4. Ⓐ Ⓑ Ⓒ Ⓓ
5. Ⓐ Ⓑ Ⓒ Ⓓ
6. Ⓐ Ⓑ Ⓒ Ⓓ
7. Ⓐ Ⓑ Ⓒ Ⓓ

Pages 76 – 77
1. Ⓐ Ⓑ Ⓒ Ⓓ
2. Ⓐ Ⓑ Ⓒ Ⓓ
3. Ⓐ Ⓑ Ⓒ Ⓓ
4. Ⓐ Ⓑ Ⓒ Ⓓ
5. Ⓐ Ⓑ Ⓒ Ⓓ
6. Ⓐ Ⓑ Ⓒ Ⓓ
7. Ⓐ Ⓑ Ⓒ Ⓓ
8. Ⓐ Ⓑ Ⓒ Ⓓ
9. Ⓐ Ⓑ Ⓒ Ⓓ
10. Ⓐ Ⓑ Ⓒ Ⓓ

Pages 68 – 69
1. Ⓐ Ⓑ Ⓒ Ⓓ
2. Ⓐ Ⓑ Ⓒ Ⓓ
3. Ⓐ Ⓑ Ⓒ Ⓓ
4. Ⓐ Ⓑ Ⓒ Ⓓ
5. Ⓐ Ⓑ Ⓒ Ⓓ
6. Ⓐ Ⓑ Ⓒ Ⓓ

Fill the bubble completely.

Use a pencil.

Sometimes you have to identify yourself on the answer sheet. Practice with this one:

First or Given Name								Last Name										
○	○	○	○	○	○	○	○	○	○	○	○	○	○	○	○	○	○	○
A	A	A	A	A	A	A	A	A	A	A	A	A	A	A	A	A	A	A
B	B	B	B	B	B	B	B	B	B	B	B	B	B	B	B	B	B	B
C	C	C	C	C	C	C	C	C	C	C	C	C	C	C	C	C	C	C
D	D	D	D	D	D	D	D	D	D	D	D	D	D	D	D	D	D	D
E	E	E	E	E	E	E	E	E	E	E	E	E	E	E	E	E	E	E
F	F	F	F	F	F	F	F	F	F	F	F	F	F	F	F	F	F	F
G	G	G	G	G	G	G	G	G	G	G	G	G	G	G	G	G	G	G
H	H	H	H	H	H	H	H	H	H	H	H	H	H	H	H	H	H	H
I	I	I	I	I	I	I	I	I	I	I	I	I	I	I	I	I	I	I
J	J	J	J	J	J	J	J	J	J	J	J	J	J	J	J	J	J	J
K	K	K	K	K	K	K	K	K	K	K	K	K	K	K	K	K	K	K
L	L	L	L	L	L	L	L	L	L	L	L	L	L	L	L	L	L	L
M	M	M	M	M	M	M	M	M	M	M	M	M	M	M	M	M	M	M
N	N	N	N	N	N	N	N	N	N	N	N	N	N	N	N	N	N	N
O	O	O	O	O	O	O	O	O	O	O	O	O	O	O	O	O	O	O
P	P	P	P	P	P	P	P	P	P	P	P	P	P	P	P	P	P	P
Q	Q	Q	Q	Q	Q	Q	Q	Q	Q	Q	Q	Q	Q	Q	Q	Q	Q	Q
R	R	R	R	R	R	R	R	R	R	R	R	R	R	R	R	R	R	R
S	S	S	S	S	S	S	S	S	S	S	S	S	S	S	S	S	S	S
T	T	T	T	T	T	T	T	T	T	T	T	T	T	T	T	T	T	T
U	U	U	U	U	U	U	U	U	U	U	U	U	U	U	U	U	U	U
V	V	V	V	V	V	V	V	V	V	V	V	V	V	V	V	V	V	V
W	W	W	W	W	W	W	W	W	W	W	W	W	W	W	W	W	W	W
X	X	X	X	X	X	X	X	X	X	X	X	X	X	X	X	X	X	X
Y	Y	Y	Y	Y	Y	Y	Y	Y	Y	Y	Y	Y	Y	Y	Y	Y	Y	Y
Z	Z	Z	Z	Z	Z	Z	Z	Z	Z	Z	Z	Z	Z	Z	Z	Z	Z	Z

This is easy when you have a name as short as mine.

Sherri's Computer

Provincial tests often give you a story with both math and language arts questions. Here's a story. The questions follow on pages 63 – 69.

Did you ever tell a lie that got you into big trouble?
Here's a story about a girl who gets caught in the lies she tells.

Sometimes words can get bigger and bigger, just like bubble gum bubbles. You start out with this tiny wad of gum, shape it with your tongue, and then if you blow carefully you get a bubble. But if you blow too hard, you get stringy bits of gum on your face. I know, because it's happened to me — and I'm not just talking about bubble gum.

It started last year, in grade 6, when I was out in the playground talking to my friend Carrie. I call her "Careless Carrie" sometimes, though she's really isn't. Carrie is about the most careful person in class ... not like me.

Anyway, I was telling Carrie that my mom had bought us a computer. It was a really junky old computer, like maybe it cost $50. It had one of those out-of-focus screens with wonky colours and the keyboard felt like somebody had spilled pop on it. But the thing worked and we had a word processing program and a couple of games. It was certainly better than NO computer, which is what we had before. So Carrie and I were talking about that — computers versus no computers — when Monica and her friends came over.

Monica is about the richest kid in our class, maybe in our school. She's got this curly, curly hair and always wears the MOST expensive running shoes and jeans. At school, Monica hangs around with her two good friends, Francine and René who are also rich ... and popular ... and stuck-up.

Anyway, while I was talking to Carrie, Monica came over with her friends. I guess they must have been listening in.

"You got a new computer?" she said, smiling with her perfect teeth.

"Yeah, kind of."

"What did you get?" she asked. "A new Pentium like my dad has?"

"My mom's got her own new Mac G4," Francine added.

"What about you?" René asked.

So I could have told them just what I told Carrie. I could have said my mom got a junky computer for maybe $50 with a fuzzy screen and wonky colours. Then the three of them would have laughed at me and gone away, feeling superior.

But something about the way Francine said "My mom's got her own new portable computer" got to me. Maybe I've got a bit of a temper, or maybe I thought she was a bit too stuck-up.

Anyway, I said, "Oh, it's a really great computer. I don't know how my mom could afford it." That's what I said, the words just getting bigger like a bubble gum bubble.

"Really?" Monica asked. She smiled like she didn't believe me.

So I blew the bubble even bigger. "Oh, yeah. There's this ENORMOUS monitor, I mean, it's bigger than our TV. My mom said there was no sense getting anything less than the best."

"Wow," René said, "ours is just a laptop."

"Did you get games?" Monica asked.

"Yeah, tons," I lied. Once you get going, it's so easy to keep lying. "I haven't even tried them all yet. And they all run so fast with that new video processor!"

The bell rang to stop me from adding any more lies, which was good because I was running out of ideas. What I know about computers would fill a very small computer file, or a really tiny book. When we went inside to our lockers, Carrie kept staring at me. She had this look on her face like I had lost my mind.

"I couldn't help it," I whispered to her. "The three of them were just so ... smug."

Smug was a good word for Monica and her group. It's better than stuck-up because anybody can be stuck-up about one thing or another. Stuck-up just means you think you're better than you are. But smug means you've got an attitude. Like, I've got all the good stuff and I deserve it ... so there!

But a funny thing happened after I told Monica and her friends about my made-up computer — they started talking to me. Before, the three of them treated me pretty much like a tree or a door knob. I was there, I existed, but who cared? But after my big computer story, they began to treat me like a person. They let me talk with them at recess. They chose me to be in their group for a history project. Francine even called me at home a couple of times to ask about homework.

Carrie didn't like it. "You're getting smug," she told me at lunch. Carrie and I always had lunch together at school because we were bussed in. Monica and her friends walked home for lunch, but they hadn't invited me to join them. Not yet, anyhow.

"I'm not smug," I said. "You're just jealous because they don't talk to you."

"I can get by without friends like that," Carrie told me.

Carrie got really jealous when Monica said I could come over to her house for lunch. Monica lives in a house about five times the size of our apartment. Her father's a lawyer and her mom does something during the day, but there's a nanny who's there all the time. I think I spent the whole lunch hour dying from envy. I mean, Monica had an antique Barbie collection that was so big it took up an entire room!

Of course, I didn't act like I was impressed or anything. I told her about how my mom collects antique furniture. I don't even know how I made that up. Most of our furniture comes from Wal-Mart.

All this went on for maybe a month, until Black Wednesday. I was home sick with the flu and spent most of the day lying in bed, watching soaps on TV. That's easy to do in our apartment because there's only one bedroom. I sleep on a pull-out couch in the living room. The TV is at the end of the bed and the junky computer is right beside it.

On Black Wednesday, I was lying there, drinking orange juice, when I heard a knock. I went to the door and looked through the little peep hole.

There they were — Monica, Francine and René.

"Come on, Sherri," Francine yelled. "We know you're home."

"Yeah, get out of bed. We've got a game to play on your computer," Monica said and the three of them laughed.

I leaned up against the other side of the door and wanted to die. They'd never been to my apartment, ever. I'd told them we lived in the penthouse, with a view over the lake. I'd told them we had antique furniture worth a gazillion dollars. I couldn't even remember every lie I'd told them.

"Open up, Sherri, you're not that sick," Francine said, pounding on the door.

That's it, I told myself, I'll be too sick. I won't let them in.

I unbolted the door and opened it just a crack. "Sorry, I'm really sick — " I said in my sickest voice. But somehow, somebody pushed the door. It flew open and the three of them could see everything — my messy bed, the blaring TV, the junky computer. Everything.

"We brought you—" Monica began, and then she stopped talking. She was was looking around at my house with these big wide eyes.

"I'm sick ..." I croaked, but it didn't matter.

"So that's your new computer," Monica said.

"It's ... well ... I ... " I tried to think of something while the gum was exploding on my face. "It's back at the store ... for repairs."

The three of them saw right through me. I knew it, even before they turned and ran, giggling, down the hall.

When I got back to school on Friday, I ate lunch by myself. Monica never invited me to her house again. René and Francine were decent to me, but that was just on the surface. We were all kind of embarrassed to be around each other.

The next week, Carrie came and sat next to me in the lunch room. She unpacked her sandwiches, just like she used to, and told me that she had just got a computer too. "It's a junky, used computer," she said loud enough for anybody to hear. Then, in a quiet voice, she asked if I wanted to come over to her place and play a game on it.

How Well Did You Read?

Here's a quiz to see whether you picked up details from the story. Look back if you need to. Mark your answers on the answer sheet on page 58.

1. In the story, Careless is a nickname for

   (A) Karen
   (B) Catherine
   (C) Carrie
   (D) Sergio

2. Sherri uses this nickname

   (A) because someone told her to
   (B) because she doesn't know her full name
   (C) because her friend is very careful
   (D) because her friend once lost a science project

3. Sherri describes Monica as

   (A) having curly hair and cheap running shoes and jeans
   (B) having curly hair and expensive running shoes and jeans
   (C) having straight hair and expensive running shoes and jeans
   (D) having straight hair and cheap running shoes and jeans

4. Francine and René are

   (A) friends of Carrie's
   (B) two computer nerds
   (C) kids on Sherri's basketball team
   (D) friends of Monica's

5. Sherri's computer is

   (A) a really junky old computer
   (B) a laptop
   (C) a brand new iMac
   (D) none of the above

6. Sherri lives in

   (A) an apartment
   (B) a penthouse
   (C) a townhouse
   (D) over a garage

7. Sherri tells Monica and the others that

   (A) her dad is a basketball coach
   (B) her computer has an enormous monitor
   (C) her new computer is really awful
   (D) her dad paid for the new computer

8. Smug means

   (A) that you love computers
   (B) that you are rich
   (C) the weather is cloudy
   (D) that you have an attitude

9. The setting of this story is

   (A) at a baseball game
   (B) at a school
   (C) at an apartment
   (D) both (B) and (C)

10. The author compares telling lies to

(A) filling a balloon with air

(B) riding a bike with no hands

(C) holding your breath

(D) blowing a bubble with bubble gum

11. What was Sherri doing on Black Wednesday?

(A) She was sick at home

(B) She was at school

(C) She was playing basketball

(D) She was painting her room

12. Why does the author call this day Black Wednesday?

(A) It was dark outside

(B) Sherri got black paint on her hands

(C) To scare the reader

(D) Because it was a horrible day for Sherri

13. What happens after Sherri tells her big lie?

(A) Monica and her friends start to treat her like a person

(B) She spends less time with Carrie

(C) She is chosen by Monica to join their group for the history project

(D) all of the above

14. When the "friends" show up at her door,

(A) Sherri invites them inside

(B) they all decide to go out for a snack

(C) Sherri's real computer is discovered

(D) Sherri's mother kicks the kids out

15. Sherri has one last lie about her computer:

(A) her dad took it

(B) it's in the store for repairs

(C) it's on loan to her brother

(D) her mother took it to work

16. How do you think Sherri felt after Monica saw the truth?

(A) alone

(B) crazy

(C) happy

(D) embarrassed

17. How do we know Sherri and Carrie are friends at the end of the story?

(A) they eat lunch together

(B) Sherri writes Carrie a letter

(C) Sherri fights with Monica and her friends

(D) they buy a new computer together

18. When Sherri says "the gum was exploding," she means

(A) her lie was exposed in a messy way

(B) her computer was not working properly

(C) her mom was mad about her chewing gum

(D) the bubble gum bubble she was blowing popped in her face

Short and Sweet

Some tests ask short-answer questions. See if you can answer these questions on "Sherri's Computer" by filling in the blanks.

1. Sherri's biggest problem is that she _____.

2. Sherri's one good friend is named _____.

3. Sherri thinks that her new computer cost about _____.

4. There are at least two things wrong with Sherri's computer:
   _____ and _____.

5. When Sherri tells Monica and her friends about the computer, she _____
   _____.

6. We know Monica is rich because she has a collection of _____
   _____.

7. When Monica and her friends visit Sherri, she tells them that _____
   _____.

8. The three girls go laughing down the hall of Sherri's apartment because
   _____.

9. For a while, Sherri has to eat lunch _____.

10. When Carrie gets a computer, she admits that it's a _____
    _____.

Paragraph answer

What do you think Sherri learned from this experience?

_____

_____

_____

_____

_____

_____

Think It Through!

For these questions, you have to think through the whole story and write some thoughtful answers. Use these pages for your rough copy. Your good answers should be on another sheet.

1. Sherri tells her friend Carrie the truth about her computer, but she lies to Monica and the others. Explain why.

_____

_____

_____

_____

_____

_____

2. Later on, Sherri adds another lie about how she lives. What is it?

_____

_____

_____

_____

_____

_____

3. There are two kinds of "friends" in the story. Explain each type and how they are shown. Which type is a true friend?

_____

_____

_____

_____

_____

_____

4. In this story, Sherri is not very nice to Carrie. Give two examples of when she treats Carrie poorly.

_____

_____

_____

5. At the end of the story, Carrie forgives Sherri. How do we see this?

_____

_____

_____

_____

6. Have you ever forgiven a friend? Explain what happened.

_____

_____

_____

_____

7. This story has a moral or a message. Try to give the moral in a sentence. Then explain it more fully.

_____

_____

_____

_____

8. The author suggests that the way someone blows up a bubble gum bubble is much like the way Sherri's lies get bigger and then explode. Find three ways this comparison works.

_____

_____

_____

_____

Sherri's Computer Math

Here are some math questions based on the story. Mark your answers on the answer sheet (page 58)

1. Sherri thinks her mom paid about $50 for the used computer. Even if she bought one that cheap, her mom would have to pay GST and PST of 15% on the price. What would the computer actually cost, including the taxes?

Ⓐ $50   Ⓑ $57.50

Ⓒ $42.50   Ⓓ $65

2. Sherri and Carrie looked at newspaper ads for computers and made a chart comparing various models. Here's the chart:

	Clone Computer	MAK Plus	Compact Computer	Bargain Computers
RAM	128	256	312	32
Hard drive	12 gig	20 gig	12 gig	6 gig
Free Extras	modem, CDRW	modem	modem, CDRW	none
Price	$1500	$1650	$1800	$970

Use your calculator to find the cost per RAM for each computer.

Clone: $1500 ÷ 128 = $11.78 per RAM

Which set of answers are correct for MAK, Compact and Bargain computers:

Ⓐ $7.42 per RAM, $6.45, $22.91

Ⓑ $7.42, $5.77, $22.91

Ⓒ $6.45, $5.77, $30.31

Ⓓ $6.45, $7.42, $22.91

3. If the cost of RAM were the only issue, which is the cheapest computer?

Ⓐ Clone

Ⓑ MAK

Ⓒ Compact

Ⓓ Bargain

4. Another way of figuring value is by hard drive memory. For each computer, calculate the cost of a gig of hard drive memory.

Clone: $1500 ÷ 12 = $125 per gig

From most expensive to least expensive for hard drive memory, how do the computers rank?

Ⓐ Bargain, Compact, Clone, MAK Plus

Ⓑ MAK Plus, Compact, Clone, Bargain

Ⓒ Clone, Bargain, MAK Plus, Compact

Ⓓ all the computers are equal

5. After charting all the variables, Sherri decided the Compact was the best value for her. Her mom will pay the taxes. Sherri makes $32 each weekend doing babysitting. If she has $500 in the bank for a new computer, how long will it take her to save the rest of the money she needs.

Ⓐ 31 weeks   Ⓑ about 41 weeks

Ⓒ about 49 weeks   Ⓓ 50.7 weeks

6. Which graph shows the way in which Sherri's money will intersect with the cost of the computer?

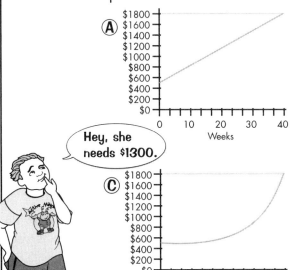

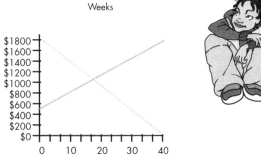

Extreme Sports

Have you ever done something really dangerous with a skateboard or on your bike? If so, you've already tried an extreme sport. Just don't get yourself hurt if you try it again.

What are extreme sports? These are sports much like regular skateboarding, snowboarding or biking, but pumped up with fancy manoeuvres. They combine skill, danger and showmanship in a way that really appeals to young people.

Extreme sports probably began with skateboarding. As most kids know, it's showy, dangerous manoeuvres that make skateboarding fun. There are four general types of tricks in skateboarding — flip tricks, grabs, grinds and stalls. Flip tricks are easy enough for novices. They involve flipping the board out from under your feet, moving it around, and getting it back under just in time to land. Grab tricks require a "lot of air" (a jump off the ground) so you can grab your board and strike a pose — at least for a second or two. For grinds and stalls, you push your board onto an edge, then do a slide, and finally hop-off to finish. Some versions of these manoeuvres are done on a "half-pipe" course to make them more difficult. Others can be done on the street — but only at the risk of scrapes and bruises.

Some experts, like famous skater Tony Hawk, make it all seem simple. At the X Games of 1999, he did the first ever "900." That means he spun around two and a half times during a jump. No one had ever been able to do that before.

Skateboarding also gave extreme sports their first special words. For instance, when a boarder crashes, she wouldn't say it was "bad." She'd say it was "gnarly." Instead of doing a trick with ease and saying it was "great," she'd call it "sick." This kind of slang has become part of the code for each sport.

Freestyle skiing is also an extreme sport. Like boarding, it adds lot of "air" and a few tricks to make it very difficult. This extreme sport has even become part of the Olympics. The goal in extreme skiing is to do tricks in mid-air similar to what a diver does on his way down to the water. Of course, in skiing it's much more dangerous. Anyone who's twisting and flipping around in mid-air can hit the snow with a real bang.

Snowboarding can also be an extreme sport. The two most popular events are the half-pipe and the boarder-cross. The half pipe for snowboarders is much like the one for skateboards — only longer and all downhill. The goal is to complete a fancy routine on the way down the hill. Each routine combines difficulty, danger and style. The boardercross is a race involving a number of snowboard racers. This is a race through an obstacle course with jumps and banked corners along the way. Much of the excitement comes from the way the snowboarders tend to run into each other, fall and then keep on going. This is a sport for those who are very fit or who don't feel much pain.

Extreme BMX events are punishing for both bikes and their riders. The two big events are the same as those for skateboarding, but now there's a bike to deal with. Most of these events call for a dangerous pose in mid-air. For instance, a rider might do a "Superman" where he or she holds onto the bike and tries to look like Superman flying through the air. On a street course, riders don't get enough "air" to do a trick like that. Instead, a street rider will do a combination of balancing tricks, grinds and stalls.

Two people are considered at the top of the heap in BMX racing: Dave Mirra and Mat Hoffman. Mirra, known as "Miracle Boy," has more X Games medals than any other BMX rider. Hoffman, known as "The Condor," has been competing since the 1980s. Both of these extreme athletes are known for their style as much as for their daring.

Lately, extreme sports seem to be very popular. They can be seen on television, at the Olympics and sometimes just down your street. Maybe it's only a matter of time before we start seeing extreme sports right beside baseball and hockey on the CBC.

Sweat the Small Stuff

Here are some questions to see how much detail you remember from your reading. Look back in the article if you need to. Mark your answers on the answer sheet. (page 58)

1. Extreme sports

   Ⓐ are safe sports

   Ⓑ are expensive sports

   Ⓒ combine skill and danger

   Ⓓ combine skill and safety

2. Three extreme sports are

   Ⓐ skateboarding, snowboarding and biking

   Ⓑ snowboarding, swimming and biking

   Ⓒ snowboarding, knitting and skateboarding

   Ⓓ tennis, basketball and hockey

3. Fancy manoeuvres

   Ⓐ are simple to do

   Ⓑ make extreme sports exciting

   Ⓒ make extreme sports boring

   Ⓓ are special dance moves

4. Flip tricks, grabs, grinds and stalls

   Ⓐ are horse-racing terms

   Ⓑ are snowboarding terms

   Ⓒ are skateboarding tricks

   Ⓓ are things that happen to older cars

5. Another word for novice is

   Ⓐ expert

   Ⓑ spectator

   Ⓒ beginner

   Ⓓ professional

6. The author suggests that a novice skateboarder should start with

   Ⓐ a grind

   Ⓑ a stall

   Ⓒ a grab

   Ⓓ flip trick

7. What do grab tricks require?

   Ⓐ expensive skateboards

   Ⓑ special axles

   Ⓒ a lot of upper body strength

   Ⓓ a lot of air

8. In a grab trick boarders try to strike a pose

   Ⓐ for at least ten minutes

   Ⓑ for at least a second or two

   Ⓒ for ten seconds

   Ⓓ for 25 seconds

900 is my IQ.

Yeah, sure.

9. Grinds and stalls can be done

   Ⓐ in a supermarket

   Ⓑ on the street

   Ⓒ in a half-pipe

   Ⓓ b and c

10. At the X Games of '99, skater _____ did the first ever "900"

   Ⓐ Tony Hawk

   Ⓑ Dave Mirra

   Ⓒ Ronald McDonald

   Ⓓ Mat Hoffman

11. A "900" occurs when

   Ⓐ a skateboarder spins around two and a half times

   Ⓑ a snowboarder flips the board once

   Ⓒ a BMX biker falls on his head

   Ⓓ a BMX biker flips his bike

12. When a boarder _____ she'd say it was "gnarly."

   Ⓐ catches air

   Ⓑ spins

   Ⓒ crashes

   Ⓓ jumps

13. Gnarly and sick

   Ⓐ are types of tricks

   Ⓑ are examples of skateboarder slang

   Ⓒ are how you feel when you get the flu

   Ⓓ come from the Latin word for skateboard

14. Two things that have made freestyle skiing very difficult are

   Ⓐ lots of air and a few lawsuits

   Ⓑ lots of air, a few tricks and huge audiences

   Ⓒ flips and grinds

   Ⓓ lots of air and a few tricks

15. The sport of freestyle skiing has made it to

   Ⓐ the Stanley Cup

   Ⓑ the Olympics

   Ⓒ the Ice Capades

   Ⓓ the Tour de France

16. In this article freestyle skiing is compared to the sport of

   Ⓐ diving

   Ⓑ gymnastics

   Ⓒ track & field

   Ⓓ soccer

17. Freestyle skiing is much more dangerous than diving because

   Ⓐ snow hurts more than water

   Ⓑ skiers practice less than divers

   Ⓒ divers don't wear helmets

   Ⓓ the coaches aren't as good

18. The two most popular snowboard events are

   Ⓐ the half-pipe and the snow-job

   Ⓑ the half-pipe and the belly-slide

   Ⓒ the half-pipe and the mo-joe

   Ⓓ the half-pipe and the boarder-cross

19. One difference between the snowboarder half-pipe and the skateboarder half-pipe is

   Ⓐ the skateboarder half-pipe is longer

   Ⓑ the snowboarder half-pipe is shorter

   Ⓒ the snowboarder half-pipe is longer

   Ⓓ the skateboarder half-pipe is covered in snow

20. In the half-pipe event snowboarders must

   Ⓐ make it down the hill

   Ⓑ complete a fancy routine on the way down the hill

   Ⓒ complete a series of jumps on the way down the hill

   Ⓓ race through an obstacle course

21. Difficulty, danger and style are

   Ⓐ common pet names

   Ⓑ part of a half-pipe routine

   Ⓒ famous skiers

   Ⓓ slang for jumps

22. The boarder-cross

   Ⓐ involves crossing the border into another country

   Ⓑ is an individual event

   Ⓒ is a race involving a number of snowboarders

   Ⓓ is a make of snowboard gear

23. Boarder-cross is a sport for those who are fit or who feel little pain because it involves

   Ⓐ boarders smashing snow sculptures

   Ⓑ boarders having a smashing good time

   Ⓒ boarders going very slow

   Ⓓ boarders smashing into each other and falling down

24. The author says that extreme BMX and skateboard events are

   Ⓐ the same

   Ⓑ different

   Ⓒ similar

   Ⓓ expensive

25. In this article, a "Superman" is

   Ⓐ an event

   Ⓑ a super hero

   Ⓒ a dangerous on-the-ground pose

   Ⓓ a dangerous midair pose

Think It Through!

1. Every sport has its own special vocabulary. Use two examples from the story to show how this applies to extreme sports. Then give some examples from another sport that you know.

_____

_____

_____

_____

_____

_____

2. What is the difference between an ordinary sport and the "extreme" version of that sport? Explain with at least two examples from the story.

_____

_____

_____

_____

_____

_____

_____

_____

3. Do you think public displays of extreme sports are a good idea? Why or why not? Take one side in this argument and explain why you feel the way you do.

_____

_____

_____

_____

So convince me! _____

_____

_____

Skateboard Math

Use the information below to answer the math questions that follow. Mark your answers on the answer sheet on page 58.

How high can they jump?

Chart of Vertical Distance of Skateboard Jumps		
	Nat	**Ned**
half-pipe	2.25 m	2.02 m
street (stationary)	0.5 m	0.72 m
street (in motion)	0.62 m	0.83 m
street ramp	0.87 m	0.85 m
curb	0.35 m	0.28 m

1. Which jumps are the highest for both Ned and Nat?

   Ⓐ street (in motion)

   Ⓑ street ramp

   Ⓒ curb

   Ⓓ half-pipe

2. How much higher is Nat's half-pipe jump than Ned's?

   Ⓐ 2.3 m

   Ⓑ 2.23 m

   Ⓒ 0.23 m

   Ⓓ 0.023 m

3. The difference between Ned's street (in motion) jump and Ned's street (stationary) jump is

   Ⓐ 11 cm

   Ⓑ 9 cm

   Ⓒ 155 cm

   Ⓓ 15 cm

4. Nat and Ned's combined street ramp height is arrived at by

   Ⓐ adding 0.5 m plus 0.72 m

   Ⓑ multiplying 0.85 m by 2

   Ⓒ subtracting 0.85 m from 0.87 m

   Ⓓ adding 0.87 m plus 0.85 m

5. Nat and Ned's average half-pipe height is

   Ⓐ 2.44 m

   Ⓑ 2.14 m

   Ⓒ 4.22 m

   Ⓓ 4.27 m

6. The average height of Ned and Nat's_____ jump is 0.86 m.

   Ⓐ street ramp

   Ⓑ street (in motion)

   Ⓒ curb

   Ⓓ street (stationary)

7. Estimate the total of all Nat's jumps to one decimal place.

(A) 570 cm

(B) 4.7 m

(C) 470 cm

(D) 5.5 m

8. Calculate the actual total of Nat's 5 jumps.

(A) 529 cm

(B) 449 cm

(C) 459 cm

(D) 470 cm

9. The difference between the estimated total to one decimal place and the actual total in metres is

(A) 11 cm

(B) 210 cm

(C) 0.21 m

(D) 0.11 m

10. It would take Ned _____ half-pipe jumps to reach a total of approximately 20 m.

(A) 12

(B) 10

(C) 100

(D) 20

If speed (velocity) equals distance divided by time (V = D ÷ T), answer the remaining questions. Show your work.

11. Nat can skate 40 m to the street ramp in 15 seconds. What is his speed in km/hour?

12. Ned goes the same distance in 18 seconds. What is his speed in km/hour?

Bicycle Geometry

Use this simplified drawing of a bicycle for the questions that follow. Choose the right answer and mark it on the answer sheet on page 58. Then explain your reasoning on this page.

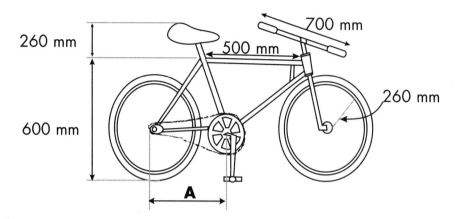

1. The wheels of the bicycle are obviously circles. If their radius is 260 mm, what is the circumference of the wheel?

   Ⓐ 408.2 mm   Ⓑ 816.4 mm

   Ⓒ 1632.8 mm   Ⓓ 2041 mm

   Explain your thinking:

   _____

   _____

   _____

   _____

2. The frame of the bicycle is almost a parallelogram. If the top tube is 500 mm from the seat post to the fork, what is the approximate distance (A) from the rear hub to the centre of the pedals?

   Ⓐ 260 mm   Ⓑ 520 mm

   Ⓒ 760 mm   Ⓓ 400 mm

   Explain your thinking:

   _____

   _____

   _____

   _____

3. The top rail of the frame is roughly 600 mm from the ground. This rail is 500 mm long. The handlebars are 700 mm across. What is the ratio of top rail to distance to ground to handlebar size?

    Ⓐ 3:4:5   Ⓑ 4:5:6

    Ⓒ 26:60:70   Ⓓ 5:6:7

Explain your thinking:

_____

_____

_____

4. The seat post is set at 240 mm for Freddie. Hiro's legs are longer than Freddie's, so a possible seat post length for him could be

    Ⓐ 220 mm   Ⓑ 240 mm

    Ⓒ 280 mm   Ⓓ 265 mm

I do have long legs!

Explain your thinking:

_____

_____

_____

5. Freddie wants to put some reflective tape on both sides of the frame of his bicycle. The top and bottom parts of the frame together are 900 mm long. If the front and rear frame pieces are each 350 cm long, how much tape will Freddie need?

    Ⓐ 850 mm   Ⓑ 1700 mm

    Ⓒ 2500 mm   Ⓓ 3200 mm

This is easy!

Explain your thinking:

_____

_____

_____

_____

Moonkid Plays Ball

Not everyone is good at sports. The character "Moonkid" in this story is lousy at baseball. But here he has to play a baseball game in gym class.

(Story by Paul Kropp, adapted from *Moonkid and Prometheus*, Stoddart Publishing 1998)

I am not a jock. I do not say this proudly, as if it were some badge of honour, but honestly. I'm just not very coordinated. I drop things; I stumble; I fall; I have no muscles. I am not proud of these things, but they are truths that I have learned to live with.

So probably the most terrifying part of the school day, for me Ian "Moonkid" McNaughton, is Phys. Ed. I am terrified of Phys. Ed because of the way it showcases everything I can't do. As anyone who knows me would tell you, I can't throw, catch, climb or contort. The things I can do — read a book, make witty comments on life and play video games — are not part of Phys. Ed.

So the idea of playing baseball was not fun for me, it was a kind of torture. My most recent torture was yesterday.

Twenty of us trooped out to the back field where some civic-minded citizen had donated a baseball diamond in the memory of his dog, or his mother or someone with the unfortunate name of "Flossie Slocum." We stood around idly while our overweight gym teacher, Mr. Newman—known affectionately as Fred— spoke knowledgeably about batting technique. I tried to pay attention, knowing there would be a multiple-choice quiz on Friday (if only Fred would set essay questions), and dreading the baseball game to follow.

Then we had one of those distressing sports rituals—choosing up. The teacher appointed two captains, jocks named Bruce and Tony whose rippling muscles and great coordination would make them first picks anyway. Then the rest of the class lined up to be picked, or not picked, as the case may be. Those with talent in the particular sport were selected first: "Ryan," calls one captain. Ryan smiles triumphantly, his status confirmed by being first-pick. The other captain, Tony, looks frustrated. He scans the line, then calls "Bill."

The first captain, Bruce, and his first-pick Ryan exchange notes. They decide to call for "Josh," who can't run because of a twisted ankle, but can certainly hit. Tony and Bill respond by picking Skye, an enormous student with a gold tooth, rumored to be wanted for armed robbery or something like that.

Once all the talent has been spoken for, the students remaining have to jostle for attention.

"Hey, man, pick me," says Bronson. "Ryan, c'mon," begs Jay. Gradually, the athletic losers are picked on a pecking order of who-knows-who, and who can maybe run to catch a ball without falling flat on his face. I make neither list.

At the end—and this is the worst part—only two or three guys remain. We are the lame and the halt. There is Trevor, who was probably OK at baseball until he got sick last year; Willie, who weighs three-hundred pounds; and me. The three Phys. Ed misfits.

"I'll take Willie if we get a pinch runner," says Tony.

A nod. The second captain stares back and forth between Trevor and me. Trevor is making muscleman postures, trying to look confident. I am trying to climb into my running shoes.

There is a general look of dismay among the others on the team. Finally the captain and Ryan make up their minds. "Okay, Moonkid, I guess it's you." There's a fair amount of laughter as I go walking over. My only consolation is that I am second-last pick and not last, as is so often the case.

We play baseball. The teacher pitches to both teams, my only break, because Fred throws the softball slow enough that I can at least see the thing. In my one turn at bat the previous week, I managed to actually hit the ball once—a foul—before striking out. This was as expected.

In baseball, the guys at the top of the batting order are expected to hit big and score the runs, and they do. As the gym period comes almost to its end, the score is tied: 15–15. Our team is at bat. Jay has been stranded on third by an out at first base. It would have been a great moment for a heavy hitter to blast one out of Flossie Slocum Park, but our team is at the bottom of the batting order. The heavy hitters are used up. All that's left is me.

"Pinch hitter," moaned Bruce and Ryan together.

There are shouts and objections from the other team. Fred ruled: "No pinch hitters. Next batter in the order is, uh, Ian."

The team looks at me with despair as I step out towards the plate. I see three bats of different sizes and weights on the ground. In despair myself, I pick up the largest and heaviest bat. In the face of doom, I decide to fight heavily-armed.

"Bunt it," hisses one guy.

"Just swing easy," advises Ryan.

Fred pitches the ball to me, slowly, so that it bounces on the base. Ball one. The catcher returns the ball and Fred throws it again, faster. I can see the ball coming at me, looking good, looking good—and I swing . . . too soon. Strike one.

"C'mon, Moonkid," shouts somebody on our team. I can feel all of them watching me: eighteen eyeballs staring at me, all looking for a miracle.

Fred pitches the ball again, a good one. Wait for it, wait for it. Oh, no.

"Strike two," Fred calls. I didn't even swing.

Fifteen-fifteen. Man on third in striking distance. Two men out. Two strikes on the batter. The situation, as they say, is tense. A chant goes up from the other team: "MOONKID! MOONKID! MOONKID!"

A million thoughts are zooming through my brain. I could bunt the ball. I could crowd the base and try to get a hit. I could fall down and fake a seizure of some kind.

"It's hopeless," grunts Ryan. He covers his face with his hands.

"Just hit it!" screams Tony, our captain, who is turning dangerously red in the face.

"You're meat," whispers the catcher behind me.

I pat the base with the tip of the bat, get in position, and squint out to the bleachers. I see Fred winding up. The pitch is coming—another good one—and maybe, just maybe—

"He hit it!" screams our captain.

"A miracle! A miracle!" shouts Ryan.

I am stunned. I actually hit the ball and it isn't going foul. It's sailing over Fred's head, over the second baseman, out to the field.

Someone is shouting "run, run" to me but I can't believe what's happened. I hit the ball. I HIT THE BALL!

From third base, Jay is running home but I'm still fascinated by the ball, by its arc in the sky, by the way someone out there is moving towards it. Who is that — Trevor? Trevor trying to catch the ball? He's so uncoordinated that he can barely button the buttons on his shirt. He couldn't—

The other side is screaming. Our side is screaming. Trevor is moving under the ball. There's no chance, no chance for someone that uncoordinated. Surely he'll miss the catch, or drop it, or fumble the ball.

None of the above. The ball sinks into Trevor's glove as if it were a leather-seeking missile.

There is a roar from the other team and an astonished smile on Trevor's face. My first hit in a lifetime of hitless games becomes an easy out.

Did You Get It?

Here are some easy, factual questions about the story. Refer back if you need to. Mark your answers on the answer sheet on page 58.

1. How does Ian "Moonkid" McNaughton describe his athletic talent?

   (A) He thinks he's fantastic.

   (B) He has trouble learning the rules to games.

   (C) He enjoys sports, but mostly watching them on TV.

   (D) He's not very coordinated and has no muscles.

2. Three things that Ian is good at include:

   (A) baseball, football and basketball

   (B) reading, playing video games and making witty comments

   (C) swimming, playing video games and bugging his sister

   (D) reading, football and making witty comments

3. The name of the park where the baseball diamond is located is

   (A) Flossie Slocum Park

   (B) Mel Firstman Square

   (C) Park Park

   (D) Ivor Wynne Stadium

4. What is the gym teacher, Mr. Newman, called by Ian?

   (A) Flossie

   (B) Fred

   (C) Dr. Newman

   (D) Alfred E.

5. The two team captains are

   (A) Ryan and Bill

   (B) Bruce and Skye

   (C) Willie and Tony

   (D) Bruce and Tony

6. Skye is said to be

   (A) a natural athlete

   (B) an enormous kid with a gold tooth

   (C) the class joker

   (D) Moonkid's best friend

7. Ian thinks that people are picked for the team based on

Ⓐ who knows who

Ⓑ who can bat the best

Ⓒ the gym teacher's favourites

Ⓓ all the above

8. Who pitches in the game?

Ⓐ Fred

Ⓑ Skye

Ⓒ Josh

Ⓓ pitching rotates

9. When Ian comes to bat, Bruce and Ryan ask for

Ⓐ one good hit

Ⓑ a pinch hitter

Ⓒ a time out

Ⓓ a new bat

10. The situation was especially tense because

Ⓐ the score was tied

Ⓑ two players were out

Ⓒ a man was on third

Ⓓ all of the above

11. At the key moment, Ian considers various possibilities:

Ⓐ bunt the ball

Ⓑ try to get hit by the ball

Ⓒ fall down and pretend to be sick

Ⓓ all of the above

12. Ryan shouts "A miracle! A miracle!" Why?

Ⓐ He's praying for help

Ⓑ He sees Fred give Ian a special bat

Ⓒ The kid on third is stealing home

Ⓓ Ian hit the ball

13. Trevor catches Ian's hit. This is surprising because

Ⓐ Trevor was asleep

Ⓑ Trevor can barely button the buttons on his shirt

Ⓒ Trevor has a broken arm

Ⓓ Trevor has only recently joined the class

14. A pinch hitter is a player who

Ⓐ hits the ball in place of a weaker player

Ⓑ never hits the ball

Ⓒ pinches the other players on the bench while they wait to play

Ⓓ runs bases in the place of a weaker player

15. At the end of the story, Ian probably feels

Ⓐ triumphant

Ⓑ angry

Ⓒ frustrated

Ⓓ all of the above

This is a true-false test. Use your knowledge of the story and the characters to come up with the better answer. There is no penalty for wrong answers.

1. Ian is athletic.   T   F
2. Mr. Newman is known as "George"   T   F
3. Ryan is the first-pick   T   F
4. Josh can't play at all well   T   F
5. There is a nasty rumour about Skye   T   F
6. The best players are often picked last   T   F
7. Willie is quite overweight   T   F
8. Ian's team needs a heavy hitter   T   F
9. Ian decides to bunt the ball   T   F
10. Ian changes to a lighter bat   T   F
11. The catcher encourages Ian   T   F
12. Ian finally hits the ball   T   F
13. Trevor is known for his baseball skills   T   F
14. Ian feels triumphant at the end   T   F
15. This story is part of a novel   T   F

No penalty means it's OK to guess if you're not sure.

But thinking still beats guessing.

Tips for true-false tests

1. The rules make a big difference. Some teachers will deduct the number wrong from the number right. In that case, a wrong answer is too risky.
2. Look for extreme statements ("Ian feels triumphant at the end") — they are often "false."
3. Look for little words like "always" and "never" that may change a true statement to a false one.

The Big Issues

Answer each of the following questions in complete sentences. Use this workbook for your rough work. Finished answers should be written on a separate sheet of paper.

1. When Ian hits the ball, the author writes "I hit the ball. I HIT THE BALL!" Explain why the author repeats the same words but uses capitals and an exclamation mark the second time.

_____

_____

_____

_____

_____

_____

2. When Ian comes to bat, the players chant "Moonkid" over and over. Do you think this makes it easier or harder for him to hit the ball? Explain your answer.

_____

_____

_____

_____

_____

_____

3. If you were the gym teacher, how could you help Ian feel more confident about his baseball skills?

_____

_____

_____

_____

_____

_____

4. Ian has an attitude about sports and baseball. What is it? Give two examples that show Ian's attitude.

_____

_____

_____

_____

_____

5. What is the relationship between Ian and Trevor? Are they friends or enemies? Will their relationship change because of the game? Use examples to prove your answer.

_____

_____

_____

_____

_____

_____

6. Have you ever faced a difficult, pressure situation? What was it? How did you handle it?

_____

_____

_____

_____

_____

Teachers give marks for paragraphs.

...and complete sentences

...and examples from the story

But they take off marks for bad spelling.

Baseball Math

Here are some math problems about Ian's baseball game.

1. When Ian is up at bat, the score is 15 to 15. The two teams have been playing for 45 minutes. On average, how long did it take to score each run?

   Ⓐ 10 minutes   Ⓑ 2 minutes

   Ⓒ 90 seconds   Ⓓ 45 seconds

2. If the two teams kept playing for 60 minutes, and kept scoring following the same pattern, what would the score be?

   Ⓐ 10 to 10   Ⓑ 20 to 20

   Ⓒ 18 to 18   Ⓓ 16 to 16

3. If Ian had hit a home run, the score would have been 17 to 15 for his team. About what percentage of the total points would Ian's team have had?

   Ⓐ 53%   Ⓑ 55%

   Ⓒ 50%   Ⓓ 47%

4. In a baseball diamond, the bases are 27.4 m apart. If Ian hit a home run, how far would he have to run?

   Ⓐ 27.4 m   Ⓑ 54.8 m

   Ⓒ 270.4 cm   Ⓓ 109.6 m

5. The closest seats at Flossie Slocum stadium are 90 m from home plate. Only Bruce and Ryan can actually hit that far. If they bat the ball and it flies at 270 km/hour, how many seconds would it take to reach the closest seat? (Assume the ball is travelling a straight line.)

   Ⓐ 0.8 second   Ⓑ 1.2 seconds

   Ⓒ 1.5 minutes   Ⓓ 1.5 seconds

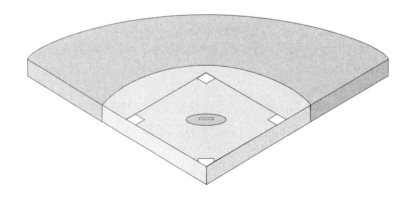

Use this drawing of a home plate for the next few problems.

Use the empty space on this page to calculate your answers if you need to.

42.5 cm

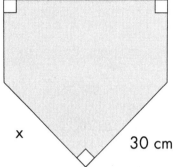

21.25 cm

x

30 cm

6. How long is the side marked x?

   Ⓐ 30 cm   Ⓑ 32.4 cm

   Ⓒ 33.6 cm   Ⓓ 3.9 dm

7. What is the perimeter of home plate?

   Ⓐ 150 cm   Ⓑ 145 cm

   Ⓒ 148.8 cm   Ⓓ 152.3 cm

8. What shape is a home plate?

   Ⓐ a rectangle   Ⓑ an octagon

   Ⓒ a triangle   Ⓓ a pentagon

9. To find the area of a home plate, you need to divide it into two shapes: a rectangle and a triangle. The area of the triangle is 450 cm^2. What is the total area of home plate?

   Ⓐ 900 cm^2 Ⓑ 1300 cm^2

   Ⓒ 1353.125 cm^2 Ⓓ 950.125 cm^2

Team Stats

Here are two players who could show Moonkid a thing or two about baseball. Answer the questions below based on the information in the chart. Then mark your answers on the answer sheet on page 58.

Name	Christine Catcher	Bob Bunter
Favourite Position	Catcher	First Base
Team	Cardinals	Beavers
Personal Information:		
Age	11	12
Years on a team	4	2
Height	125 cm	121 cm
Weight	40 kg	45 kg
Statistics last year:		
Hits	64	80
Runs	25	24
Home runs	3	5
Errors	20	20
Strike outs	8	4

> I'm pretty good at baseball.

1. Christine is 5 kg _____ than Bob.

   Ⓐ heavier   Ⓑ lighter

   Ⓒ taller   Ⓓ shorter

2. Bob is _____ shorter than Christine.

   Ⓐ 4 m   Ⓑ 0.04 m

   Ⓒ 0.4 m   Ⓓ 40 mm

3. Five years from now, Christine will have played _____ years for the Cardinals and Bob will have played _____ years for the Beavers.

   Ⓐ 9 and 7   Ⓑ 5 and 5

   Ⓒ 7 and 9   Ⓓ 9 and 6

> Yeah, sure.

4. How many more hits did Bob have than Christine?

   Ⓐ 16   Ⓑ 9

   Ⓒ 7   Ⓓ 20

5. If Bob bats as well for the next two years as he did this past year, how many home runs will he have hit altogether?

    (A) 9   (B) 15

    (C) 30   (D) 45

6. Christine had twice as many strike outs as Bob. If Christine strikes out 32 times this season, how many times will Bob strike out if their pattern holds?

    (A) 64   (B) 32

    (C) 30   (D) 16

7. Last season, Christine got 15 stolen bases and Bob got 5. We can write this as a ratio of 3:1. Which one of these sets does not follow that pattern:

    (A) 15 to 5   (B) three to one

    (C) 12:4   (D) 9 to 6

8. Bob has been practicing stealing bases to try to do better. Next season, he wants to steal two bases to every three of Christine's. This ratio can be written as

_____ .

    (A) 1:3   (B) 2:4

    (C) 2:3   (D) 1:4

9. What was the ratio of Bob's hits to home runs?

    (A) 1:8   (B) 80:15

    (C) 4:5   (D) 16:1

10. Christine's ratio of hits to strike outs was 64:8, which reduces to 8:1. What is Bob's ratio of hits to strike outs?

    (A) 20:1   (B) 6:1

    (C) 10:4   (D) 8:2

11. Which player would you rather have on your team? Use the statistics from the chart to explain your choice in the space below.

_____

_____

_____

Flossie Facts

Here's a diagram of the Flossie Slocum Park. Use it for the next set of problems. Mark your answers on the answer sheet on page 58.

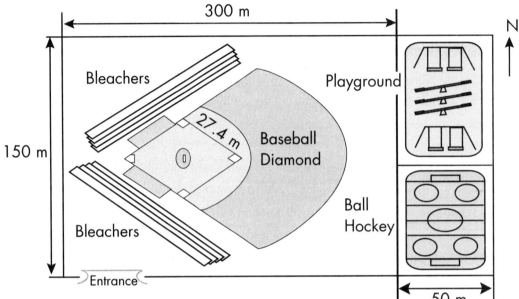

1. What is the perimeter of the ballpark (not including the playground or hockey arena)?

Ⓐ 450 m   Ⓑ 4500 m

Ⓒ 900 m   Ⓓ 652 m

2. The city is thinking of putting a pathway around the entire ballpark area. If they use paving blocks, they'll need 15 paving blocks for each metre of the path. How many paving blocks will they need?

Ⓐ 13 500   Ⓑ 16 500

Ⓒ 9780   Ⓓ 750

3. Another idea is to plant trees along the western edge of the park. If the trees are planted 3 metres apart, how many trees would be needed?

Ⓐ 15   Ⓑ 50

Ⓒ 75   Ⓓ 100

4. The two sets of bleachers currently hold 800 people for baseball games. If the city added another set of bleachers at the western side, how many people could be seated altogether?

Ⓐ 1200   Ⓑ 1000

Ⓒ 900   Ⓓ Not enough information

For these three questions, mark the right answer on the answer sheet on page 58. Then write your reasoning on this page.

5. When there are no games being played, a person can walk from the park entrance to the playground by crossing the playing field. How far is that distance?

Ⓐ 300 m   Ⓑ 335.4 m   Ⓒ 350.8 m   Ⓓ 450 m

Explain how you got your answer:

_____

_____

_____

_____

6. When a game is being played, it takes Francine four minutes to go from the park entrance to the playground. About how long will it take her if she can cut across the field?

Ⓐ 3 minutes   Ⓑ 5 minutes   Ⓒ $3\frac{3}{4}$ minutes   Ⓓ just under 3 minutes

Explain how you got your answer:

_____

_____

_____

_____

7. Some mothers in the neighbourhood are worried that kids in the playground might be hit by a ball batted from the baseball diamond. If a good baseball player can sometimes hit a ball 150 m, do the mothers have reason to be fearful?

Ⓐ yes   Ⓑ no   Ⓒ maybe   Ⓓ not enough information

Explain your reasoning:

_____

_____

_____

_____

A Test on Tests

Use your test-taking skills for this test-taking test!
Mark your answers right in this workbook.

Here are the words you need—and three more, just to make it harder.

estimate	planning	explain	spelling	work
eliminate	guess	skip	remove	reread
answer	punctuation	extra	checking	colouring

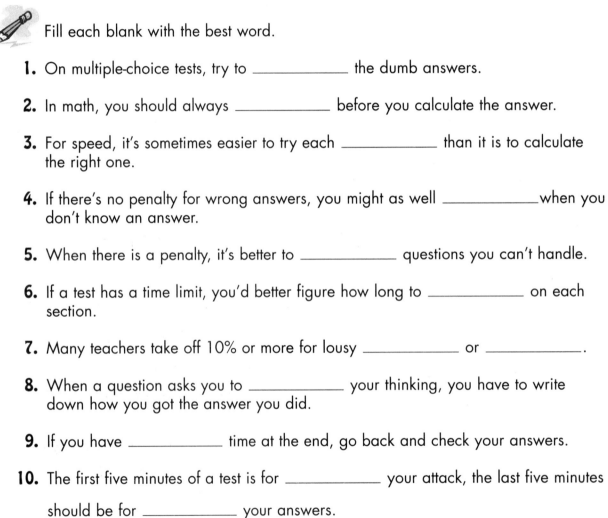

Fill each blank with the best word.

1. On multiple-choice tests, try to _____ the dumb answers.

2. In math, you should always _____ before you calculate the answer.

3. For speed, it's sometimes easier to try each _____ than it is to calculate the right one.

4. If there's no penalty for wrong answers, you might as well _____when you don't know an answer.

5. When there is a penalty, it's better to _____ questions you can't handle.

6. If a test has a time limit, you'd better figure how long to _____ on each section.

7. Many teachers take off 10% or more for lousy _____ or _____.

8. When a question asks you to _____ your thinking, you have to write down how you got the answer you did.

9. If you have _____ time at the end, go back and check your answers.

10. The first five minutes of a test is for _____ your attack, the last five minutes should be for _____ your answers.